**biochemical
predestination**

biochemical predestination

Dean H. Kenyon
Department of Cell and Molecular Biology
San Francisco State College

Gary Steinman
Department of Biochemistry
Pennsylvania State University

McGraw-Hill Book Company

New York   St. Louis   San Francisco
London   Sydney   Toronto   Mexico   Panama

biochemical
predestination

Some say that in the origin of things,
When all creation started into birth,
The infant elements receiv'd a law
From which they swerve not since...That under force
Of that controlling ordinance they move,
And need not his immediate hand who first
Prescrib'd their course, to regulate it now.

William Cowper (1731–1800),
The Winter Walk at Noon

foreword

Answers to the question of the origin of life on the Earth have been sought in various forms almost since men became human. Attempts to provide such answers in the technical or scientific context are, of course, of more recent vintage, but even these stem back several generations. It is, however, only in the last two dozen years that it has been possible to make an approach to this problem in chemical and molecular terms.

While several books have been written in the last decade addressing themselves to one or another aspect of the problem, they have, in general, been either collections of symposia papers or limited essays from one or another disciplinary point of view. In a sense, the present volume is of the latter type, but it is broader in concern than prior ones and is written primarily from the point of view of two young organic and biophysical scientists. It is the adjective "young" that is important here. These young men have actually begun their scientific careers, following the basic disciplines in chemistry and biophysics, with experimental research toward the elucidation of one or another of the specific experimentally formulatable questions that arise when one begins to think about the problem as a whole. It is this that lends them their unique position and gives this book its special character. The book is really the first attempt to produce what might be called a comprehensive essay which could be used as the basic textbook for a systematic discussion of the problem in an academic and scientific environment.

I have no doubt that it will find its place on the shelves of the beginning student in chemistry, biochemistry, and biology as well as the researcher, both new and mature, in the field.

Melvin Calvin

Director, Laboratory of Chemical Biodynamics
University of California

preface

In a number of laboratories around the world, small groups of investigators are devoting their full-time research efforts to a new kind of experimental activity variously known as chemical evolution, protobiochemistry, primordial biogenesis, abiogenic molecular evolution, experimental organic cosmochemistry, or, simply, origin of life studies. Twenty years ago, there was only one such laboratory, and, if we go back eighty years, we find that no experimental work whatsoever was being done on the origin of life problem. Today, investigators already established in some other field of science who devote part of their research time to origin of life studies number in the hundreds. These scientists have widely differing backgrounds and areas of competence ranging from astrophysics to zoology. This diversity of talent emphasizes the multidisciplinary character of the origin of life problem—a theme which will recur throughout this book.

Objectives

Our aim in the present book is not only to present in detail what we consider to be the major experimental approaches to the origin of life problem (including our own) but at the same time to evaluate critically the *underlying assumptions* (as well as the explicitly stated hypotheses) upon which current work is being carried out. Our presentation will be illustrative rather than exhaustive since we believe that the number of distinguishable kinds of experiments is far smaller than the total number of experiments actually performed and published.

We have attempted to write this book for both the undergraduate student encountering the origin of life problem for the first time and for the advanced investigator who seeks to keep abreast of new developments, whether they be in an area of his primary research concern or allied to it. The widespread, general interest in this problem is shared by enlightened laymen as well as by scientists and students in the natural and physical sciences. Although we have avoided the overly simplified discussions characteristic of most reviews now available, the use of technical terminology has been kept to a minimum in most instances and defined wherever possible. The tyro in biochemistry is advised to have on hand any one of the several good general texts now available to aid in appreciating such things as amino acid structures, since such a background is helpful (but is not absolutely essential for good comprehension) here. The book has been put out in soft-cover edition in order to bring it within the realm of financially acceptable references or secondary sources of the student.

It is our hope that this volume will serve to identify and illuminate general conclusions that can be drawn at this point of progress and to stimulate new thinking and investigations into primordial biogenesis.

Interest and applications

Up until a few years ago, virtually no American college or university offered a course on the origin of life. Very recently a few graduate seminar courses have been given, such as those at Pennsylvania State University and San Francisco State College, and one of these has already developed into a regular catalog course at Stanford University. Today the origin of life is discussed briefly in most introductory biology, botany, zoology, and microbiology courses, largely because textbooks for these courses routinely contain short sections on the subject. These treatments are for the most part, however, very sketchy and out-of-date. Discussion of the problem is also included in some of the new "core curricula" being developed at several schools (e.g., in the second year of the two-year Science Courses for Baccalaureate Education at Rensselaer Polytechnic Institute). It seems likely that within the next couple of decades an appreciable number of American colleges and universities will be offering regular courses on the origin of life.

Already, a substantial number of M.S. and Ph.D. dissertations on the subject have been completed, and it is likely that their authors will continue to devote at least some of their subsequent research time to the problem.

The number of research papers describing experiments explicitly

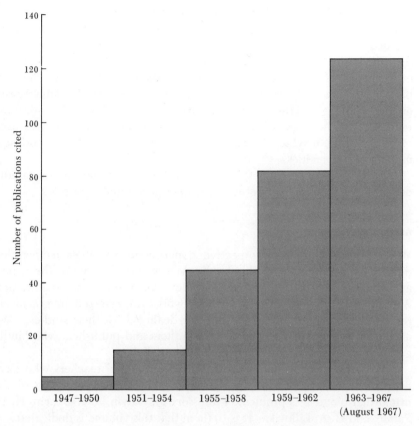

Number of publications cited in Chaps. 4 to 6 of this book which originally appeared during the periods noted.   The increase with time is indicative of a rapidly developing general interest in the origin of life problem and its related areas.

related to the origin of life problem has risen steadily since the early 1950s, and the literature now contains hundreds of references (see Fig. 1).   The principal journals in which these papers have appeared are *Science, Nature, Proceedings of the National Academy of Science of the United States, Biochimica Biophysica Acta,* and *The Journal of the American Chemical Society,* although many other sources occasionally contain origin of life papers.

Since the International Union of Biochemistry devoted its first volume (Moscow, 1957) exclusively to the origin of life on the Earth, a number of other national and international meetings have been held on the subject.   In addition, the Biophysical Society, the American Association for the Advancement of Science, the American Chemical Society, and the Chemical Institute of Canada have recently devoted special sections of their annual meetings to discussions of chemical evolution and the origin of life.

The U.S. government sponsors and finances a number of federal research programs designed to provide information possibly relevant to the origin of terrestrial life and to help establish a consistent rationale for carrying out and interpreting the results of extraterrestrial biological experiments. Perhaps the best known of these programs are the exobiology and chemical evolution studies being conducted in laboratories of the National Aeronautics and Space Administration. In addition, federal grants help support origin of life investigations at various research institutes (one of which is exclusively devoted to the subject) and at a number of universities.

From these observations, it is evident that there now exists a rapidly developing active interest in the problem of primordial biogenesis.

Acknowledgments

We are grateful to our respective departments for their cooperation during the preparation of this book. We would like to cite the expert assistance of Mrs. Elisabeth Lake and her staff in typing the manuscript. A number of the investigators whose works are referred to graciously reviewed those parts of the manuscript dealing with their studies. We also wish to acknowledge the several authors and publishers who kindly granted permission to use copyrighted material.

We are especially indebted to the scientists and teachers who have been most instrumental in the development of our appreciation of the primordial biogenesis problem: Professors M. Calvin, A. I. Oparin, H. H. Pattee, and H. A. Lillevik. It is to them that this volume is dedicated.

Dean H. Kenyon
Gary Steinman

contents

the nature of the origin of life problem

1-1 INTRODUCTION

Defining the problem

It is likely that many of you, particularly those of you who are actively involved in research on the origin of life, will have your own conceptions of the nature of the problem and of the methods by which it might be attacked. However, if you are a student meeting the problem for the first time, you will need to understand some of the assumptions and lines of reasoning underlying current formulations of the problem in order to evaluate critically much of what follows in this book. In attempting to arrive at an adequate statement of the problem, we shall adopt a highly intuitive approach consisting of a series of related questions about biological origins.

It is immediately obvious to everyone that in addition to ourselves there is a great diversity of living things in the world. Not only are there innumerable types or species of living things, but also many individual organisms of any given type. With respect to this totality of biological nature several different types of questions of origins can be raised. The first such question one might ask is: How did a particular individual organism (e.g., this koala bear or that sardine) of a given species originate? Using man as a familiar example, we can reply that the person in question was not always the way he is now (obvious), and that there was a time before which the individual probably did not exist (plausible). In the language of modern biology, he came to be what he is now by means of the biological processes of growth and development, starting out from a fertilized egg (not obvious) in

1

his mother's womb. The details of the processes by which a zygote develops into a fully formed individual are the subject matter of embryology and will not concern us here. If this kind of origin of life question is asked about any other sexually reproducing species, the answer is the same, namely, that any given individual of the species arises by development from a fertilized egg. In the case of asexually reproducing species, other processes, such as fission, budding, or simply growth and splitting away from a multicellular portion of the parent, are involved in the origin of new living individuals. In all cases, individuals of a given species arise from preexisting members of the same species.

Having settled the question of how individuals of a given species originate, we might next ask a question which concerns the origin of the species itself. (In this connection it is interesting to note that in the natural development of curiosity in a child the first question usually asked concerning biological origins is some version of "Where did I come from?"; of course, this is the personal version of the question asked above. The child is usually not given the scientific answer on the occasion of his first inquiry, but some time later he learns the biological details of reproduction. If his curiosity remains alive, it is likely that, as his intellect matures, he will begin to inquire about the origin of man.) Retaining man as the most familiar example, the question may be rephrased as follows: Although individual men live and die, have the general biological characteristics of mankind remained constant for endless generations throughout all time? Or, was there a time in the history of the Earth before which man did not exist?

Concern with this fundamental question existed very early in history as is shown by the elaborate creation mythologies of most major civilizations. Since Plato and Aristotle, many philosophers have attempted to deal with the question. Throughout the ancient and medieval history of Western civilization, it was commonly believed that fully formed individual insects, reptiles, and even mammals arose spontaneously from previously nonliving matter [1]. Today, most of the scientific and intellectual community, as well as many laymen, accept an explanation of the origin of man based on Darwin's theory of the origin of species by natural selection of previously existing variants of a similar species. The same kind of question about biological origins can, of course, be posed for any species of living or fossil organism. The creation mythologies, ancient and medieval folklore, and Darwin's theory of evolution all give the same general answer: There was a time in the history of the Earth before which any given species did not exist, although the origin is attributed to different causes in each case. However, it is only within the framework of Darwinian evolution that a third kind of question about biological origins naturally emerges and leads directly to a formulation of the origin of life problem.

Darwin's theory of evolution offers an immensely plausible and virtually undeniable explanation of how the great diversity of currently existing species arose by natural means.   One of the main features of the evolution of living nature on the Earth is that throughout the fossil record there is a progressively increasing number of types of organisms. As evolution proceeds, the diversification of phylogeny increases.   Let us assume that this diversification also occurred during very early stages in the history of life before hard-shelled species arose, that is, before the Cambrian-Precambrian barrier 600 million years ago.

By extrapolating backward, further and further beyond the Cambrian-Precambrian barrier, we shall eventually arrive at a point in time at which very few species of relatively simple organisms existed.   Further extrapolation will presumably lead to one (or at most a few) primordial population, probably similar in morphology to the simplest of contemporary bacteria or blue-green algae, from which all other species in the history of life (both plants and animals) evolved.   This backward extrapolation is shown in Fig. 1-1.

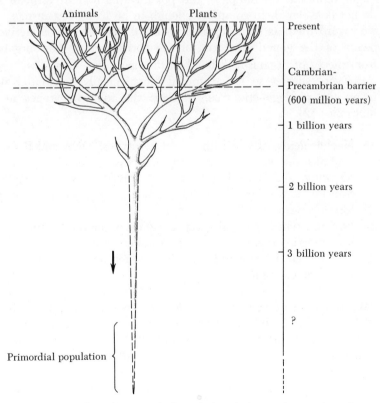

FIG. 1-1   Backward extrapolation of the phylogenetic tree to a hypothetical common ancestral population of microorganisms (see text).

The idea that all of contemporary living nature was derived from a common ancestral population is strongly supported by the results of comparative biochemistry [2]. Although different types of organisms exhibit some differences in their biochemical composition and reaction pathways, there is a remarkable degree of similarity and, in many instances, of identity running through the biochemical organization of all of life, with the possible exception of the virus particles. These latter problematic entities do not conform to the general patterns to be discussed even though they have some features of biochemical organization, such as the presence of proteins and of genetic information stored in nucleic acid molecules (either DNA or RNA) which are common to all terrestrial (earth-bound) life forms. A major feature of viral nonconformity is that virus particles are incapable of replication outside the complex internal environment of a particular host cell. Also, replication of a virus particle involves a taking over of a large part of the metabolic machinery of the host cell, to the extent that the latter is eventually destroyed. Therefore, even though virus particles exhibit a structural simplicity appealing enough to suggest to some that they might represent the simplest and possibly the earliest form of life, we do not consider them complete enough to be living organisms. Rather, we regard them as being most probably degenerate forms derived from pieces of the genetic material of the corresponding host organisms or from pieces of organisms related to the hosts (see Chap. 7).

Every species so far examined biochemically, no matter where it is on the phylogenetic tree, contains the following types of macromolecules [2]:

1. Nucleic acids, of which there are two types: DNA and RNA. DNA contains the genetic information necessary for the production of offspring, and RNA is intimately involved at several stages in the transfer of the hereditary information in the genes to the protein-forming systems of living cells.
2. Proteins, which generally act as catalysts for the chemical reactions occurring in organisms or as structural components.
3. Polysaccharides and lipids, both of which act as energy sources and structural components.

Also, the same types of small molecules, such as α-amino acids, purines and pyrimidines, and the organic cofactors, are found universally. Perhaps more significantly, many *sequences* and *patterns* of biochemical reactions (e.g., anaerobic glycolysis, the citric acid cycle, nucleic acid replication and transcription, protein biosynthesis, and fatty acid biosynthesis) are virtually identical, even down to their most subtle details, in nearly all forms of terrestrial life so far studied.

It could be argued that the universality of much of biochemistry is merely consistent with the concept of a common ancestral population but does not in any sense prove it since the same basic reaction patterns may be *required* for all life.   In other words, the comparative biochemical data are not inconsistent with the possibility that several independent primordial populations each having the same basic biochemical organization occurred at different times and at different sites on the Earth, and that each of these gave rise to its own phylogeny [3].

However, for our purposes, it does not matter whether life in fact arose monophyletically, i.e., from a single ancestral population, or polyphyletically (although our inquiries may incidentally shed some light on this question).   In either case we can still formulate a third kind of question regarding biological origins: How did the common ancestral population forming the base of the phylogenetic tree arise on the Earth? Or, phrasing the question somewhat more generally to take into account polyphyletic origins, how did any one of possibly several independent primordial populations arise?   Even if several primordial populations gave rise to different parts of present phylogeny, it is very likely that they all had the same basic biochemical organization; thus we can rephrase the question as follows: How did the universal basic pattern of contemporary biochemical organization originate?   This form of the question is a logical extension of the questions on origins of individuals and species.   It represents an essentially *historical* formulation of the origin of life problem.   Most of the experimental work to be discussed in this book was carried out with this kind of statement of the problem in mind.   Alternative formulations of the problem are briefly discussed near the end of this chapter.

You will note that one of the assumptions underlying the above formulation of the origin of life problem is that there was a time in the history of the Earth before which the primordial ancestral population itself did not exist, i.e., that the history of terrestrial life is *finite* in duration.   The validity of this assumption rests in part on the lines of evidence suggesting that the Earth itself has a finite age.

Briefly summarized, some of these lines of evidence are as follows: (1) Naturally radioactive elements exist in the crust of the Earth. Eternal existence would require infinite masses of these elements. (2) A rotating body which is dissipating energy as frictional heat must lose angular momentum.   Due to tidal friction, the Earth has been slowly losing angular momentum throughout geologic time [4].   Eternal existence would require infinite angular momentum.   (3) If we assume that the sun and the Earth have the same age, then the fact that the sun is continuously radiating energy implies a finite age for the Earth. Otherwise, infinite solar mass is required.

It could, of course, be argued that life originated elsewhere in the cosmos before the solar system was formed and was later somehow transported through interstellar space and deposited on the Earth, possibly in the form of heat- and radiation-resistant spores, there to flourish and proliferate [5]. However, this suggestion, known as the *panspermy* hypothesis, is considered highly improbable [6]. For the present, we shall assume that life arose on the Earth by natural means from previously nonliving matter.

The solution of the origin of life problem as formulated above requires an understanding of the molecular details of those chemical and physical processes occurring on the surface of the primitive Earth which were directly involved in the transformation of inert matter into living matter.

Possible methods of attacking the problem

How might one attack this problem experimentally? In order to gain some preliminary clues about possible experimental methods and strategies, we can ask how problems of origin are approached in some of the classical disciplines. Here again our approach will be intuitive, relying on common knowledge and some elementary biology.

Let us begin with the first kind of question regarding biological origins raised above. In order to understand how a particular individual of a given species originates, it is necessary to know the details of the entire *life cycle* of that species. At certain times in the cycle, new offspring individuals are formed. By repeated observation of the reproductive phases of the cycle, more and more details of the processes by which new individuals originate can be learned. A simple example of such a life cycle is provided by the single-celled green alga, *Chlamydomonas* (see Fig. 1-2). New individuals of this organism are produced either asexually via the formation of zoospores, or sexually by the formation and subsequent pairwise fusion of gametes. The entire life cycle, whether the organism is reproducing sexually or asexually, takes place in less than 1 hr [7].

The simplest life cycle found in contemporary organisms is represented by the rod-shaped bacterium, *E. coli*, which simply elongates and divides into two new individual cells by forming a fission plate halfway along its length (see Fig. 1-3). Under optimal conditions the generation time is less than 30 min [8].

The possibility of learning the microscopic, and eventually the molecular, details of the origin of new individuals in these simple cases, and for any other contemporary organism, depends upon the existence of a life cycle short enough to be conveniently observed in nature or in the laboratory. In this type of problem it is always possible (though not always easy) to directly observe the actual phenomenon and to subject it to variation of experimental conditions such as temperature or nutrient concentration. A similar situation exists in the case of the origin of a particular kind of cellular organelle, such as the centriole.

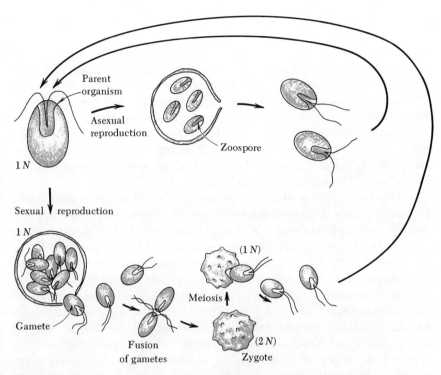

FIG. 1-2   Life cycle of the single-celled alga *Chlamydomonas.*   (*After* [7].)

What is required here is a series of stages in the development of a particular kind of cell which can be repeatedly observed in the laboratory and which exhibits the transition from the nonexistence to the existence of the daughter centriole.   In developmental cell biology it is always possible, at least in principle, to return to the phenomenon in this way.

However, it is not possible to use this approach in the case of the origin of life problem since the phenomenon most probably is not occurring under natural conditions now.   Some reasons why this is so

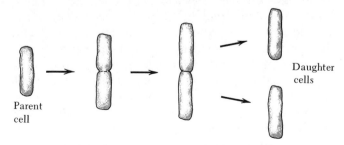

FIG. 1-3   Life cycle of the rod-shaped bacterium *Escherichia coli.*

will be discussed in later chapters. It is sufficient to say here that any assemblage of organic molecules, whether or not it is undergoing the kind of self-organizing chemical evolution required for the transition from the nonliving to the living state, would almost certainly be devoured by ubiquitous microorganisms and eventually oxidized to CO_2 through combination with the abundant molecular oxygen of the contemporary atmosphere. Also, it is highly probable that chemical evolution resulting in the formation of living organisms has not been in operation throughout Earth history. Rather it appears that the process took place during a single epoch (or at most during a few epochs in possibly different regions of the primitive Earth) in the remote antiquity of the Earth before Darwinian evolution began.

Although methods used to answer questions of origin in the biology of contemporary organisms are not applicable to the origin of life problem for rather obvious reasons, it might be thought that an appropriate strategy would be suggested by the methods used in *evolutionary biology* and *paleontology* for working out the phylogenetic relationships among fossil organisms. The difficulty here is that information bearing on the phylogeny of ancient organisms is obtained exclusively from morphological examination of surviving fossil remains. We have already mentioned, however, that the fossil record undergoes an abrupt thinning out at the Cambrian-Precambrian barrier, which corresponds roughly to a transition period in the history of life during which many types of organisms with easily preservable hard shells arose [9]. Several rather extensive fossil assemblages of Precambrian hard-shelled organisms have been discovered [10], but these fossils represent past life forms which are much more highly evolved than the rudimentary kind of protobacterial population we imagine to be at the base of the phylogenetic tree.

Apparently much more relevant to the origin of life problem are the recently discovered intact organic remains of several kinds of primitive algae and bacteria in ancient Precambrian sediments of ages ranging up to 3.2 billion years. To date only a handful of such microfossil finds have been reported, but already they have opened up the possibility that vestiges of the common ancestral populations of microorganisms might have survived down to the present day. These microfossils will be discussed in detail in Chap. 2. Such discoveries have stimulated a good deal of interest and discussion among "origin-of-lifers" since they provide direct evidence of the great antiquity of life on the Earth. However, aside from giving information bearing on the minimum age of terrestrial life, these fossils provide us with virtually no clues about the *origin* of life since even the simplest of the microfossil structures presumably represents an already fully functioning organism capable of self-replication. Although detailed evidence on the chemical composition of these microfossils must await further investigation, it seems likely that the corresponding living microorganisms contained the same types of substances and patterns of biochemical organization found universally in contemporary life.

Direct micropaleontologic evidence bearing on the origin of life would consist of surviving assemblages and states of organization of biochemical substances considerably less complex than the known Precambrian microfossils. However, in order for an assemblage of fossil organic matter to be recognized as a morphological precursor to the common ancestral population, it must be large enough to be observable by some microscopic means (light microscopy or electron microscopy). It must also have some characteristic morphological features (such as similarity to current rod-shaped or coccoid bacteria) which enable it to be distinguished from the surrounding inorganic sedimentary material. It is unlikely that both of these criteria would be satisfied by the simplest kinds of prebiological systems.

It is conceivable that direct evidence bearing on the states of organization of prebiological organic matter might be obtained through the discovery of certain kinds of organic molecules preserved within ancient Precambrian sediments. Very recently, a number of reports have appeared describing the extraction and purification of several classes of complex organic molecules from very ancient sediments [11]. The highly nonrandom structures of these molecules suggest that they may have been derived from biological material. The possible implications of these fascinating results will be discussed in the next chapter. This kind of discovery may provide us with the only hope we have of obtaining *direct* evidence on the nature of *prebiological* aggregates of organic matter. The central difficulty here is that we need some kind of criterion for recognizing a given kind of "molecular fossil" as *prebiological* (i.e., once directly involved in processes leading to life) as opposed to *biological* (derived from some preexisting, full-blown organism through some sequence of geochemical degradation steps).

Although it is perhaps too early to say, the establishment of such a criterion seems exceedingly difficult since the different molecular species must be separated from one another before they can be identified, thus removing any surviving traces of their original state of organization. Secondly, the only available criterion for identifying a given extractable organic molecule as a molecular fossil is structural similarity to some contemporary biological molecule. Application of this same criterion to possible prebiological molecular fossils would require that we already knew the structures of a set of molecules uniquely characteristic of prebiological systems.

The same kinds of problems would arise in the case of possible future discoveries of biochemical or prebiochemical substances on the surfaces of other planets by means of the kind of automated laboratory currently being designed for a soft landing on Mars [12]. The discovery of indigenous biological substances on the surface of another planet would prove to be one of the most sensational scientific discoveries of the century and would greatly enhance our confidence in the view that life arises by natural means under appropriate conditions. However, it seems improbable that such discoveries would provide any essential clues about the *processes* involved in the transition of an assemblage of organic molecules from the lifeless to the living state, unless it should turn out that some recognizable intermediate stage characterized by an abundance of functioning *prebiological* systems just happens to be occurring right now.

If methods used in biology and paleontology to solve certain types of questions about origins are not applicable to the origin of life problem, one might think that methods analogous to those used in human historical studies might prove of some help. For example, the problem of how a particular contemporary institution originated in the ancient past of some culture seems to be somewhat similar to the origin of life problem. The conditions giving rise to the institution may have occurred only once and may not be occurring at present.

The present structure and organization of the institution may be exceedingly complex and bear little resemblance to the original form of the institution. In the simplest terms the historical problem is "How did the institution get started?" The historian will immediately recognize that this form of the question has some obvious defects, not the least of which is the fact that any social institution has a long series of precursor institutions extending deep into the remote past (possibly beyond the dawn of modern man), so that one cannot speak of the origin of an institution without ultimately speaking about the origin of man. However, for the purpose of this discussion, we may consider a simpler situation involving the origin of particular physical structures such as the Athenian Acropolis or the Great Pyramids of ancient Egypt. One type of origin question might be concerned with the mechanical details of the actual construction work; i.e., how was the structure built? Relevant information might be obtained by examination of the surviving remains of the structures for inscriptions which might possibly contain the dates and purpose of construction. Surviving documents written near the time of construction might also contain clues about the origin. Are there similar procedures which might be fruitful in the origin of life problem?

The data of comparative biochemistry yield information relevant to the nature of the common ancestral population. These data are obtained by methods crudely analogous to the above-mentioned historiographic procedures, i.e., by studying diverse forms of contemporary (surviving) life. However, to date, no definite tangible traces of the transition from nonliving to living matter have been found, so that methods strictly analogous to the historiographical methods of examining, for example, a half-completed pyramid or surviving documents and other artifacts, cannot be applied to the origin of life problem.

Since many problems of origin are dealt with in historical geology and very often the time spans are immense, it might seem that some of the thinking employed in this discipline would be useful in the problem of biogenesis.   For example, we might be concerned with the formation of a particular valley or canyon.   Although the origins in question might have occurred in the remote past, the relevant geological processes (erosion by rivers, mountain building, etc.) are occurring in nature at present (although very slowly) and thus are amenable to direct observation.   Of course, these processes might be occurring now at different sites and in different combinations than those actually involved in the formation of the particular geological feature in question, but the point is that by studying currently operating processes, one can construct a very plausible picture of how certain features of the terrain were formed in the past.

The origins of some types of geological formations, such as the Precambrian iron ores of Finland, however, seem to have required conditions no longer present on the surface of the Earth—in particular, a reducing, or at least an oxygen-deficient, atmosphere rather than the oxygen-rich contemporary atmosphere.   In the case of the origin of life problem it is likely that many of the required conditions (such as an atmosphere with only trace amounts of molecular O_2) or processes no longer occur to any appreciable extent on the Earth.   However, some possibly relevant processes undoubtedly have persisted down to the present day, such as vulcanism or catalysis by mineral surfaces.

In conclusion it is apparent that approaches or strategies used to attack questions of origin in other subjects are not directly applicable to the origin of life problem.   The nature of this problem makes it fundamentally different from typical problems in the classical disciplines for the reasons outlined above.   In fact, one might be left with the impression that there is little justification for an experimental approach. The usual kinds of problems encountered in chemistry and physics involve phenomena which can be repeatedly observed at will in the laboratory.   The emphasis there is on obtaining a detailed understanding of the fine structure of the events underlying the directly observed phenomena.   In the case of the origin of life problem, however, we cannot repeatedly return to observation of the phenomena since we do not know what the phenomena are and since they occurred in the remote antiquity of the Earth and presumably are not occurring under natural conditions now.

Nevertheless, with all of the above limitations, a substantial amount of definitive experimental work on the problem has been and is being

done. In order to understand the reasons for this, it will first be necessary to discuss briefly some of the ways in which the problem has been
approached in the past.

1-2   SOME HISTORICAL ASPECTS

From ancient times to the late nineteenth century it was a common belief
in many cultures that all sorts of fully formed living things could, and
in fact often did, originate "all at once" from previously dead material,
in addition to arising from parent organisms. Many fascinating accounts
of presumed instances of this kind of spontaneous generation of organisms, ranging in size from small, barely perceptible (with the unaided
eye) insects and worms up to frogs, mice, and even crocodiles, have
survived to the present day.* In general, the organisms were observed
to arise from decaying organic matter such as putrefying meat, rotting
plant material, excreta, slimes of various origins, and, in some cases,
simply from mud and silt. Moisture, warmth, and sunlight were frequently mentioned as beneficial factors in the environment. For example, in ancient Egypt it was commonly believed that various amphibians,
reptiles, and even mammals arose spontaneously out of the muddy banks
of the Nile under the influence of sunlight. The following lines from
Shakespeare's "Antony and Cleopatra" indicate that such a belief was
still prevalent in Elizabethan England:

> *Your serpent† of Egypt is bred now of your mud*
> *By the operation of your sun: so is your crocodile.*
> Lepidus, Act II, Scene 7

In the surviving works of Aristotle many alleged instances of spontaneous generation are cited involving a great variety of organisms including various plants, insects, worms, frogs, salamanders, and mice,
as well as many marine animals such as crayfish and eels. Again the
characteristic conditions involved decaying organic matter such as dung
or rotting meat, various kinds of filth and refuse, moist sand, mud, and,
in some cases, sweat [14]. Belief in spontaneous generation was extant
in ancient Far Eastern cultures as well. For example, the ancient Chi-
nese thought that aphids suddenly arose fully formed on young bamboo
shoots growing under warm humid conditions [1].

Numerous allusions to instances of spontaneous generation were
made throughout the late Roman and medieval periods in the writings
of eminent Christian scholars such as St. Basil the Great and Albertus
Magnus. In his "Hexaemeron" St. Basil asserts that insects, frogs, eels,

---

* For a detailed discussion of observations and theories of spontaneous generation,
you are referred to Oparin's excellent monograph [1].
† "Any noxious creature that creeps, hisses or stings" [13].

and mice all arise spontaneously without predecessors directly from the Earth in hot humid weather [15].

Although most of the known accounts of spontaneous generation involve various animals, Albertus Magnus also cites many instances of the spontaneous generation of assorted fungi, bushes, and even trees. The conditions under which this kind of origin of life occurred consisted of the usual decaying organic matter, moisture, and, in addition, a somewhat novel ingredient, namely, starlight [16].

In addition to the great abundance of recorded observations of spontaneous generation, there have been many philosophical and theological discussions of the subject. Such major figures in the history of thought as Thales, Plato, Epicurus, Democritus, Cicero, Plutarch, St. Augustine, St. Thomas Aquinas, Alexander Neckham, Cardinal Damian, Paracelsus, Goethe, Copernicus, Galileo, Harvey, Francis Bacon, Descartes, Hegel, and Schelling, in addition to the figures mentioned above, all accepted the spontaneous generation of plants and animals as a fact and differed only in their theoretical interpretations of the phenomenon [1].

Detailed discussion of the various schools of thought on this matter is beyond the scope of this book. It is sufficient to say here that until the nineteenth century there was no such thing as an origin of life *problem*. People knew perfectly well on the basis of their own observations how organisms originated—they either came from parent organisms or arose directly from the inanimate Earth, although admittedly under somewhat unpleasant conditions.

During the sixteenth and seventeenth centuries, the major emphasis in the study of nature began to shift rapidly from philosophical speculation and direct observations of naturally occurring phenomena to deliberate and systematic manipulations of phenomena in the *laboratory*. This development of systematic experimental science initially had very little effect on the general belief in spontaneous generation. Instead, methodical and sometimes quite elaborate procedures for artificially producing various kinds of organisms began to appear in the scientific and philosophical literature in addition to accounts of observed cases of spontaneous generation in nature.

Perhaps the most striking of these recipes is that of Johann Baptista van Helmont for making mice from wheat (Fig. 1-4). Van Helmont is highly regarded in the history of biology for his elegant and quantitative studies of plant nutrition. The following lines from his "Ortus Medicinae" [17] suggest, however, that the eminent physician did not bring the same degree of experimental precision to all of his investigations [18]:

. . . For creatures such as body lice, bugs, fleas and worms are our miserable guests and neighbors, but they are born from our entrails

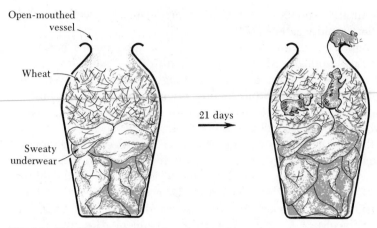

FIG. 1-4   Van Helmont's procedure for making mice from wheat with the aid of sweaty underwear (see text).   (*Based on* [17].)

and excrements. For if you press a piece of underwear soiled with sweat together with some wheat in an open mouth jar, after about twenty-one days the odor changes and the ferment, coming out of the underwear and penetrating through the husks of the wheat, changes the wheat into mice. But what is more remarkable is that mice of both sexes emerge (from the wheat) and these mice successfully reproduce with mice born naturally from parents. . . . But what is even more remarkable is that the mice which came out of the wheat and underwear were not small mice, not even miniature adults or aborted mice, but adult mice emerge!

If van Helmont's experimental procedures occasionally left something to be desired (by twentieth-century standards), those of the great seventeenth-century physician Francesco Redi did not.   As a result of Redi's carefully conducted (and in the context of his time brilliantly conceived) experiments on the alleged spontaneous generation of worms in putrefying meat, serious doubts that spontaneous generation did in fact occur were entertained for the first time.

In an early experiment designed simply to reproduce a commonly described instance of spontaneous generation, Redi stored meat from a freshly killed snake in an open box.   After several days, he observed the expected small worms swarming over the decaying meat.   However, instead of losing interest in further observation at this point, as his numerous predecessors had apparently done, he continued the experiment [19]:

. . . When the meat was all consumed, the worms eagerly sought an exit, but I had closed every aperture.   On the nineteenth day of the same month some of the worms ceased all movements, as if they were asleep, and appeared to shrink and gradually to assume the shape like

*an egg . . .   I placed these balls separately in glass vessels, well covered
with paper, and at the end of eight days, from each came forth a fly. . . .*

Thus the maggots which had been observed for centuries to appear
spontaneously in rotting meat were really the larvae of insects.

Redi might not have investigated the phenomenon further if William
Harvey had not concluded that every living thing (including flies) originated ultimately from an egg [1], even though Harvey himself did not
contend that his generalization excluded the possibility of spontaneous
generation (see Ref. 1, p. 16). Redi saw two possible explanations
for his experiment with decaying snake meat.   One was the commonly
held belief that the fly larvae had in fact arisen spontaneously from
the decaying meat.   The other was that they had somehow arisen from
eggs.   In an attempt to resolve the question, Redi conducted an experiment which to this day remains a monument to ingenuity and clarity.
He simply took two pieces of freshly killed meat, wrapped one of them
in Neapolitan muslin and stored it in a large container covered with
additional muslin stretched on a wooden frame, and stored the other
unwrapped piece in an open container.   Figure 1-5 shows the results.   It

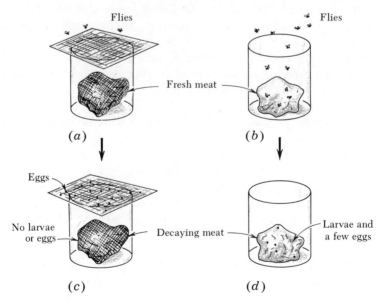

FIG. 1-5   Diagram of Francesco Redi's experiment disproving the spontaneous generation of "worms" in decomposing meat.   (*a*) Freshly killed
meat wrapped in Neapolitan muslin and stored in container covered with a
muslin screen; (*b*) freshly killed unwrapped meat stored in open container;
(*c*) wrapped meat after standing several days.   Eggs are present on the
muslin screen, but neither larvae nor eggs are present in the decaying meat;
(*d*) unwrapped meat after standing several days.   Decaying meat covered
with hordes of larvae and a few eggs.   (*Based on* [19].)

is apparent that the small worms (larvae) did not arise spontaneously from the meat as had been thought for so long, but rather from eggs previously deposited on the meat by flies.

Redi repeated his experiment many times with many types of meat [19] and in all cases obtained the same result, namely, that the prior laying of eggs was required for the appearance of larvae. Thus, William Harvey's conclusion that all life comes from eggs was shown to be correct in this case, and the doctrine of spontaneous generation was dealt a severe blow.

When the results of Redi's experiments became widely known, belief in the spontaneous generation of *any* kind of macroscopic organism slowly began to wane; by the middle of the nineteenth century, the last outpost of the doctrine were the microorganisms [20]. Ever since the microbial world had been revealed for the first time in Leeuwenhoek's microscopes in the late seventeenth century, numerous presumed instances of the spontaneous generation of bacteria and other microorganisms were recorded. Just as in the case of larger organisms, the characteristic conditions involved decomposing organic matter. If a small bit of the decaying meat in Redi's experiment (Fig. 1-5c or d) had been observed under the microscope, it would have been found to be teeming with microbes. (Of course, we know today that the decay itself is *due* to the activities of the microbes.) Microorganisms were observed to abound in virtually any sort of fermenting or decomposing water extract of animal or plant material, such as hay infusions, yeast water* with sugar, spoiled mutton broth, souring milk, beet and grape juices, and vinegar, which was exposed to the air and allowed to stand without special treatment [1,20].

However, because of the undeniable clarity of Redi's demonstration that insect larvae do *not* arise spontaneously from decaying meat but rather from previously deposited eggs, opinion on the spontaneous generation of microbes was divided. Some highly imaginative microscopists maintained that sexual reproduction was common among the infusoria and, therefore, that the corresponding microbial "eggs" must have gotten into those infusions which exhibited the growth of microorganisms. Others, however, saw no indication of sexual reproduction and maintained, therefore, that spontaneous generation had occurred [20].

Experimental evidence apparently supporting the spontaneous generation hypothesis was published in the mid-eighteenth century by John Turberville Needham [1]. This very skillful naturalist and Jesuit priest had conducted a systematic series of experiments in which he introduced various kinds of infusions into glass vials, boiled the contents for several minutes, and then sealed the flasks (occasionally hermetically) usually simply with corks. In all cases, he observed hordes of "animacules" in the flasks after several days. Needham claimed that he had "ne-

* An extract obtained by boiling yeast with water.

glected no precautions" to ensure that any germs of microorganisms originally present in the infusion or on the walls of the vial were destroyed and that "animacules" had not entered his vials from the outside. Thus, after boiling the contents and sealing the vial, he went [1] ". . . even so far as to heat violently in hot ashes the body of the vial so that if anything existed even in that little portion of air which filled up the neck it might be destroyed and lose its productive faculty." Needham maintained that his work unequivocally demonstrated the spontaneous origin of microorganisms from nonliving organic matter.

Needham's conclusions, however, were by no means universally accepted, even though they were widely publicized and had received the stamp of approval of the highly influential naturalist George Louis Leclerc, Comte de Buffon. In particular, many Italian naturalists, presumably firmly convinced of the universality of Redi's refutation of the spontaneous generation of insect larvae, rejected Needham's results out of hand, though without experimental proof [1].

Evidence contradicting Needham's conclusions was provided by a brilliantly conceived and carefully executed set of experiments conducted by the Abbé Lazaro Spallanzani [1]. The kind of experiment he carried out was very similar to that of Needham, except that instead of sealing the vessel containing the infusion *after* a *few minutes* of boiling, he *first* sealed the vessel (hermetically in all cases) and *then* boiled the contents for times as long as 30 min to 1 hr. When the flasks were broken open several days later (a period of time more than sufficient to guarantee the appearance of swarms of "animacules" in Needham's vials) and the contents subjected to microscopic observation, no microorganisms of any kind were found. As a result of having run many careful experiments, Spallanzani concluded that Needham's findings were a result of either the entry of airborne animacules into the infusions from the outside when cork-sealed vials were used or of inadequate time of boiling in the case of hermetically sealed flasks [1].

In spite of Spallanzani's apparently clear-cut results, Needham, as well as many of his supporters, still did not abandon his belief in the doctrine of spontaneous generation. He replied that the Abbé had treated his infusions brutally and thus destroyed the vital force in the infusions as well as the capacity of the air in the flasks to support life [21]:

He [Spallanzani] hermetically sealed nineteen vessels filled with different vegetable substances and he boiled them thus closed, for the period of an hour. But from the method of treatment by which he had tortured his nineteen vegetable infusions, it is plain that he has greatly weakened, or perhaps entirely destroyed, the vegetative force of the infused substances. And, not only this, he has by the exhalations [from the vegetables] and by the intensity of the fire, entirely spoiled the small amount of air that remained in the empty part of his vessels. Consequently,

*it is not surprizing that his infusions, thus treated, gave no sign of
life. This is as it should have been.*

Although today we find it difficult to understand how Needham's
objections could have been taken seriously, it nevertheless is true that
many physiologists and naturalists including Lamarck, Dujardin, and
Pouchet believed that his criticisms were valid and consequently retained
their belief in spontaneous generation [1]. Apparent support of Needham's criticism was provided by Gay-Lussac's finding that the air remaining in hermetically sealed vials prepared according to the method of
Appert (the inventor of the canning process) contained no oxygen [20].
This discovery lent support to Needham's contention that Spallanzani
had so vigorously heated his flasks that the air in them could no longer
support life.

A decisive step in the refutation of Needham's position was taken
by the German physician and deft experimentalist Theodor Schwann
(who is traditionally credited with having been a coconsolidator of the
cell doctrine). He modified Spallanzani's experiment in such a way as
to compensate for the alteration of the air in the flasks (i.e., conversion
of the oxygen to CO_2 through reaction with the organic material in
the infusion during prolonged boiling) feared by Needham and his supporters. A sketch of Schwann's apparatus is shown in Fig. 1-6. The
round-bottomed flask containing a meat infusion was tightly fitted with
a cork which had been coated with a rubber solution in linseed oil
and oil of turpentine. The cork was fitted with two lengths of glass
tubing as shown in the diagram. One of these tubes extended down
into a pool of mercury overlaid by corrosive sublimate (to kill any
organisms which might grow in the aqueous layer formed by the condensation of steam issuing from the flask during boiling) and finally by
a layer of oil. A section of the other tube was bent into a spiral and
finally drawn out into an open capillary tip [22].

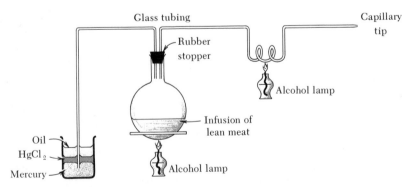

FIG. 1-6 Theodor Schwann's apparatus for conducting a modified version of
Spallanzani's experiment (see text for details). (*Based on* [23].)

A typical experiment was carried out as follows: first, the infusion was boiled until the steam issuing from the open end of the left-hand glass tube could no longer be condensed by the oil and mercury (about 15 min). While the infusion was boiling, the spiral section of the right-hand glass tube was heated almost to the softening point by means of an alcohol lamp. The red-hot temperature of the spiral section was maintained throughout the time the flask was cooling. This was done in order to ensure that the returning air was heated to this temperature before entering the flask. (This process is called *calcining*.) The section of tubing between the spiral section and the flask was long enough so that the air was cool again by the time it reached the flask. When the flask had completely cooled to room temperature, the capillary tip was sealed in the flame of the alcohol lamp. Periodically, the air in the flask was renewed by reheating the glass spiral, breaking the capillary tip, forcing a stream of fresh air through the apparatus by means of an aspirator, and finally resealing the tube. In experiments of this type the results were consistently negative; that is, no microbes or moulds of any kind were observed in the flasks, even though some of the experiments were run as long as 6 weeks.

If Schwann had relied solely upon the results of the above experiments to counter the views of the remaining supporters of Needham, his case would have been no stronger than Spallanzani's. Schwann went on to demonstrate that frogs respire normally in calcined air and therefore that the air in his flasks (unlike the air in Spallanzani's flasks) contained enough oxygen to easily support life [20].

This finding, however, did not banish all vestiges of belief in microbial spontaneous generation. Biologists of Needham's persuasion could still object that some unknown, nonliving but active principle required for spontaneous generation was in fact initially present in the infusion or in the air but was destroyed by prolonged boiling or by calcining. Schwann himself, on the basis of the results outlined above and other similar work on alcoholic fermentation, concluded [24] only that "It is not oxygen, or at least not just the oxygen of atmospheric air, which occasions alcoholic fermentation and putrefaction, but a principle present in ordinary air, a principle destroyed by heat."

Not until this heat-labile, active principle was unequivocally identified could the last vestiges of the belief in microbial spontaneous generation be finally and decisively put to rest. This identification was achieved by Pasteur in a monumental series of exceptionally lucid experiments described in his "Memoir on the Organized Corpuscles which Exist in the Atmosphere: A Study of the Doctrine of Spontaneous Generation" [25].

Pasteur was induced to take an active interest in the spontaneous-generation controversy by certain preliminary conclusions he had drawn from his studies on the nature of ferments [26]. However, some of his eminent mentors apparently did not share his enthusiasm. In particular, Jean Baptiste Dumas politely admonished him by saying [26] that "I would not advise anyone to spend too long on the subject." (Echoes of this sentiment can still be heard today with respect to the contemporary pursuit of experimental studies of the origin of life.) Nevertheless, Pasteur was eventually (1862) to win a special prize (the Prix Alhumbert) from the French Academy of Sciences for a dissertation describing "attempts by well-conceived experiments to throw new light on the question of spontaneous generation" [27].

In Pasteur's day it was well known that various boiled infusions and juices containing nitrogenous substances acquired the ability to ferment sugars and other simple organic compounds, such as lactic acid or tartaric acid, upon being exposed to air. From his earlier investigations, particularly those involving the conversion of sugar to alcohol in solutions containing living yeast, Pasteur had concluded that all fermentations were mediated by living organisms. He reasoned, therefore, that either living organisms must arise spontaneously from previously inert matter in the fermenting infusions upon contact of the latter with the oxygen in the air, or that the air itself carried viable "germs" of microorganisms into the infusion [25].

It is obvious that in order for the second of these two explanations to be correct, ordinary air must contain viable germs of microorganisms. Pasteur drew a stream of air through a wad of gun cotton until a substantial amount of dust had lodged in it. He then dissolved the gun cotton with a mixture of alcohol and ether and examined the insoluble dust under the microscope. He saw innumerable spherical and ellipsoidal objects identical in appearance to certain plant spores or gametes of various microorganisms [25]. Of course, because of the ether and alcohol these microscopic objects were not viable, so that the evidence, although highly suggestive, was inconclusive.

Further evidence that airborne spores and gametes were responsible for growths in boiled infusions was obtained in an elegant set of experiments involving the famous "swan-neck" flasks [25]. Sugared yeast water was introduced into round-bottomed flasks, the necks of which had been drawn out into S-shaped curves as shown in Fig. 1-7. If the solutions were boiled for several minutes, they remained sterile indefinitely, even though the ends of the necks were open to the air. However, if the swan neck was broken off (Fig. 1-7b), within 1 to 2 days life was abounding in the flask. Airborne spores or gametes apparently entered the open end of the swan neck and fell to the low point of the first curve (Fig. 1-7a) from which they could not ascend over the hump and hence could not reach the boiled solution (since they were heavier than air and were not subjected to uplifting air currents). However, when the S-shaped neck was broken off as shown

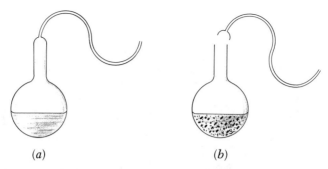

(a)   (b)

FIG. 1-7 Pasteur's swan-neck flask experiment. (a) Sugared
yeast water boiled in a swan-neck flask. Solution remains
sterile upon standing; (b) same flask teeming with microscopic
life 48 hr after swan-neck removed as shown. (*After* [25].)

in Fig. 1-7b, airborne spores fell directly into the sugared yeast water
where they initiated growth.

Although the results of the experiments described above strongly
suggested that fermentation or putrefaction of boiled infusions is caused
by viable germs, the possibility could not logically be excluded that
some other (nonliving) substance in the air was responsible for the
growths and that therefore spontaneous generation might have occurred
in the flasks after all. With this contingency in mind Pasteur performed
an elegant experiment using the apparatus diagramed in Fig. 1-8 [25].

The flask containing the sugared yeast water was sterilized according to the method of Theodor Schwann (see Fig. 1-6). The contents
of the flask were first boiled for several minutes. Calcined air was
then allowed to replace the air which had been driven out of the flask
during the boiling, and finally the open neck of the flask was sealed.
The sealed flask was then allowed to stand for a month at 30°C. It
exhibited no growth whatsoever during this time and was assumed to
be completely sterile.

The neck of the flask was then connected to the rest of the apparatus
as shown in the diagram (Fig. 1-8). Individual components are described in the caption to the figure. After the platinum tube P had
been brought to red-hot temperature by the furnace, stopcock S_3 was
closed while S_1 and S_2 remained open. The air in the section of the
apparatus running from R_1 to S_3 was then evacuated by means of the
vacuum pump. Following this, S_2 was closed, and calcined air was
admitted by opening S_3. The evacuation was repeated, after which
calcined air was again admitted. This cycle was repeated a dozen times
in order to ensure that all of the air originally in contact with the dust
particles on the cotton was replaced by calcined air. Then, with stopcock S_2 closed, the sealed tip of the flask was broken at the location

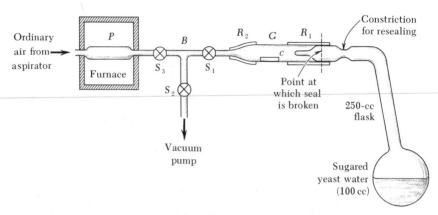

FIG. 1-8 Pasteur's apparatus for introducing airborne dust in an atmosphere of calcined air into a previously boiled solution of sugar in yeast water. *R*, connecting segments of rubber tubing; *G*, glass tubing; *B*, brass T-section; *P*, platinum tube heated red-hot in furnace; *S*, stopcocks; *c*, open-ended glass tube filled with cotton or asbestos fibers containing atmospheric dust. (*After* [27].)

shown by the dotted line, and the apparatus tipped so that the small cotton-containing tube *c* entered the flask and fell down into the infusion. Finally, the flask was resealed at the constriction point and allowed to stand at room temperature. The following excerpts from Pasteur's notebook [27] describe the results of the experiment (the cotton with its load of dust was introduced into the infusion at 9:00 A.M., January 8, 1860):

> *On January 9th, at 9:00 A.M., the liquid in the flask showed no change. At 6:00 P.M. the same day little tufts of mould could be seen very distinctly, growing from the tube containing the dust. The liquid remained perfectly transparent.*
>
> *On January 10th, at 5:00 P.M., the liquid still maintained its perfect transparency, aside from the silky tufts of mould. . . .*
>
> *On January 11th, the liquid had lost its transparency. It was entirely turbid, so much so that the tufts of the mycelium could no longer be distinguished.*
>
> *Then, using a file, I opened the flask and studied with a microscope the different growths which had originated therein.*
>
> *The turbidity of the liquid was due to a crowd of little bacteria, of the smallest dimension, very rapid in their movements, pirouetting in a lively manner. . . . The silky turfs were formed by a mycelium with branched tubes.*

The above experiment was repeated several times with the same results. In order to counter the possible objection that the cotton, having itself been synthesized by a living organism, might have influenced the results, Pasteur repeated the experiment using asbestos fibers in place of cotton to trap the airborne dust.   Again microbial growth was observed in the resealed flask after 2 days.   If the little tube containing the wad of cotton was heated while in the glass tube G before being introduced into the flask, no growth was observed [25,27].

This decisive experiment and other similar ones all but silenced the proponents of spontaneous generation.   In his "Memoir," Pasteur discussed the alleged instances of microbial spontaneous generation and very clearly demonstrated that in each case the observations were erroneous.   In most cases the experimenters were ignorant of the presence of viable microbial spores and gametes in ordinary air, and consequently they failed to take special precautions in order to prevent these viable germs from getting into the infusions after boiling.   Thus, Needham's results were most probably ascribable to the entry of unheated air bearing viable germs into his vials after boiling and before sealing.   The negative results, of course, were also readily understandable.   Spallanzani did not observe growths in his flasks because he first sealed them and *then* boiled the contents, thus destroying any viable spores originally present in the flasks.   Schwann's process of calcining destroyed all of the viable germs in the air admitted to the flask before the capillary tip (Fig. 1-6) was sealed.

However, Felix Pouchet's claim of spontaneous generation in hay infusions [28] deserves special consideration since it involved a contingency not taken into account by Pasteur.   The controversy surrounding it was largely responsible for the fact that all but one of the last vestiges of belief in the doctrine did not die until a dozen years after the publication of Pasteur's "Memoir."

Pouchet boiled infusions of hay and sealed the flasks without replacing the expelled air.   As long as the flasks remained sealed no growth was observed [28].   Pasteur had treated flasks containing yeast water in a similar manner and, as expected, no growth was observed as long as the flasks remained sealed.   If the seals were broken and a small amount of air allowed to enter the flasks, following which the flasks were again sealed, Pouchet *invariably* obtained growths whether the experiment was conducted in the Museum of Natural History in Paris (of which Pouchet was the director) or on top of the Pyrenees Mountains.   Pasteur, on the other hand, obtained growths in only a fraction of his flasks, the size of the fraction depending on the type of air admitted.   For example, only 4 out of 19 vessels opened and resealed in the Natural History Museum developed microbial growth, whereas 16 out of 18 exposed outdoors under a tree gave positive results.   The results of these experiments provided Pasteur with additional (although indirect) evidence that the growths were due not to the air itself, as Pouchet's results seemed to indicate, but rather to viable germs *unevenly* distributed in the air [25].

John Tyndall finally settled the matter by showing unequivocally that the hay germs originally present in the infusions survive boiling for long periods of time and that upon contact with the oxygen in the air, they give rise to the growths obtained by Pouchet. Subsequently, many types of heat-resistant bacterial spores came to light as a result of Pasteur's dispute with Henry Bastian [27].

When the monumental works of Louis Pasteur and John Tyndall were published and became widely known, the doctrine of spontaneous generation, after a long, distinguished, and often stormy career, during the greater part of which it, in Oparin's [1] words, "held undivided sway over people's minds," finally all but died (Bastian persisted alone in his belief in spontaneous generation until his death in 1915).

A long period of experimental pessimism followed during which many eminent scientists believed the question of the origin of life could not be profitably studied by the scientific method. As a result of Pasteur's work many were convinced that life could only come from preexisting life, and therefore that life was eternal in the universe, although it may not have necessarily existed eternally on the Earth. The following quotation taken from a nineteenth century French botany textbook is a typical illustration of this conviction [1,29]:

> The vegetation of the Earth had a beginning and will have an end [determined presumably by the beginning and end of the Earth itself], but the vegetation of the universe, like the universe itself, is eternal.

In this new climate of opinion, virtually no experiments related to the origin of life were performed for the next 50 years, although philosophical speculation continued [1].

It is important to note that although many of his supporters thought otherwise, Pasteur did not really disprove the possibility of spontaneous generation. What he did show was that spontaneous generation had not been demonstrated to occur as previously claimed [1]. In fact, the doctrine was to be resurrected later in a much more elaborate and highly ramified form. The corresponding renewal of interest in the possibility of experimental investigation of the origin of life depended upon the rapid progress in other areas of science which occurred during the quietus on the spontaneous-generation question following Pasteur's work.

1-3 REBIRTH OF THE INQUIRY

Rapid growth of knowledge in many scientific disciplines

In Pasteur's day virtually nothing was known about the internal workings of bacterial cells. Although some internal structures had been seen by the microscopists (particularly in the case of the larger protozoa), for the most part microbial organisms, especially the bacteria, were regarded simply as tiny featureless globs or bags of living matter. This apparent structural simplicity helped to sustain the fervor with which the proponents of spontaneous generation defended their position, since they could see no *logical* barrier to the sudden appearance of such living units.

However, by the mid-1920s a vast amount of detailed information about the chemistry occurring in living cells had been accumulated. In particular, to mention only a few of the highlights of these developments, it was learned that protoplasm exhibits many colloidal properties, such as reversible sol-gel transformations, and that most of the dry weight of living matter consists of several different classes of macromolecules, the most abundant of which are the proteins [30].

Nucleic acids were extracted from cell nuclei and chemically characterized. Crude enzyme preparations containing proteolytic or dehydrogenase activities were obtained from cell extracts. Also, numerous types of low-molecular-weight substances such as amino acids, sugars, and various pigments were identified in cell extracts. Biochemical processes such as glycolysis and fermentation were shown to consist of complex sequences of reactions in which proteins were involved as catalysts.

During the last quarter of the nineteenth century much was learned, through detailed microscopic observation and the application of the newly discovered specific staining techniques, about the intricate behavior of chromosomes during cell division in protozoa and higher organisms. Aside from the major division of eukaryotic cells into nucleus and cytoplasm, various other structural units and organelles were discovered, such as the plasma membrane, the various kinds of vacuoles, the nucleolus, the centrioles, and the so-called Golgi bodies [30].

During the first two decades of the twentieth century, a concept of the living cell characterized by great structural and functional complexity began to emerge [30]. The general picture consisted of a division of labor among various specialized organelles together with an enormously complex and highly organized pattern of interlocking reaction sequences involving substances of much higher molecular weight and architectural complexity than the compounds investigated by the organic chemists in the first half of the nineteenth century.

After Wohler succeeding in artificially synthesizing urea in 1832 [31], many of the simpler, low-molecular-weight substances (such as sugars and amino acids) known to be characteristically present in living matter were synthesized without the aid of cells. The simplicity of some of these syntheses was later on to suggest that they might have occurred on the surface of the Earth in the remotest antiquity before life began, given suitable natural conditions.

Rapid, and in many ways astounding, progress was made in physics during the 60 years following Pasteur's work on spontaneous generation.

Maxwell's equations describing the behavior of electromagnetic fields, and the atomicity of both electricity and matter were firmly established during this time [32]. Although many other advances occurred during this period, perhaps the most significant for our purposes was the development of atomic spectroscopy, and in particular its application to the identification of elements in stars and other astronomical bodies. The new astronomical knowledge stimulated speculation about the origin of the solar system [33].

Evidence of the great antiquity of the Earth and of terrestrial life was obtained by the methods of historical geology—in particular through the study of strata and of the distribution of fossils in the geologic column [34].

Perhaps the most significant advance of all was the enlargement of perspective produced by Darwin's theory of organic evolution, i.e., that phylogeny had increased in complexity during the history of the Earth by virtually imperceptible degrees over immense spans of time. The possibility of extending the Darwinian concept to the gradual increase in complexity of carbon compounds on the surface of the primitive Earth before the emergence of the primordial population allowed the origin of life problem to be reopened in a new scientific context in the 1920s by J. B. S. Haldane [35] and A. I. Oparin [36].

The Haldane-Oparin hypothesis

The new knowledge of the chemical and fine-structural complexity of living cells, geological information suggesting the great antiquity of the Earth, and Darwinian evolution together made possible the conception of a novel and very fruitful hypothetical scheme for the gradual emergence of self-replicating chemical systems by purely natural means on the primitive Earth. The implications of the negative results of Pasteur's experiments on spontaneous generation were reexamined [36]. It was argued that these experiments *did not* disprove the possibility of spontaneous generation. They merely showed that under Pasteur's experimental conditions, which involved very short times compared to geologic spans of time, life did not arise from sterile organic matter.

This negative result was understandable if one considered the great complexity of protoplasm. The proponents of spontaneous generation had claimed that living cells could originate "all-at-once." It was much more reasonable to suppose that even the "simplest" units of living matter (i.e., bacteria) very gradually came into being in a series of stages of increasing complexity. Consequently, both Haldane [35] and Oparin [36] proposed that the origin of life on the Earth was preceded by an immensely long period of "abiogenic molecular evolution." The final results of this molecular evolution were the primordial ancestral populations of microorganisms referred to above.

The starting point for the general scheme of biogenesis now known as the Haldane-Oparin hypothesis depends on astronomical and astrophysical data on the distribution of elements in the cosmos. Spectroscopic analysis of light from numerous astronomical objects demonstrated that hydrogen occurs universally and is by far the most abundant element in the cosmos [1,36]. The spectra also revealed the ubiquitous occurrence of relatively abundant amounts of carbon in various states of ionization and in covalent linkage with other elements. For example, stars and comets were shown to contain C^{++}, C^{+}, C, C_2, CH, CH_4, and CN^- [1]. In fact, if the unreactive noble gas helium is excluded, the three most abundant elements in the cosmos besides hydrogen are carbon, oxygen, and nitrogen (see Table 3-5). Carbon is also the most characteristic element of contemporary terrestrial living systems and along with hydrogen, oxygen, and nitrogen constitutes the bulk of living matter [37].

The next ingredient in the overall scheme involved some hypothesis about the origin of the solar system. However, the specific details of such a hypothesis are not crucial to the origin of life problem. For our purposes it does not matter whether we subscribe to a "cold" or a "hot" theory of the origin of the Earth, since in either case the solar system is thought to have been formed from matter having the average elemental composition of the universe as a whole (see Sec. 3-3). Let us assume for the sake of argument that the Earth was formed by a process of slow accretion or condensation of originally highly dispersed interstellar material. During this contraction process various kinds of materials underwent continuous separation according to their relative densities. Before this contraction had resulted in anything approaching the current size of the Earth, gaseous, liquid, and solid phases were present.

Because of the great excess of hydrogen in the original material and therefore the high partial pressure of H_2 in the primitive atmosphere,* the lighter elements became saturated with hydrogen (assuming that thermodynamic equilibrium was continuously maintained) and entered the atmosphere of the nascent planet as highly reduced gases such as CH_4, C_2H_6, NH_3, and H_2O.

A central part of the Haldane-Oparin hypothesis is the assumption that throughout the Earth's formation and after it was fully formed, simple carbon compounds were being transformed into a great variety of more complex carbon compounds by means of heat and solar radiations. Solar ultraviolet radiation (UV) was a prominent form of free energy available for promoting chemical reactions (since the UV-absorbing ozone screen had not formed yet). Most of the organic chemistry occurring during the earliest stages of chemical evolution is presumed

---

* The current distinctions between a "primary" and a "secondary" primitive atmosphere and the supporting evidence are discussed in Sec. 3-3.

to have taken place in the primitive atmosphere. The simple reduced gases were continuously subjected to an influx of solar radiation. Under the influence of this radiation they underwent a variety of reactions involving formation of many kinds of more complex organic compounds among which, presumably, were the simpler of the substances occurring in contemporary living organisms, such as fatty acids, amino acids, sugars, purines, and pyrimidines.

These compounds, being nonvolatile, diffused into the primitive seas, there to undergo further chemical transformations leading to the production of, among myriad other substances, the polypeptides and polynucleotides. In this way the primitive seas became a kind of "thin organic soup" in which a great many types of organic chemical transformations were taking place. The overall complexity of the soup was imagined to increase slowly and thus undergo molecular evolution.

Oparin postulated that eventually, when enough high-molecular-weight material accumulated (particularly the polypeptides), a phase separation began to take place in the primitive hydrosphere, resulting in the production of the so-called *coacervate droplets*—small colloidal organic inclusions (of the order of microns in size) which have various osmotic properties [1,36]. Simple organic compounds are imagined to accumulate preferentially within the droplets (see Chap. 6). Eventually, sequences of coupled reactions began to emerge. Oparin envisioned competition between individual coacervate systems and a primitive kind of natural selection. Those systems which could most effectively accumulate the raw materials required for the production of more of the coacervate substance itself, and hence grow and eventually divide by surface tension effects, would survive and flourish.

Finally, after millions (or perhaps hundreds of millions) of years of such competition, primordial populations of microorganisms arose containing all of the universally occurring biochemical reaction patterns fundamental to contemporary life. These populations then gave rise to contemporary phylogeny by means of Darwinian evolution.

The new paradigm

Although an experimental approach to the origin of life problem is limited for the reasons discussed above, nevertheless the Haldane-Oparin hypothesis does suggest at least one kind of experiment which might be performed. Since the hypothesis visualizes a long series of intermediate steps in the gradual emergence of living systems on the primitive Earth, it would seem reasonable to scale down the purposes of the experiment. Instead of attempting to demonstrate experimentally the spontaneous generation of a fully formed microorganism from previously sterile organic matter, attention is focused on one particular stage of the entire hypothetical process of molecular evolution. For example, the transformations of the simple reduced gases of the primitive secondary atmosphere under the action of a particular kind of free-energy flux likely to have been present at the surface of the primitive Earth might be studied. This kind of experiment was in fact performed by Miller at the University of Chicago in 1953 [38].*

It is obvious that one of the central assumptions of such an experimental approach is that one can more or less accurately *simulate* the relevant primitive Earth conditions in a laboratory apparatus. In order to carry out such an experiment at all, since there is no phenomenon to return to in the sense of the classical disciplines, one must be able to (1) simulate the general conditions thought to prevail at the time the phenomenon did take place, (2) perform the experiment, and (3) attempt to interpret the results within some framework of assumptions. All of this involves a considerable amount of uncertainty. Nevertheless, Miller's experiments produced some remarkable, unexpected, and very exciting results.

Miller [38,40] simulated the primitive secondary atmosphere in a closed glass system, subjected it to a continuous silent electric discharge for a period of 1 week, and then analyzed the resulting mixture for nonvolatile products. The starting mixture of gases consisted of methane, ammonia, hydrogen, and water vapor at a total gas pressure of 1 atm. By paper-chromatographic analysis of the resulting reaction mixture, Miller found several of the α-amino acids which occur in contemporary proteins.

Miller's experiment was considered to be a striking success. After his short report was published, a number of other investigators set out to confirm and extend his results. Since 1953, many variations of Miller's original experiments have been carried out. Some of these variations will be discussed in detail in Chap. 4.

What is important here is that all of these experiments have been performed within the framework of a new paradigm in which the possibility of returning to the phenomenon under study virtually at will, as required in the classical scientific disciplines as well as in the spontaneous-generation problem discussed above, has necessarily been abandoned. We do not know at the outset of our investigations which observable phenomena might have been involved in the origin of life. Instead, hypothetical primitive Earth conditions of the most general kind are simulated in a closed system, and by means of some criterion of relevance an attempt is made to determine which, if any, of the observable chemical transformations occurring in the system might be relevant to biogenesis.

One essential feature of this kind of experimental approach is that

* Prof. M. Calvin and his associates performed a somewhat similar experiment in 1951 [39], but they used an atmosphere of CO_2 and water vapor instead of a reducing atmosphere as proposed in the Haldane-Oparin hypothesis.

once the apparatus is turned on, that is, once the initial mixture of gas is provided with a continuous influx of free energy, the investigator no longer interferes with the reactions except by carrying out the manipulations necessary to withdraw and analyze samples. Furthermore, these manipulations must be designed so as not to influence appreciably the chemical and physical processes occurring in the apparatus. These ground rules make the Miller experiments (as well as variations and extensions of them) fundamentally different from typical organic syntheses, which often require elaborate and sometimes drastic manipulations of the experimental conditions. The numerous assumptions underlying such an approach are discussed below.

Although we have described what Miller did, we have not said how he came to decide on the particular experimental conditions he used. The kinds of evidence suggesting that Miller's experimental conditions did in fact simulate in a general way at least some of the main features of the primitive secondary atmosphere will be discussed critically in Chap. 3. It is sufficient to say here that estimates of the probable ranges of partial pressures of the primitive gases were made by means of thermodynamic calculations, making the assumptions that thermodynamic equilibrium was reached, that certain geochemical equilibria were limiting, and that the partial pressure of hydrogen gas was above a critical limiting value.

1-4 FUNDAMENTAL ASSUMPTIONS UNDERLYING CURRENT EXPERIMENTAL STUDIES

The doctrine of uniformitarianism

It is universally assumed by everyone working in the field that the details of physical and chemical laws have remained essentially the same from the epoch of origin down to the present day; that is, regularities in the observable behavior of natural phenomena discovered in the last several hundred years are presumed to have been operable throughout the history of the universe, or at least throughout the history of the Earth, and throughout the extent of the universe at any one time. This assumption is necessary if the formulation of the origin of life problem as an essentially historical problem is to have any meaning. If our problem is to find out as much as possible about those physical and chemical processes occurring on the primitive Earth which were directly involved in the origin of life, then we must assume that it is possible to duplicate, at least to some extent, those processes in the laboratory. Implicit in this assumption is the requirement that no supernatural agency "entered nature" at the time of the origin, was crucial to it, and then withdrew from history.

Direct evidence bearing on this doctrine is very hard to come by.

Among the possibilities are the pleochroitic rings representing the termini of α-particle tracks found in some very old rock specimens [9]. Discrete rings are found since α-particles of several different well-defined energies are emitted by radioactive material at the center of the ring system. These rings are very sharply delineated, showing that the physical laws associated with the emission processes and the processes associated with slowing down the α-particles in their passage through the crystalline lattice have remained constant throughout geologic spans of time. Strictly speaking, this evidence bears directly only on the validity of absolute geologic dating by means of α-particle-emitting natural radioactive isotopes. However, it does lend support to the assumption that physical laws in general have remained constant throughout geologic time. Any additional evidence would of course be immediately welcomed.

Probable events versus rare events

It must be assumed that the origin of life on the primitive Earth involved a series of relatively probable chemical and physical events and did not crucially depend on the chance occurrence of very rare events. Special, very rare, or miraculous events may actually have been crucially involved, but if they were, we cannot hope to reproduce them in the laboratory. The above assumption is required if the problem is to be subject to investigation by the scientific method.

It is sometimes argued in speculative papers on the origin of life that highly improbable events (such as the spontaneous formation of a molecule of DNA *and* a molecule of DNA-polymerase in the same region of space at the same time) become virtually inevitable over the vast stretches of geological time. No serious quantitative arguments, however, are given in support of such conclusions. One of the major themes of this book will be the degree to which nonrandom, highly constrained chemical processes were probably involved in the origin of life. It will be argued that not only is any hypothesis based on the chance occurrence of rare events not subject to experimental test, but also that such hypotheses are contrary to most of the available evidence.

The biochemical similarity principle

It has been assumed in nearly all of the experimental work to date that the compounds which occur ubiquitously in *contemporary* life were also essential to the origin of life. This assumption provides one of the criteria of success for the Miller-type simulation experiment as well as for later extensions to the aqueous phase. The assumption is by no means necessary, but provides the simplest working hypothesis [41].

In a Miller-type experiment, many different products are formed from a few simple starting materials, as expected. (What is remarkable is that many more conceivable low-molecular-weight compounds are *not* formed in detectable yields [42].)

In order to determine if the results have any relevance for the origin of life problem, one needs some plausible guidelines for the interpretation of the results. The guideline most commonly used results in a search among the reaction products for substances of contemporary biological interest. In the sparking experiment described above, the striking success was due to the fact that α-amino acids were found among the reaction products. Of course, other substances were formed as well, many of which were not identified [43]. Some of these unknown substances quite probably do not occur in contemporary life.

Although the biochemical similarity principle *as applied to specific biological compounds* is the most commonly used criterion of experimental success, it is not the only one, nor is it necessarily the most relevant one. For example, one could attempt to detect the occurrence of specific kinds of *processes* rather than specific products in these experiments. Such processes as radiation-induced oxidation-reduction, increasing average molecular weight, or nonrandom sequence ordering of amino acid residues in growing polypeptides might all be relevant since they occur in some way in contemporary life. The first of these processes was in fact demonstrated under very simple conditions in Calvin's pioneering experiment involving the radiation-induced reduction of carbon dioxide to formic acid and formaldehyde [39].

As an additional alternative to the biochemical similarity hypothesis it has been argued that many more types of compounds than those presently functioning in living systems might have been crucially involved in the origin of life [44]. However, it is not clear how this hypothesis of biochemical diversity might be tested experimentally.

1-5 EXPERIMENTAL TECHNIQUES AND THE STATUS OF CONCLUSIONS

Experimental procedures

Many of the actual laboratory manipulations carried out by investigators working on the origin of life problem are indistinguishable from those used in other fields such as analytical chemistry or protein biochemistry. For example, during the analytic phase of the work in primitive atmosphere experiments, it is not possible to tell by inspection from the outside that the work is concerned with the origin of life problem. The paper chromatography, the electrophoresis, and the other techniques are identical to those used in connection with other chemical problems. The same kinds of results, subject to the same kinds of limitations and experimental errors, are obtained whether or not the work is connected with the problem of biogenesis. Other kinds of experimental procedures are more uniquely related to the origin of life problem, such as filling and turning on a spark apparatus. But even here many of the individual operations, e.g., vacuum techniques and the use of high-voltage equipment, are identical to those employed in the study of various problems in chemistry and physics.

Status of conclusions

The most characteristic features of research on the origin of life problem are associated with the formulation of the problem, the setting up of hypotheses, the criteria of success for a given experiment, and the status of conclusions, and not with the individual laboratory operations. What emerges from the results of many kinds of simulation experiments is a very complex and detailed partial picture of slowly increasing plausibility. The status of conclusions derived in this way is akin to that of historical conclusions.

Proof in the sense in which one thinks of it in chemistry and physics is not attainable in the problem of primordial biogenesis. In one very important sense, the origin of life problem does not allow the degree of certainty obtainable in human historical studies because tangible evidence of the type ordinarily used in the solution of human historical problems, such as documents and artifacts, has not been available.

Even with these limitations, however, some remarkably consistent major themes recur in the experimental data. These themes will be discussed in detail in Chaps. 4 to 6. Their occurrence strongly suggests that current investigations and inquiries are revealing to us at least the *general features* of processes that were involved in biogenesis. In addition, very recent work on the biochemical fossils identifiable in Precambrian sediments may help remedy the lack of direct historical evidence bearing on the origin [11].

1-6 ALTERNATIVE FORMULATIONS OF THE PROBLEM: SOME ADDITIONAL DIFFICULTIES

The formulation of the origin of life problem as a historical problem requires that in a given experiment some attempt be made to simulate some particular set of primitive Earth conditions thought to be most relevant to the particular hypothetical phase of molecular evolution being investigated. The degree to which a given set of experimental conditions actually simulates primitive Earth conditions is very often the subject of considerable controversy among workers in the field. In Chap. 3, the evidence supporting various theories about the nature of primitive Earth conditions will be presented and discussed in some detail.

It is only by means of an exhaustive analysis of the available geochemical and geophysical data on the surface and interior of the Earth, on meteorites, and on the rest of the solar system, as well as the spectroscopic evidence on the distribution of elements in the cosmos (and this carried out with extraordinary ingenuity), that one can make a case for any particular model of the early history of the Earth. Urey [45] has made such a survey of the available evidence (up until 1952) and has drawn some highly plausible conclusions about some of the *general* conditions prevailing on the primitive Earth. For example, he has considered the probable composition of the primitive secondary atmosphere, the probable volume of the primitive oceans, the state of oxidation of the surface rocks, and the probable surface temperature ranges. Most of his conclusions have been disputed to some extent, but there is general agreement at least among "origin-of-lifers" on major points such as the virtual absence of molecular oxygen in the primitive secondary atmosphere.

However, many of the *details* of the primitive environment are not known and may not even be knowable in principle, e.g., the exact composition of the atmosphere, the pH of the oceans, the kinds, amounts, and distributions of mineral surfaces, and the fine structure of highly specialized microenvironments. Some of these detailed features of the surface of the primitive Earth may have been necessary for the origin of life. In particular, a very specific kind of collection of diurnal cycles such as variation in tides, temperature, deposition of organic material on estuary banks, solar radiation, and local concentrations of various substances might have been required for the origin. Because of the uncertainties in primitive geochemistry, some workers have been pessimistic about the prospects for meaningful experimental work on the problem; others have tried to formulate the problem somewhat differently in order to avoid the necessity of a dependence on the details of primitive Earth conditions [46].

At this point it may be useful to reiterate why the problem is of such great interest in order to give you some intuitive insight into why persistent efforts have been made to study the problem experimentally despite all of the above limitations. We have already described how the origin of life problem arises naturally from a backward extrapolation of the diversification of phylogeny over geologic time. Also, we have suggested how a given individual may come to pose the problem through a kind of dialectic in the evolution of his own curiosity about biological origins, starting out with the child's question "Where did I come from?" However, we have not yet mentioned Oparin's argument that in order to understand fully the chemical nature of *contemporary life,* one must know how life originated [47]. Molecular biologists will probably elucidate most, if not all, of the molecular processes occurring in living cells, but we shall not even then be able to explain why certain reaction sequences occur and others do not. In this sense the origin of life problem is worth pursuing for one of the same reasons that historical studies are worth pursuing—the results of these studies presumably help us to understand the present.

Another much more practical impetus for studying the origin of life is the potential commercial utility of some of the new chemical reactions discovered in simulation experiments. For example, it has recently been shown that adenine can be efficiently produced on a commercial scale by a slightly modified version of a reaction scheme originally discovered and elucidated in a primitive Earth experiment [48]. Also, information obtained in primitive atmosphere experiments might help provide useful guidelines in the search for possible early stages in prebiological evolution occurring at the present time on other planets.

One alternative way to formulate the problem poses the following question: What are the general conditions required for the spontaneous formation of self-replicating systems from an originally nonliving environment? This formulation is considerably more general than the historical one and allows for the emergence of life under conditions differing from those occurring on the Earth. The general emphasis here is to find minimum sufficient requirements of a very general sort. Therefore, most of the work directed toward finding a solution of this type has been theoretical in nature and involved with model systems, based on computer theory, which in some way exhibit autonomic increase in complexity of behavior toward self-replication [49]. This approach is clearly not tied to specific primitive Earth conditions. However, it is difficult, but not impossible, to conceive of meaningful experimental tests for theories of this type.

A third formulation poses the following question: Can we find any single set of chemical and physical steps whatsoever which exhibit a transition from nonliving to living behavior? Such a sequence of events could be completely independent of what actually took place on the primitive Earth. We are thinking here specifically of the suggestion that *any* such demonstration would enormously aid our attempts to understand the emergence of life on the Earth [50].

Although these two alternative formulations have given rise to some experimental work, the bulk of the work to date has been consciously directed toward the solution of the historical problem. Experiments have been performed under laboratory conditions not grossly different from the hypothetical primitive Earth conditions.

The uncertainties caused by not knowing primitive geochemical conditions in detail are ameliorated to some extent by the following experimental observation: α-amino acids are consistently produced in primitive atmosphere experiments even though a variety of different initial gaseous mixtures and a variety of different free-energy sources have been employed. Therefore, not knowing the relative quantitative significance of each of the free-energy sources or not knowing the exact composition of the primitive secondary atmosphere does not invalidate the conclusion that α-amino acids were produced in fair abundance in the primitive atmosphere. However, we must still have some evidence to back up our contentions about the main features of the primitive atmosphere, e.g., its overall *reducing* character, as opposed to the *oxidizing* character of the contemporary atmosphere.

In the same vein, if several different experimental sets of conditions for the polymerization of biological monomers into biopolymers can be found, all of which are more or less geochemically plausible (or at least are not grossly inconsistent with what little we know with relative certainty about the surface of the primitive Earth), then the major problem of whether or not polymers could have formed nonenzymatically under natural conditions is resolved. However, we may never know the fine details of the process as it actually took place on the primitive Earth.

So far we have alluded only to those experiments in which only a very limited part of molecular evolution was being investigated, usually under rather simple reaction conditions. Another experimental approach has been suggested recently in which it is proposed that a much more complex set of conditions be simulated in a single apparatus. In fact, it is suggested that a complete artificial primitive seashore be set up [49].

In order to understand the basis for such a proposal, it is necessary to discuss a particular kind of theory of the origin of self-replicating macromolecular systems. This is done briefly in Chap. 7. However, in most of the simulation studies carried out to date, major emphasis has been placed on the production of particular kinds of biochemical substances, rather than on a search for mechanisms by which these substances might have spontaneously organized into self-maintaining, *dynamic*, self-replicating chemical systems.

It has been suggested that quite complex microscopic environments, such as imperfections in mineral lattices or regions near particular conformations of growing polypeptides, might have been crucial to this kind of self-organization [49]. Therefore, it is argued, one ought to try to include in a simulation experiment *all* of the general surface conditions likely to have been present on the primitive Earth—sterile sea water, sand and clay minerals, reducing gases, ultraviolet radiation, periodic tilting of the whole apparatus to simulate the tides, and light and dark periods to simulate the diurnal cycle. The apparatus is then turned on, and one periodically examines the various parts of the system for evidence that the chemical complexity is moving from chaos (the initial condition) toward more and more organized behavior and eventually to some kind of rudimentary self-reproduction.

The difficulty which immediately arises when one actually tries to do such an experiment is that it is not at all clear what one should look for. Short of full-blown bacteria, what kind of phenomenon should be taken as evidence of life or of a trend toward life? What is needed is some kind of definition of the minimum requirements for life. Although this may seem to be a simple problem, it is actually very difficult, and a good deal of discussion of it has appeared in the scientific literature. All of the three major formulations of the origin of life problem, as well as the search for extraterrestrial life, require some kind of definition of the term "life." It will be recalled that at the beginning of this chapter the problem was formulated in terms of a hypothetical primordial population of microorganisms similar in organization to the simplest of contemporary microorganisms. It might be thought that the properties of these organisms could provide a suitable approximate definition of the first life—that they might suggest what to look for in, say, an artificial seashore experiment. This is fine if we ever have the phenomenal luck of finding a fully developed organism arising in such a simulation experiment. What we need are some useful criteria to aid us in recognizing the *intermediate* stages in dynamic organization. The difficulty of formulating such criteria is perhaps the most serious challenge confronting us.

In the next chapter we shall briefly survey the few known fossil remains of ancient Precambrian organisms and the methods used to determine the absolute ages of these fossils. Chapter 3 is devoted to a discussion of lines of evidence drawn from many different disciplines which have been used to support current conceptions of the primeval scenario in which the origin of terrestrial life might have taken place.

REFERENCES

1. Oparin, A. I.: "The Origin of Life on the Earth," Academic Press Inc., New York, 1957.
2. Florkin, M.: "Comparative Biochemistry," Academic Press Inc., New York, 1964.
3. Kerkut, G. A.: "Implications of Evolution," Pergamon Press, New York, 1960.
4. Munk, W. H., and G. L. F. MacDonald: "The Rotation of the Earth," Cambridge University Press, London, 1960.
5. Arrhenius, S.: "Worlds in the Making," H. Borns (trans.), Harper & Row, Publishers, Incorporated, New York, 1908.
6. Shklovskii, I. S., and C. Sagan: "Intelligent Life in the Universe," Holden-Day, San Francisco, 1966.
7. Nason, A.: "Textbook of Modern Biology," John Wiley & Sons, Inc., New York, 1965.
8. Thimann, K. V.: "The Life of Bacteria," The Macmillan Company, New York, 1955.
9. Rutten, M. G.: "The Geological Aspects of the Origin of Life on Earth," Elsevier Publishing Company, Amsterdam, 1962.
10. Glaessner, M. F.: *Biol. Rev. Cambridge Phil. Soc.*, 37:467 (1962).
11. Eglington, G., and M. Calvin: *Sci. Am.*, 32 (January, 1967).

12. Horowitz, N. H.: *Science,* **151**:789 (1966).
13. "Webster's New Collegiate Dictionary," p. 773, G. C. Merriam Company, Springfield, Mass., 1953.
14. Aristotle: "De generatione animalium," A. L. Peck (trans.), Harvard University Press, Cambridge, Mass., 1953.
15. St. Basil the Great: in "A Select Library of Nicene and Post-Nicene Fathers of the Christian Church," ser. 2, vol. 8, p. 102, B. Jackson (trans.), Oxford University Press, London, 1895.
16. Sighart, J.: "Albertus Magnus, sein Leben und seine Wissenschaft," G. J. Manz, Regensburg, 1857.
17. Van Helmont, J. B.: "Ortus Medicinae," p. 70.9, Mercurius van Helmont, Amsterodami, 1667.
18. Hawkins, R. (trans.): personal communication.
19. Redi, F.: "Experiments on the Generation of Insects," M. Bigelow (trans.), The Open Court Publishing Company, La Salle, Ill., 1909.
20. Bulloch, W.: "The History of Bacteriology," Oxford University Press, London, 1936.
21. Needham, J. T.: *Phil. Trans. Royal Soc. London,* no. 490, p. 615 (1749).
22. Schwann, T.: *Ann. Physik,* **41**:184 (1837).
23. Cheyne, W. Watson: "Antiseptic Surgery," Smith, Elder and Co., London, 1882.
24. Original in Ref. 22; English translation in Ref. 27.
25. Pasteur, L.: *Ann. Physik,* **64**:5 (1862).
26. Dubos, R. J.: "Pasteur and Modern Science," Doubleday & Company, Inc., Garden City, N.Y., 1960.
27. Conant, J. B.: "Pasteur's and Tyndall's Study of Spontaneous Generation," Harvard University Press, Cambridge, Mass., 1953.
28. Pouchet, F.: "Hétérogénie ou traité de la génération spontanée basé sur de nouvelles expériences," J. B. Baillière et fils, Paris, 1859.
29. van Tieghem, P.: "Traité de botanique," Libraire F. Savy, Paris, 1884.
30. Stern, H., and D. L. Nanney: "The Biology of Cells," John Wiley & Sons, Inc., New York, 1965.
31. Wohler, F.: *Pogg. Ann.,* **3**:177 (1825); **12**:253 (1828).
32. Richtmyer, F. K., E. H. Kennard, and T. Lauritsen: "Introduction to Modern Physics," McGraw-Hill Book Company, New York, 1955.
33. Pannekoek, A.: "A History of Astronomy," Interscience Publishers, New York, 1961.
34. Grabau, A. W.: "A Textbook of Geology," D. C. Heath and Company, Boston, 1921.
35. Haldane, J. B. S.: *Rationalists Ann.,* 148 (1929).
36. Oparin, A. I.: "Proiskhozhdenie zhizni," Izd. Moskovskii Rabochii, Moscow, 1924; "The Origin of Life," The Macmillan Company, New York, 1938.
37. Oró, J.: *Annals N.Y. Acad. Sci.,* **108**:464 (1963).
38. Miller, S. L.: *Science,* **117**:528 (1953).
39. Garrison, W. M., et al.: *Science,* **114**:416 (1951).
40. Miller, S. L.: *J. Am. Chem. Soc.,* **77**:2351 (1955).
41. Young, R. S., and C. Ponnamperuma: Early Evolution of Life, *BSCS Pamphlet* #11, D. C. Heath and Company, Boston, 1964.
42. Palm, C., and M. Calvin: *J. Am. Chem. Soc.,* **84**:2115 (1962).
43. Miller, S. L.: in A. I. Oparin (ed.), "The Origin of Life on the Earth," p. 123, The Macmillan Company, New York, 1959.
44. Pirie, N. W.: in A. I. Oparin (ed.), "The Origin of Life on the Earth," p. 76, The Macmillan Company, New York, 1959.
45. Urey, H.: "The Planets," Yale University Press, New Haven, Conn., 1952.

46. Pattee, H. H.: in F. F. Nord (ed), "Advances in Enzymology," vol. 27, p. 381, Interscience Publishers, New York, 1965.
47. Oparin, A. I.: "Life: Its Nature, Origin and Development," Oliver & Boyd Ltd., Edinburgh, 1961.
48. *Chem. Eng. News,* p. 39, August, 8, 1966.
49. Pattee, H. H.: *Biophys. J.,* 1:683 (1961); in S. W. Fox (ed.), "The Origins of Prebiological Systems," p. 385, Academic Press Inc., New York, 1965.
50. Schramm, G.: in S. W. Fox (ed.), "The Origins of Prebiological Systems," p. 299, Academic Press Inc., New York, 1965.

the antiquity of terrestrial life

2-1 THE CONCEPT OF ABSOLUTE AGE

In this chapter we shall be concerned with two questions:

1. How long has life, in some form, existed on the Earth?
2. How long has the Earth itself existed as an organized spherical body?

Before turning to current lines of evidence bearing on these questions, let us first briefly discuss some of our most immediate perceptions of age. It is a commonplace fact of our experience that different individual living people have different ages. These ages can, of course, vary over the entire life span of man and in most cases they can be ascertained unequivocally. The fact that we can easily find out the chronological age of a given individual may seem so trivial as to be totally unrelated to our present inquiry. However, the factors on which the determination of human chronological ages depends are not so obvious, and, indeed, these factors provide us with important clues about the nature of the relatively much more difficult problem of determining the chronological age of life in general.

First of all, the age of a given individual is a statement of the number of years which have elapsed since that person was born. No information at all is provided about the lengths of time that have elapsed since individual material components (e.g., chemical elements, inorganic ions, and simple compounds such as water) of the person's body were formed. The age of a person is essentially a measure of the length of time during which *some* assemblage of matter has been *organized* into that particular human being.

Secondly, the possibility of assigning chronological age depends upon man's ancient perceptions of some quite general and reliable periodic processes in the environment. These include the diurnal cycle of light and dark, the lunar cycle, the annual progression of the seasons, and the corresponding apparent motion of the sun against the pattern of the fixed stars. The latter process provides the units in which chronological ages are conventionally measured.

Thirdly, we must have some means of reliably recording the number of times the standard periodic process, i.e., the revolution of the Earth about the sun, has occurred between the birth of the individual and the present. Perhaps the minimum requirements here are a reasonably good memory and some system of counting. However, without the aid of writing, age determinations would be more than mildly bothersome and subject to much uncertainty, particularly with respect to older persons. Writing provides us a means of constructing a tangible enduring record of the number of annual cycles which have occurred since some arbitrarily chosen starting point. If we assign consecutive numbers to the annual cycles, we have the ingredients of a calendar. This in turn provides us with an unequivocal means of assigning absolute chronological ages since all we need is a surviving written record of the number of the year in which the person was born. The same method applies to persons who lived at various times in the past, provided we have, in addition, surviving records of the years in which the individuals died.

The existence of surviving written records allows us to assign ages not only to individual people, but also to many other entities as well. For example, the age of a given building is easily determined if we have a record of the year in which it was constructed. Again, the term "age" refers to the number of years which have elapsed since the materials from which the building was constructed were first organized into the structure and does not refer to the ages of the materials themselves. By repeated explicit associations of certain calendar years with particular objects we can gradually build up an intuitive sense of the antiquities of various kinds of material objects of human culture, so that eventually the ages can be approximated without explicit reference to the calendar. In this way individual examples of various historical artifacts, such as pottery chards, weapons, and tools, can be dated even though they bear no specific chronological inscriptions. In all cases, however, some prior reference of similarly constructed objects to specific dates is required.

Written records can also allow us to discover and to assign absolute dates to particular events in human history, even though no other artifacts of the events may have survived to the present day. But if we

proceed chronologically backward through the surviving written records
of the human past in an attempt to gain some sense of the antiquity
of man, we find that for periods older than about 5,000 years ago virtually no such records exist. The oldest known examples of human
writing, for example, the cuneiform tablets of the Tigris-Euphrates Valley, date back to about 3000 B.C. [1]. This date apparently corresponds
to the earliest invention of writing, and thus in assigning absolute dates
to earlier periods of human "prehistory" and beyond that to the epochs
of Earth history before the dawn of man, evidence other than written
records must be sought.

Perhaps the most familiar method for determining absolute ages
without the benefit of written records involves simply counting the number of annual growth rings in a cross section of the trunk in certain
kinds of trees. Although this technique does not involve written records
of the succession of years, it nevertheless satisfies the same fundamental
criteria for absolute age determination discussed above. The annual
growth rings represent tangible surviving traces of a periodic biological
process [2]. Of course, application of the method depends upon the
discovery of a correlation between the currently observable annual
growth pattern of the tree trunk, on the one hand, and the discernible
pattern of discrete concentric rings, on the other. It must be remem-
bered that what is being measured here is the age of the tree, and
consequently the method is of no value whatsoever in dating the origin
of life since trees are highly evolved species. However, the maximum
ages so far obtained by this method for contemporary trees are only
several thousand years. For fossil trees, the lifetime must be distinguished from the number of years which have elapsed since the death
of the tree.

An additional method of absolute dating, similar in principle to
ring counting in trees but relying instead on a periodic geological rather
than biological process, might at first glance appear to provide us with
a means of extending our absolute time scale considerably beyond the
earliest written records of man. This procedure involves counting the
number of alternating fine and coarse layers of particular minerals in
certain specialized kinds of sedimentary formations. For example, the
so-called varved clays deposited in glacial lakes exhibit a regular alterna-
tion of clearly distinguishable summer and winter bands [2,3]. Thus,
by simply counting the number of bands, we can determine the number
of years required for the deposition of a given thickness of the corresponding sedimentary bed. In this way, absolute ages of several tens
of thousands of years have been reckoned, corresponding to the time
elapsed since the last Ice Age.

Again the same fundamental criteria are satisfied. A repeating annual sequence of geological events can be observed to be taking place
at the present time in glacial lakes. Each repetition of the cycle results

in the deposition of a tangible, enduring pattern of bands which correspond to the enduring growth rings of trees and to the tangible marks and symbols of surviving written records of the succession of years. In the case of the varved clays, the "writing" is accomplished by the geological process of mineral deposition. The "numbering" of successive years is achieved by the annual deposition of succeeding layers one upon the other. However, just as in the case of the growth rings of the trees, we are still dealing with times which, at most, amount to only thousands of years [3]. We still have no hint about the immense antiquity of the Earth.

So far we have considered only those methods of absolute age determination which, in one way or another, involve tangible records containing a discrete number of recognizable marks or structures which corresponds in a direct way to the number of years elapsed. As we have seen, such methods do not carry us very far along the way to the remotest antiquities of the Earth. In the following discussion we shall make a transition to a group of dating methods which differ from those described above in one important way: the natural processes on which they depend are not periodic; rather, they occur continuously. In every case, however, the natural process can be observed to be taking place at the present time at rates which can be estimated. With techniques utilizing the decay of naturally occurring radioactive isotopes, the rate of the process is precisely measured, even though in most cases the values are exceedingly small.

Before turning to the radioactive dating methods, which provide us with our most reliable information about the almost incredibly immense spans of time over which Earth history is spread, let us consider two specific examples of somewhat simpler methods which have been used in the past. These ingenious methods, although they are now known to give answers which are erroneous by wide margins, will nevertheless provide us with some intuitive sense of the kind of numbers encountered in Earth history.

The first example involves an attempt to estimate the average rate at which eroded materials have been deposited into sediments throughout geological time. The igneous and metamorphic rocks of the continental land masses are continuously being worn down primarily by the weathering action of water in streams and rivers [4]. The eroded rock-forming substances are carried some distance by the moving bodies of water and eventually may be deposited in sedimentary beds such as the flood plain of the Nile River.

If we could estimate the average rate at which the thickness of sedimentary deposits has been increasing during geologic time (assuming the process of deposition to be cumulative in a simple way), then we could estimate the time required for the formation of these sediments. The following observation provides a clue [4]: in 1854, a statue of Rameses II, which dates from about 1200 B.C., was found at Memphis, in the Nile Delta, buried under 9 ft of river sediment. Thus, the average rate at which sedimentary material was deposited at Memphis is simply 9×12 in./3,000 years or about 3.5 in./century. Various estimates of the global average total thickness of sedimentary rocks lie somewhere between 2,500 and about 8,000 ft [5]. Let us then simply calculate the time required to form a sedimentary column 5,000 ft thick, assuming an average rate of deposition of 3.5 in./century; the answer turns out to be 1.7 million years.

Of course, this result is only a very crude estimate of the minimum time required for formation of the sedimentary rocks since the 9 ft of alluvial mud under which Rameses II was buried corresponds to a much shorter column of sedimentary rock because of compression and water removal during the formation of the latter. Secondly, sedimentary rocks themselves participate in the so-called *geochemical cycle* by undergoing conversion to metamorphic rock under high pressure at, for example, the base of the sedimentary column [5]. Thus, the present total thickness of sedimentary rock does not reflect the total amount of sediments formed during geologic time. Nevertheless, the calculation does seem to indicate that the antiquity of the Earth must be reckoned, at the very least, in millions of years.

As a second example, we shall consider a method for estimating the minimum age of the oceans based on the rate at which dissolved salts are currently transported to the oceans via rivers and streams [4]. The method is very straightforward, at least in principle, and simply involves a comparison of two numbers: the total amount of dissolved salts in the contemporary oceans and the total amount of dissolved materials supplied to the oceans per year. The first number is relatively easy to obtain since many data are available on the concentrations of various salts in different oceanic regions, and the total volume of the oceans is reasonably accurately known ($1,370 \times 10^6$ km^3 [5]). The average salinity of the oceans is about 3.6 gm of dissolved materials per 100 cc of ocean water, so that the total amount of dissolved salts is about 50×10^{21} gm, or roughly 5×10^{16} tons [5]. As you might readily expect, the second of the required numbers, the total annual inflow of salts, is much more difficult to obtain, and estimates vary from 1.6×10^8 tons/year [4] to 30×10^8 tons/year [5]. If we assume that the average rate of inflow throughout the history of the oceans is somewhere near 5×10^8 tons/year, then we can readily calculate the length of time required for the salt content to rise from an assumed initial value of zero to its present value. The answer turns out to be 100 million years.

In the above calculation, several important factors were neglected [4]. For example, the current rate at which salts are delivered to the oceans is probably considerably higher than the average value throughout geological time since various lines of geologic evidence suggest that during much of Earth's history, the surface of the Earth exhibited much less relief than at present. Therefore, much less erosion was taking place. Also, it is probable that uplifting of previously submerged land resulted in the removal of large amounts of salt from the oceans. Subsequent erosion would then return the salt to the oceans, and in fact much of the dissolved material currently being transported by rivers might have been recycled many times in this way. Therefore, in order to obtain a reasonably accurate estimate of the net rate of accumulation of salts in the oceans, it is necessary to subtract the amounts of recycled salts from the total measured contributions of the major river systems. We must conclude that even a period as long as 100 million years represents only a bare minimum for the duration of geologic time.

2-2 THE GEOLOGIC COLUMN

Sedimentary rocks

Now that we have some intuitive sense of the concept of absolute duration in geology and of the numerous difficulties associated with accurate determinations of such time spans, let us briefly consider another kind of general procedure for assigning ages. The method begins with the observation that the sedimentary rocks of the world exhibit a more or less regular pattern of superimposed beds, or strata, of varying texture, color, and thickness [6]. Indeed, the presence of such a system of layers is one of the major diagnostic features of sedimentary rocks, as opposed to igneous and metamorphic rocks.

Our earlier example of sedimentation in the Nile River Delta provides a convenient illustration of the beginning stages of the formation of sedimentary rocks. Various kinds of debris removed from rocks by the process of weathering are transported by the river to the site of deposition. As the weight of accumulated sediment builds up, the pressure at lower-lying regions increases, with the result that the material at these depths is compressed and dehydrated to some extent. Eventually, a bed of compact, hard rock is formed [7]. The variation in texture and color of the successive strata reflects differences in the average composition of the deposited material during different spans of time. The relevance of these sedimentary formations for the problem of age determination lies in the principle of superposition; that is, successive layers were formed in strict chronological sequence so that the lower-lying strata are older than those situated near the top of the formation [3].

The classical fossil record

If some means could be found for correlating a given set of layers at one locale with a corresponding set formed simultaneously at another site, then it might be possible to construct a quite general chronology of geological history which might extend a considerable distance along the way toward the remotest antiquities of the Earth. So far we have written very little about the fossil record of past life, even though one of the principal questions we are concerned with in this chapter is that of the absolute age of terrestrial life. Perhaps this is the most appropriate place to include a consideration of the fossil record, since the latter is imprisoned for the most part in sedimentary rocks and since it in fact provides us with an elegant procedure for matching one set of strata with another, even on a worldwide scale. The reason for this is that different layers contain different characteristic assemblages of fossils [3].

A few general points are worth mentioning [8]. First of all, examination of progressively deeper-lying sedimentary beds reveals an overall trend toward morphologically simpler types of fossils. Secondly, with increasing depth, there is an overall decline in the number of distinguishable species. Finally, many slowly varying sequences of similar fossils, such as those of ancient marine snails, can be continuously traced through many layers. All of these facts are consistent with the general picture of increasing diversification of phylogeny during Darwinian evolution discussed in Chap. 1.

What is important for our purposes is the fact that the succession of sedimentary layers can be divided into major epochs in the history of life, depending upon the predominant kinds of fossils prevailing in each set of layers. If a given kind of fossil occurs in only a few contiguous layers and is of widespread occurrence in sediments around the world, it can be used as an "index fossil" for correlating the ages of rock layers found at different locations. If the index fossil occurs at a number of different sites, it is a reasonable assumption that the corresponding strata were formed simultaneously in Earth history. By means of several such index fossils, such as the marine invertebrate *Hypothyridina cuboides* [4], it is possible to place many different areas of the globe on the same relative time scale, although we have no means as yet of assigning absolute numbers of years to the various epochs of our worldwide geologic column. However, since historical geologists and paleontologists had already investigated the fossil record in great detail and had solved many of the problems of establishing relative ages before radioactive dating came into prominence, the affixing of an absolute time scale to the epochs of the geologic column was like the frosting on the cake.

On the basis of the above discussion, you might think that the absolute age of the oldest terrestrial sediments would tell us how long life has existed on the Earth since there is no reason to suspect at the outset that the fossil record would not be continuous all the way down to the base of the geologic column. However, the fossil record undergoes an abrupt thinning out considerably before the oldest sediments are reached [9]. The break occurs at the so-called Cambrian-Precambrian boundary, which corresponds to the epoch in the history of life during which species with easily preservable hard parts such as shells first became abundant. At greater depths in the geologic column, the surviving remains of past life are few and far between. The few assemblages of Precambrian fossils discovered to date consist largely of such organisms as radiolaria and crustaceans, which are much more highly evolved than the hypothetical primordial population of protobacteria discussed in Chap. 1 [3,9]. Fortunately, however, fossil remains of some very ancient Precambrian microorganisms, including forms resembling blue-green algae and bacteria, have been recently discovered. We shall discuss these remarkable finds in detail.

In summary, we have seen, first of all, that two fundamental requirements must be satisfied by an absolute dating procedure:

1. Surviving tangible traces must exist of the operation of some cumulative geological or biological process which may be either periodic or continuous.
2. The time-dependent process must be currently observable and its absolute rate must be measurable.

Dating methods dependent upon the operation of annually recurring processes have yielded maximum ages of the order of only several thousand years. Procedures based on very slow, cumulative geological processes extend the absolute geochronological scale to hundreds of thousands of years, but they still do not accurately reflect the immense antiquity of the Earth.

Secondly, we emphasized the point that the *relative* chronology of much of the classical fossil record has been established by correlation of corresponding strata over wide geographic ranges. Reliable establishment of the absolute dates for a few key points in the worldwide geologic column, such as the beginning of each major epoch, would thus allow the construction of an absolute time scale for a substantial fraction of past terrestrial life. In order to achieve this, it is necessary to utilize a technique of recent development and high sophistication, namely, the method of radioactive dating. The cumulative time-dependent process upon which the method depends is the decay of certain very long-lived, unstable atomic nuclei in the surface rocks of the Earth. In the following sections we shall discuss in some detail how the radioactive clocks have given us the ages of terrestrial life and of the Earth itself.

2-3 RADIOACTIVE ISOTOPES AS GEOLOGIC CLOCKS

General principles

Any given chunk of igneous rock is made up of a number of different kinds of minerals, each of which consists of specific, very regular crystalline arrays of atoms [5]. The elements which occur most commonly in the rock-forming minerals of the crust of the Earth are, in order of decreasing relative abundance, O, Si, Al, Fe, Mg, Ca, Na, and K, with many other minor constituents represented as well [5]. The individual atoms in the crystalline arrays are locked in place by very strong electrostatic forces.

Although some degree of slow chemical change may take place on the exposed surfaces of the crystals, virtually no exchange of materials (e.g., substitution of one atom for another) takes place in the interior of the crystal lattices. Thus, the relative positions of the atoms may remain undisturbed for vast stretches of time. Since any currently existing piece of igneous rock was originally formed by the crystallization of its constituent minerals during cooling of a molten volcanic magma, the absolute age of that rock may be simply defined as the number of years which have elapsed since the original crystallization took place [5,10]. We cannot make a corresponding definition for the absolute age of a given sedimentary bed. The constituent minerals had already existed for various unknown spans of time in other sediments and in igneous and metamorphic rocks before they were weathered away and eventually deposited in the sedimentary bed. In the case of an ore vein, the absolute age corresponds to the time elapsed since the ore minerals were first deposited in the vein, either from a dense gaseous phase derived from a magma or from a hydrothermal aqueous solution [3].

One important feature of rock-forming minerals deserves mention here. Although the elemental composition of a given mineral sample is well defined and measurable, submicroscopic domains of the crystal lattices exhibit occasional irregularities in lattice ion content [5]. Typically, several elements will predominate in the repeating spatial configuration of ions, and each element will have its own characteristic set of lattice positions. Thus, the overall composition of biotite, a particularly stable mica found in granite and frequently used in absolute dating, can be represented by the following formula: $K(Mg, Fe)_3(AlSi_3O_{10})(OH)_2$. The iron and magnesium content is variable from sample to sample, but within well-defined limits. In addition, the crystals contain small and variable amounts of many other elements not noted in the formula. In fact, in some minerals, trace amounts of a substantial fraction of all the elements in the periodic table are detectable.

It is apparent that minerals cannot be considered pure chemical compounds in the ordinary sense since individual samples may exhibit different compositions. The minor constituents are incorporated into the mineral during its original crystallization from the magma and generally remain as permanent features of the crystal structure. The noble gases, however, present a special difficulty since they can participate, at best, in only very weak chemical bonds and, therefore, might conceivably escape the mineral lattice during the course of geologic time [11]. This factor will be significant in connection with two of the principal methods of radioactive dating we shall discuss.

The majority of the atoms in mineral crystals have stable nuclei which presumably have persisted in their present forms since the origin of the elements themselves and, therefore, surely since the time at which they were originally incorporated into a crystal lattice. For each element present in a given sample of rock there are several different isotopes. The possibility of determining the absolute age of a given sample of igneous rock depends upon the remarkable fact that some of these isotopes are unstable and are undergoing characteristic, detectable nuclear transformations yielding stable isotopes of other chemical elements [10]. For example, one of the isotopes of the common rock-forming element potassium is continuously undergoing the following transformation into the elements argon and calcium [3,10]:

$$^{40}K \overset{\beta \text{ emission}}{\nearrow} \; ^{40}Ca$$
$$\underset{\gamma \text{ emission}}{\overset{\text{electron capture}}{\searrow}} \; ^{40}Ar$$

An isotope of the element rubidium, which may substitute for potassium in mineral lattices, transmuters into a single daughter product, namely, an isotope of strontium [3,10], as follows:

$$^{87}Rb \xrightarrow{\beta \text{ emission}} \; ^{87}Sr$$

The isotopes ^{40}K and ^{87}Rb are said to be *radioactive* since the nuclear transformations which they undergo are accompanied by the emission of characteristic, detectable radiations. Both of the above processes have been investigated in detail in the laboratory, and the rates at which they occur have been measured with considerable precision. Such decay rates are conventionally expressed in terms of the half-life, which is the length of time required for one-half the original number of radioactive atoms to decay into the stable daughter products. In the case of ^{40}K, the half-life turns out to be 12.4 billion years. For ^{87}Rb, the value is even higher, namely, 47×10^9 years [12]. By comparison, the half-life of carbon 14, which is perhaps the most widely known radioisotope used for absolute age determinations in history and archeology, is only 5,680 years [12].

The radioactive heavy elements uranium and thorium are present in small, measurable amounts in many minerals and are major components of some minerals, such as UO_2 and ThO_2, both of which are major components of pitchblende [3,13]. Three isotopes of these elements are of interest in the present discussion, namely, ^{235}U (half-life $\tau = 0.7$ billion years), ^{238}U ($\tau = 4.5$ billion years), and ^{232}Th ($\tau = 13.9$

billion years) [12]. Each of these isotopes is the starting point for a different, complex series of radioactive decay processes, culminating in the production of stable isotopes of lead. These sequences are diagramed in Fig. 2-1.

You will note that, in principle, all of the radioactive isotopes discussed above qualify as geologic clocks for determining the absolute ages of igneous rocks or of ores in which they are incorporated. The isotopes are undergoing a currently detectable process, i.e., radioactive decay, resulting in the continuous accumulation of identifiable, stable daughter products. Even though the rates of the various decay processes are exceedingly small, they can be accurately measured with the aid suitable electronic instrumentation.

In order to see how such a method might be applied in practice, let us consider the granitic black mica biotite [10]. This mineral is rich in potassium. The predominant isotope occurring at the lattice points occupied by potassium atoms is ^{39}K, which has a stable nucleus. However, a small fraction of the potassium sites will be occupied by the radioactive isotope ^{40}K. During any given interval of time, say 1,000 or 1 million years, a minute fraction of the ^{40}K atoms will undergo spontaneous decay to argon 40 and calcium 40 atoms, which remain fixed at the original lattice points. The proportion of decay events resulting in the formation of ^{40}Ar remains constant (12 percent) with time [10,12]. With increasing time, there is a steady accumulation of the two daughter products at the expense of ^{40}K. Therefore, the older a given crystal of biotite, the more argon 40 it should contain.* Determination of the age in years would then simply require measurement of the amounts of ^{40}K and ^{40}Ar in the sample. Such measurements can be made with considerable accuracy by means of mass spectrometry, provided that certain precautions are taken to minimize contamination of the sample with ^{40}Ar from the air [10]. All that is required is a suitable mathematical expression which relates the amounts of parent and daughter elements to the absolute age.

In order to obtain the required equation, let us begin with the law of radioactive decay, which applies to all the radioactive isotopes discussed above:

$$P(t) = P(0)e^{-\lambda t} \tag{1}$$

where $P(t)$ is the number of atoms (in a given mineral sample of known mass) of the parent radioactive isotope remaining in the mineral lattice at a time t after the original magmatic crystallization. $P(0)$ denotes the number of parent atoms present at the time of crystallization. The time t is identical to the absolute age of the mineral sample. The radio-

---

* As we shall see later, it is not necessary to know the amount of ^{40}Ca present in the mineral.

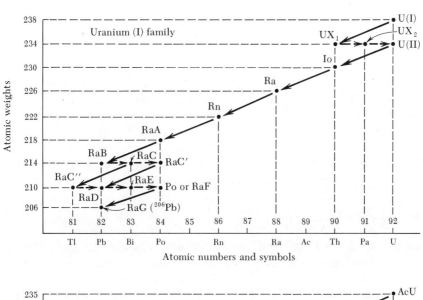

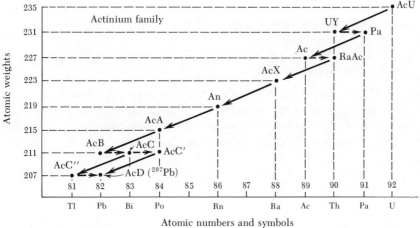

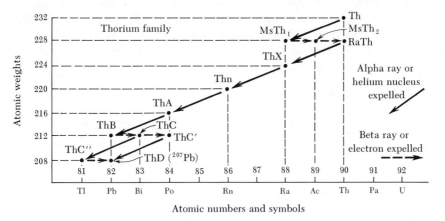

FIG. 2-1 The decay schemes of the uranium, actinium, and thorium series of natural radioactive elements. (*After* [14].)

active decay constant λ is inversely related to the half-life ($\lambda = \ln 2/\tau$). The decay law simply expresses the experimental fact that in equal intervals of time a constant fraction of the remaining radioactive atoms undergo conversion to the daughter products. In the following discussion, we shall denote daughter products by the general symbol D.

If we assume that the sample has remained a *closed system* throughout its entire history (i.e., that it has neither lost nor gained any atoms of the parent and daughter isotopes or any atoms of the intermediate isotopes in the case of the uranium and thorium decay schemes), then the sum of parent and daughter atoms remains constant, and we can write

$$P(0) = P(t) + \Delta D \tag{2}$$

where ΔD denotes the total number of atoms of the daughter species produced radiogenically during the lifetime of the sample.

Let us focus on the ^{40}K–^{40}Ar dating method. In this case, ΔD contains contributions from both ^{40}Ar and ^{40}Ca. However, since the fraction of decay events resulting in ^{40}Ar is known to remain constant at 12 percent, we can write

$$\Delta D_A = 0.12[P(0) - P(t)] \tag{3}$$

where ΔD_A is simply the number of ^{40}Ar atoms produced radiogenically during the lifetime of the mineral. The term in brackets denotes the total number of ^{40}K atoms which underwent radioactive decay. Solving for $P(0)$ from Eq. (1) and substituting the answer into Eq. (3), we obtain

$$\frac{\Delta D_A}{P(t)} = 0.12(e^{\lambda t} - 1) \tag{4}$$

In practice only the *total amount* of daughter species in the sample is measurable. This quantity, however, may have two contributions since at the outset we cannot exclude the possibility that some of the daughter species might have been incorporated into the mineral at the time of its formation. Therefore, the total amount of argon 40 [$D_A(t)$] must be expressed as follows:

$$D_A(t) = D_A(0) + \Delta D_A \tag{5}$$

where $D_A(0)$ is the amount of ^{40}Ar initially present. Fortunately, it turns out that argon apparently does not enter into the growing crystal lattices of any mineral forming in a cooling magma [5,10]. We may safely assume then that $D_A(0) = 0.$*

---

* In the case of the uranium-lead and thorium-lead methods, such a simplification is not possible since, in general, varying amounts of the radiogenic isotopes ^{206}Pb, ^{207}Pb, and ^{208}Pb will have been present initially in the crystallizing minerals [10,11

Eliminating $D_A(0)$ from Eq. (5) and substituting the solution for ΔD_A into Eq. (4), we obtain the following:

$$\frac{D_A(t)}{P(t)} = 0.12(e^{\lambda t} - 1) \tag{6}$$

Solving this equation for t, we obtain

$$t = \frac{1}{\lambda} \ln \left[\frac{D_A(t)}{0.12P(t)} + 1 \right] \tag{7}$$

Similar equations can be derived for the other commonly used radioactive dating methods. In the next section we shall illustrate the use of such equations by means of an explicit example of absolute age determination.

Although our brief sketch of the general principles of radioactive dating might have suggested to you that the procedures are relatively simple and straightforward, such an impression is a delusion. Aside from the fact that exceedingly sophisticated instrumentation* is required to measure minute amounts of particular radiogenic isotopes, the method involves a number of fundamental uncertainties, not the least important of which are those associated with the assumption that the given rock sample has remained a closed system. This is especially significant in the case of the lead methods since one of the intermediates is the gaseous elements radon (see Fig. 2-1), which can diffuse out of the rock over geologic time, resulting in low age determinations.† Also, acidic ground water is known to remove ^{208}Pb from thorium minerals preferentially, thus making the ages determined by the ^{232}Th–^{208}Pb method consistently lower than those obtained by other methods [15]. Similarly, argon may slowly leak out of some potassium minerals but not others. Thus, it is not possible to use indiscriminately any sample of an ore mineral or an igneous rock for an absolute age determination.

Indications of the suitability of a given rock sample for reliable absolute age determination are provided by a comparison of the results obtained on that sample by two or more different isotopic methods. If the resulting ages differ widely, the rock is unsuitable. On the other hand, if similar answers are obtained by different procedures, the resulting estimate of the age is likely to represent the actual age of the rock since it is unlikely that different isotopes would leach out of the mineral lattices at the same rate. A clear example of such a "concordant" age is provided by a biotite sample from Colorado. A variation of the lead method, in which the $^{207}Pb/^{206}Pb$ ratio is determined, yielded an age

* For lucid elementary discussions of this instrumentation, we refer you to the excellent accounts of Rutten [3] and Hurley [10].
† Such leakage may occur to an appreciable extent in certain very ancient uranium-rihc rocks which have undergone extensive internal radiation damage resulting in numerous imperfections in the crystal lattices.

of 1.7 billion years, whereas the $^{87}Rb–^{87}Sr$ procedure yielded a result of 1.65 billion years [16].

The fundamental assumption underlying our whole discussion of absolute age determination by means of radioactive isotopes is that the absolute rates of decay of the various isotopes have remained constant throughout geologic time. If, at any time in the past, the rates differed appreciably from the presently observable rates, it is obvious that the age results would be completely vitiated. The assumption represents a special case of the more general doctrine of uniformitarianism already discussed in Chap. 1. We pointed out that virtually the only relatively direct evidence bearing on the validity of the doctrine relates to the radioactive decay of certain alpha-particle-emitting isotopes in the uranium decay sequences. The evidence consists of the so-called *pleochroitic rings* which are microscopically discernible around uranium inclusions in certain minerals [3,20]. It is the sharp definition of these rings which bears testimony to the constancy of those physical parameters associated with the alpha-emission process.

At this point it might be useful to list all the criteria which must be satisfied by a mineral sample if it is to be suitable for a reliable absolute age determination. These are as follows:

1. The sample must be part of an igneous rock or an ore deposit. The modes of formation of most metamorphic and sedimentary rocks preclude the possibility of meaningful isotopic age determinations.

2. The sample must contain measurable amounts of the parent and stable daughter products of a radioactive decay process, or sequence of processes. The absolute rates of these decay processes must be accurately known.

3. The half-lives of the parent isotopes must be comparable to the absolute age of the mineral. If the half-life of a given isotope is very short compared to the absolute age, it will have long since entirely disappeared. Correlated with this requirement is the fact that essentially no short-lived isotopes such as ^{59}Fe ($\tau = 45$ days) [12] are detectable in ancient rocks. The exceptions are the intermediate isotopes in the uranium and thorium decay schemes, some of which have half-lives of the order of seconds or minutes, although these isotopes are present only in exceedingly minute amounts. If the half-life of the parent isotope is orders of magnitude higher than the absolute age of an ancient Precambrian rock, then no detectable decay will have occurred over the entire lifetime of the mineral, and criterion 3 will not be met. The corollary is that such isotopes will be classified as nonradioactive.

4. The mineral must have remained a closed system with respect to leakage or addition of the parent and daughter isotopes, as well as all intermediate isotopes, throughout its lifetime. If age deter-

minations by two or more different isotopic methods agree, it is likely that the sample satisfies this criterion.

5. Some procedure must be available for accurately estimating the amounts of the daughter isotopes likely to have been incorporated into the mineral lattice at the time of crystallization.

6. Experimental means must be available for estimating the extent to which extraneous laboratory sources have contaminated the sample with radiogenic isotopes.

7. The doctrine of uniformitarianism, at least insofar as it bears on radioactive decay of the relevant isotopes, must be true.

As we have emphasized above for ancient Precambrian formations, isotopic age determinations can be performed only on ore deposits or igneous rocks. However, our original goal was to establish an absolute time scale for sedimentary beds since these alone contain traces of ancient life. Is it possible to correlate the absolute ages of igneous rocks with the absolute ages of the sedimentary layers of the geologic column? The answer, fortunately, is yes. Sedimentary formations are frequently penetrated by magmatic intrusions of various ages [3]. A typical situation is illustrated in Fig. 2-2. The geology of how the particular pattern of sedimentary beds shown in this figure was formed is indicated in the caption. It is sufficient to say here that intrusion A must be older than the overlying strata, but younger than the layers into which it originally penetrated. Likewise, intrusion B must be younger than both the upper and lower series of beds through which it penetrated. This sets the minimum age of the upper beds at the absolute age of intrusion B. By the principle of superposition, the beds lying immediately on top of the uppermost boundary of intrusion A must be close to 500 million years old, whereas those lying near the upper extremity of intrusion B have ages near 400 million years. By similar methods, the absolute durations of all the eras in the geologic column have been determined. In particular, the Cambrian-Precambrian boundary has been assigned an absolute age of 600 million years.

Example of an absolute age determination

In order to provide you with some basis for understanding how absolute age determinations are actually carried out in the laboratory, we shall discuss here in some detail a specific application of the ^{87}Rb–^{87}Sr method of dating [17]. In particular, we shall be concerned with a certain exposure of very ancient Precambrian granite in the central Transvaal of southern Africa. Similar large tracts of granite are exposed over many regions of South Africa and are among the most ancient surface rocks known [18]. They are of particular interest in our present discussion since at one location at least sedimentary beds in close stratigraphic

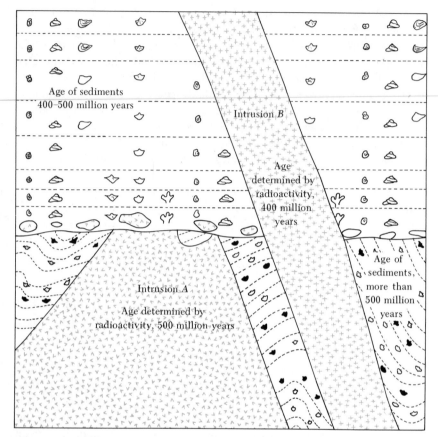

FIG. 2-2 Scheme of relative and absolute dating in geology. A pile of older sediments has been folded during an orogeny. At the end of the orogenetic period magma intruded into the sediments. This now forms the igneous rocks of intrusion *A*. The folded crust was later eroded and denudated, whereupon a pile of younger sediments was laid down. This contains pebbles of the igneous rock of intrusion *A* at its base, so intrusion *A* is older relative to the overlying series of sediments. Both the older and the younger rocks were later intruded by a second magma (intrusion *B*). Relative ages of beds of the younger sediments can be established locally by noting the superposition of individual beds. Regionally, a relative age can be established by the use of index fossils found in this series. The same method can also be applied to older series of sediments. Although the series was folded, it is still possible to distinguish between the upper and the lower beds. The series still contains recognizable index fossils, which have not been obliterated by metamorphism accompanying the orogeny.

The relative age of intrusion *A* is younger than the lower series of sediments and older than the upper series. The relative age of intrusion *B* is younger than the upper sediments and a great deal younger than the lower sediments.

Absolute dating is possible for the two intrusions. The absolute age of the sediments can, however, only be approximated as either older or younger than the dated intrusions [3].

relationship to the granites have been found to contain indications of ancient bacteria [19].

Let us focus on a series of rock samples which were collected from the same geologic stratum at a number of different sites in the Transvaal [17]. In order to determine the absolute age of these samples by the rubidium-strontium method, it is necessary to measure the total amounts of ^{87}Rb and ^{87}Sr in the samples and to estimate what fraction of the total ^{87}Sr was present at the time of initial crystallization. Once these values are obtained, the age is calculated by means of the following slightly modified version of Eq. (7):

$$t = \frac{1}{\lambda} \ln \left(\frac{^{87}\text{sr}^*}{^{87}\text{rb}} + 1 \right) \tag{8}$$

where ^{87}rb denotes the total number of ^{87}Rb atoms per gram of rock, and ^{87}sr* denotes the number of ^{87}Sr atoms (per gram) which were produced radiogenically from ^{87}Rb during the lifetime of the sample. A fractional branching constant [i.e., 0.12 in Eq. (7)] does not occur in Eq. (8) since ^{87}Rb decays only to ^{87}Sr (see page 49).

A given chunk of granite was first crushed and mixed thoroughly, following which small amounts of it (≈ 1 gm) were weighed out for the analysis. The samples were treated with HF to remove the silicon as the gaseous compound SiF_4, and with $HClO_4$ to form the perchlorates of various cations including Rb^+ and Sr^{++}. After drying the mixture, the perchlorates were taken up in a known volume of $3N$ HCl. The concentrations of the rubidium and strontium isotopes in the rock solution were determined by means of mass spectrometry. In this technique, the various isotopes are resolved one from another on the basis of their slightly different charge-to-mass ratios [20].

For instrumentation reasons it was desirable to obtain separate, relatively pure strontium and rubidium fractions from each solution before mass spectrometry. This was readily achieved by a series of simple chemical treatments coupled with ion exchange chromotography on a suitable resin. The individual fractions were then subjected to mass spectroscopy and the isotope ratios determined from the amplified ion currents. The absolute amounts of ^{87}Rb and ^{87}Sr present in a given sample were determined by the "isotope dilution" procedure [17,20]. Known amounts of reference isotopes (^{87}Rb and the nonradiogenic isotope ^{86}Sr) were added to sample solutions, and the new isotope ratios were determined. The desired quantities were then readily obtained by simple calculations [17].

Estimation of the radiogenic component of the total strontium 87 (that is, ^{87}sr*) presents perhaps the greatest experimental difficulty. In the original work upon which our present discussion is based, this problem was solved in the following way: the ratio of radiogenically produced strontium 87 to rubidium 87 [^{87}sr*/^{87}rb; see Eq. (8)] was deter-

TABLE 2-1 Rubidium-strontium mass spectrometric data on five different samples of an ancient granite from southern Africa [17]
See text for details

Granite sample number	$^{87}sr/^{86}sr$	^{86}sr	^{87}rb	$^{87}rb/^{86}sr$
1	0.753	32.2*	30.4*	0.934
2	0.789	26.7	46.7	1.729
3	0.862	17.3	58.3	3.321
4	0.915	13.7	62.1	4.488
5	1.089	12.1	101.7	8.321

* Micrograms per gram of rock sample.

mined graphically from isotopic data on a series of rocks from the same stratum exhibiting different ratios of *total* rubidium to *total* strontium, rb_t/sr_t. The fact that the Rb to Sr ratios may differ from rock to rock does not by itself imply that the samples are of different absolute ages since only the ^{87}Sr to ^{87}Rb ratios bear on the age.

Table 2-1 lists the results of isotope determinations on five different granite samples. The ratios in the first column were determined directly from mass spectrometric data on rock extract solutions. The values in the second and third columns were determined by the isotope dilution procedure. Finally, the ratios in the fourth column were calculated from the data in columns 2 and 3. If one isotope ratio is plotted against the other, it can easily be shown that the resulting points should lie along a straight line described by the following equation:

$$\frac{^{87}sr}{^{86}sr} = \left[\frac{^{87}sr^*}{^{87}rb}\right]\frac{^{87}rb}{^{86}sr} + \left[\frac{^{87}sr_0}{^{86}sr}\right] \tag{9}$$

where $^{87}sr_0$ is the amount of strontium 87 present in the sample at the time of crystallization. Now, the unbracketed terms may vary from sample to sample, but if all the samples are of the same age (as they should be on stratigraphic grounds), then the bracketed terms should remain constant. Therefore, the ratio we are seeking, namely, $^{87}sr^*/^{87}rb$, is simply given by the slope, which in this case turns out to be 0.0455. Inserting this value into Eq. (8) and using a decay constant of $\lambda = 1.39 \times 10^{-11}$ years^{-1}, we obtain the following value for the absolute age of the granite samples:

$$t = \frac{1}{1.39 \times 10^{-11} \text{ years}^{-1}} \ln(0.0455 + 1)$$

$$= 3.2 \text{ billion years}$$

You will note that the above method does not require explicit determination of the values of $^{87}sr_0$ for the various samples. These numbers can, however, be calculated from the intercept on the vertical axis, which is equal to $^{87}sr_0/^{86}sr$, and from the values of ^{86}sr listed in Table 2-1. The fact that the value of $^{87}sr^*/^{87}rb$ is the same for all the rock samples indicates that the granites have remained closed systems since they originally crystallized.

Similar measurements have been made on samples of many other ancient granites in South Africa with resulting ages ranging up to 3.4 billion years [18]. In some cases it has been possible to corroborate the Rb–Sr ages by means of the potassium-argon and the various lead methods. Although the specific details of the experimental procedures may vary depending upon the type of rock or upon the investigators making the age determination, the major features of the example discussed here occur in virtually every instance of absolute dating to which we shall make reference in discussing Precambrian fossils. With this somewhat lengthy excursion into dating methods out of the way, let us consider the problem of the age of the Earth.

The age of the Earth

At the outset we must define what is meant by "the age of the Earth." If we adopt the cold planetesimal theory of the origin of the solar system as a working hypothesis (Sec. 3-3), then the most reasonable starting point would appear to be the time at which the consolidated terrestrial mass differentiated into crust and mantle. As we shall see in the next chapter, the segregation of molten iron into the core probably took place over a considerable fraction of early Earth history and hence will not be considered here.

Since the oldest reliably dated terrestrial rocks have ages in excess of 3 billion years [18], the Earth must be *at least* that old. Our problem then is essentially that of determining how much time elapsed between the formation of the crust and the crystallization of these ancient surface rocks. One possible approach is to consider the average relative abundances of uranium and lead isotopes in crustal materials. If we assume that the crust has remained a closed system (at least with respect to uranium and lead) since the time of its formation, then the abundances of the radiogenic isotopes ^{207}Pb and ^{206}Pb, together with the known half-lives of the uranium isotopes, should allow calculation of the age. However, we also need to know how much ^{206}Pb and ^{207}Pb was present at the outset in order to determine what fraction of the contemporary radiogenic Pb was produced by decay of uranium during Earth history. We need to know the appropraite values of $D(0)$ in Eq.(5). There is no reason for assuming that these isotopes were absent from the original crust. However, we can obtain an upper limit for the age of the Earth by assuming that, for example, the present average abundance of ^{207}Pb resulted *entirely* from decay of ^{235}U. The result turns out to be 5.5 to 6.0 billion years [10]. Thus, the age of the Earth must lie somewhere between 3.2 and about 5.7 billion years.

Our problem would be discouragingly difficult were it not for the fortunate fact that the isotopic ratios in primeval terrestrial lead can be estimated from data obtained on the troilite phases of iron meteorites [11,12]. The underlying assumption is that the Earth and the parent body of the meteorites were formed at the same time so that the lead isotope ratios in uranium-free regions of meteorites are essentially the same as those of the original terrestrial crust.

For instrumentation reasons it is easier to measure isotope ratios than absolute amounts, and the nonradiogenic isotope ^{204}Pb provides a convenient reference standard for mass spectrometric determinations. The following equation is used to perform the age calculation [11,22]:

$$\frac{(^{207}Pb/^{204}Pb) - (^{207}Pb/^{204}Pb)_0}{(^{206}Pb/^{204}Pb) - (^{206}Pb/^{204}Pb)_0} = \frac{1}{137.7}\frac{e^{\lambda T} - 1}{e^{\lambda' T} - 1} \tag{10}$$

where $^{207}Pb/^{204}Pb$ and $^{206}Pb/^{204}Pb$ are the average isotope ratios in the present crust, determined by analysis of marine sediments; $(^{207}Pb/^{204}Pb)_0$ and $(^{206}Pb/^{204}Pb)_0$ represent average isotope ratios in lead extracted from the troilite phase of iron meteorites (taken to be equal to the values for primeval terrestrial lead); λ and λ' are the decay constants of ^{235}U and ^{238}U, respectively; and T is the age of the Earth. The factor $1/137.7$ represents the present ratio of ^{235}U to ^{238}U. In one application of the above equation, the following values of isotope ratios were used [11]:

$$\left.\begin{array}{ll} ^{207}Pb/^{204}Pb & 15.61 \\ ^{206}Pb/^{204}Pb & 18.45 \end{array}\right\} \quad \text{marine sediments}$$

$$\left.\begin{array}{ll} (^{207}Pb/^{204}Pb)_0 & 10.42 \\ (^{206}Pb/^{204}Pb)_0 & 9.56 \end{array}\right\} \quad \text{troilite phase of iron meteorites}$$

The resulting age of the Earth is 4.55 billion years.

A variation of the above procedure, in which the lead isotope ratios in an ancient rock of known age were used instead of the average present crustal ratios represented by marine sediments, yielded a value of 4.75 billion years [23]. More elaborate uranium-lead methods have been developed, including one based upon isotopic data on oceanic basalts of differing U to Pb ratios. This latter technique resulted in an age of 4.53 ± 0.04 billion years [21]. All of these procedures require estimates of primeval lead derived from measurements on iron meteorites.

A further implication of the assumption that the Earth and the parent body of meteorites were formed at the same time is that direct age determinations on the meteorites themselves should confirm the results discussed above. This expectation is abundantly fulfilled, at least by two of the dating methods. Application of the uranium-lead technique to the siliceous phase of stony meteorites yields results clustering around 4.5 billion years [24]. A number of stony meteorites with differing ratios of total rubidium to total strontium have been ana-

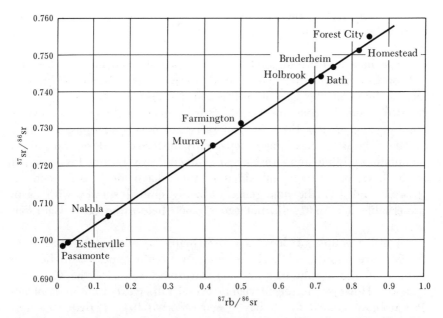

FIG. 2-3 Rb–Sr isochron diagram for stony meteorites. The slope of the line gives an age of about 4.3 billion years. (*After* [11].)

lyzed for isotopic content by the method discussed in the previous section [11]. Data of the type shown in Table 2-1 were obtained from each meteorite sample, and the results are shown graphically in Fig. 2-3. The slope of the line [see Eq. (9)] corresponds to an absolute age of about 4.3 billion years. The corresponding answer in the case of iron meteorites turns out to be approximately 4.4 billion years [11].

Only the potassium-argon method gives widely divergent results ranging from 0.5 to 5 billion years in the case of stony meteorites and from 7 to 10 billion years in the case of some iron meteorites [11]. However, there exists the distinct possibility that varying degrees of argon loss may account for the discrepancies.

In spite of the uncertainties introduced by the K–Ar results, the available evidence indicates that the probable absolute age of the crust of the Earth is about 4.55 billion years.

2-4 SURVIVING TRACES OF PRECAMBRIAN LIFE

Introduction

Now that we have established an upper limit for the antiquity of terrestrial life, let us proceed with an examination of ancient fossil remains in an attempt to find a lower limit. We shall be concerned primarily with actual morphological remains, reserving discussion of "fossil" organic compounds to the last section. The sequence of fossil finds has been arranged in reverse chronological order beginning with the most recent.

We have already alluded to the somewhat annoying fact that the rich profusion of fossils appears to diminish rather suddenly in the geologic column at the Cambrian-Precambrian barrier. There appear to be two major reasons for this fact: (1) many sedimentary rocks of absolute age greater than 600 million years have undergone extensive metamorphosis or have been repeatedly distorted and rearranged by mountain building and erosion, so that conceivably any fossils which might have once been embedded in them have long since been destroyed; and (2) the emergence of many animal species with easily preservable hard parts did not occur much before the Early Cambrian period.

Until a couple of decades ago virtually no authentic Precambrian fossils were known, so that the antiquity of life appeared to be little more than the absolute age of the lowermost strata of the Cambrian system. However, in recent years, several rather extensive finds of late Precambrian animal fossils have been reported [9]. Perhaps the most notable of these assemblages is the one located in the Ediacara Hills of South Australia [9,25]. At this site, numerous fossil impressions or casts of extinct genera of jellyfish, soft corals, segmented and bilaterally symmetric flatworms, as well as worm trails and novel animal forms of unknown affinity, have been found embedded in ancient sandstones. Apparently all of the fossil organisms represented in the assemblage were soft-bodied since no characteristic indications of hard shells, such as fracture lines, are present. Although suitable minerals for absolute age determination are not present in the fossil-bearing sandstones, the latter are clearly Precambrian since they lie 500 ft below beds of dolomitic limestone bearing fossils characteristic of the beginning of the Cambrian.

All of the known fossils in the Ediacara Hills assemblage are large enough to be seen with the unaided eye. For example, individual specimens of *Dickinsonia costata* may range in size from several inches to 2 ft. Thus, compared to our hypothetical common ancestral population of protobacteria, the Ediacara Hills organisms were very highly evolved metazoa.

The Nonesuch shale

The Nonesuch shale is a massive Precambrian sedimentary formation located in northern Michigan [26]. The strata of this system, whose total thickness is nearly 600 ft, are extensively exposed in the White Pine area near the southern shore of Lake Superior. Determination of the absolute age of the formation by means of the rubidium-strontium whole-rock technique already discussed has resulted in a value of 1.05 billion years [26].

Chemical and micropaleontological investigations on samples of gray siltstone removed from the lowermost 30 to 35 feet of the Nonesuch formation have revealed the presence of appreciable amounts of indigenous organic matter. We shall return to the latter in the section on chemical fossils. In the present discussion we are concerned mainly with morphological remains. At the microscopic level this material exhibits three distinguishable kinds of morphological organization: (1) angular opaque bodies lying between individual mineral grains, (2) irregular globular masses, and (3) fragments of primitive plant tissue consisting of individual filaments 1 to 15 μ long and aggregates of filaments which may exceed 100 μ in length.

The microscopic organization of the plant microfossils of category 3 is much more clearly exhibited in preparations from which the surrounding mineral matrix has been removed. This was accomplished by dissolving a given siltstone sample in an aqueous solution of HCl and HF. The liberated organic material was then centrifuged down and washed in $ZnBr_2$ solution following which it was mounted in glycerine jelly on a glass microscope slide. Examination of these slides revealed structures such as those shown in Figs. 2-4a, b, and c. Note that indications of cellular structure are present in Figs. 2-4a and c. Because of the rather poor state of preservation of these plant remains, it is difficult to establish their phylogenetic affinities with any degree of precision. It seems plausible, however, that they represent primitive algal or fungal forms.

The Gunflint iron formation

The most extensively studied and perhaps the most spectacular assemblage of primitive Precambrian microfossils occurs in beds of black chert (microcrystalline quartz containing fine-grained pyrite as well as organic matter ranging in color from yellow to black), situated near the base of the Gunflint iron formation of Ontario [27,28]. This sedimentary formation has apparently undergone very little metamorphism. Organic fossil remains in a remarkable state of preservation have been recovered from samples of the black chert obtained from exposures of the formation at several different localities extending over a 190-km range. Samples of mica granules embedded in the formation have been dated by the $^{40}K-^{40}Ar$ method, and the results suggest that the Gunflint sediments are about 1.9 billion years old [29]. The granite which underlies the sediments at one site has been dated by both the $^{40}K-^{40}Ar$ and the $^{87}Rb-^{87}Sr$ methods with a resulting absolute age of 2.3 to 2.6 billion years.

Attempts to isolate the organic remains from the crystalline matrix

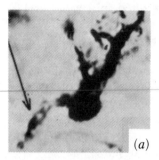 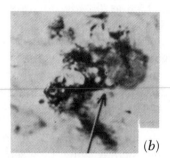

(a)   (b)

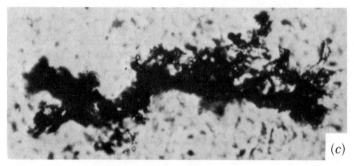

(c)

FIG. 2-4 Microscopic fossil plants present in an organic slurry prepared from gray siltstone (see text) in the lowermost sedimentary beds
of the Nonesuch shale of northern Michigan (absolute age 1.05 billion
years). (a) Branched and unbranched filaments in association with a
solid glob of amorphous organic material. Arrow indicates cell-like
structures approximately 1 μ wide. Magnification is ×1,600; (b)
aggregate of filaments associated with a solid spherical body of organic
matter. The arrow indicates a branched filament. Magnification is
×1,300; (c) sheet of plant tissue made up of the residues of cellular
filaments. Magnification is ×675 [26].

of the chert by treatment with HF nearly always resulted in considerable
damage to the delicate architecture of the fossils.   Therefore, the procedure which resulted in structural resolution of the more resilient Nonesuch organic remains could not be used here.   This, however, was no
great loss since the specimens preserved within the chert exhibited a
wealth of morphological detail when examined with the light microscope
in very thin (30 to 60 μ) sections of the translucent mineral.   Examination of hundreds of such thin sections revealed the presence of many
different types of fossil plants varying from single-celled types to
branched and unbranched filaments.   Some of these fossil organisms
bear close structural similarities to some simple contemporary plants,
such as certain of the filamentous blue-green algae, whereas others resemble no known contemporary or fossil organism.   Our sampling of
the Gunflint microfossils must necessarily be highly selective, but the

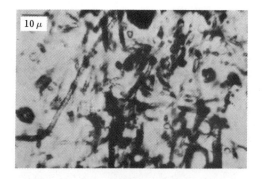

FIG. 2-5 Complex conglomeration of organic structures, including numerous filaments, present in Gunflint chert. Absolute age is 1.9 billion years [28].

examples which we have chosen for representation in Figs. 2-5 to 2-8 do serve to indicate some of the major categories of structural types which have been described and classified to date. In all cases, the specimens were photographed in thin sections of chert by means of transmitted light [28].

Filaments both with and without cross walls are the most numerous structures found in the Gunflint assemblage (Figs. 2-5 and 2-6). The

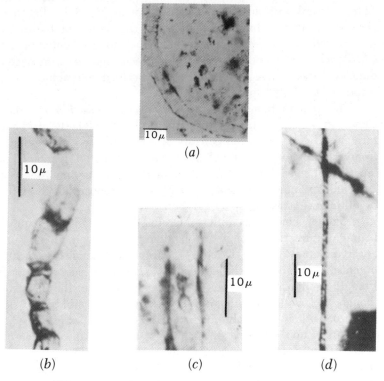

(a)

(b)   (c)   (d)

FIG. 2-6 Filamentous microfossils in Gunflint chert. These forms resemble certain of the contemporary blue-green algae [28].

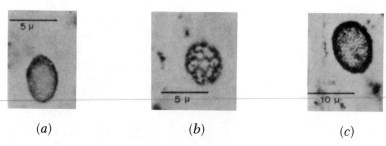

(a)   (b)   (c)

FIG. 2-7 Organic spore-like bodies observed in thin (30 to 50 μ), polished sections of the Gunflint chert [28].

diameters of individual filaments range from 0.5 to 6.0 μ. Certain of the forms with closely spaced cross walls (Figs. 2-6a and d) resemble contemporary blue-green algae of the genus *Oscillatoria*. By far the most prevalent diameter occurring among filamentous forms is 1.1 μ, suggesting that one particular species of blue-green alga predominated over the others.

The Gunflint chert also contains numerous more or less spherical sporelike structures of varying diameter (1 to 16 μ) and wall thickness. Three examples of such bodies are shown in Fig. 2-7. Barghoorn suggests the following four possibilities for the nature of these structures: (1) unicellular blue-green algae analogous to the contemporary genus *Chroococcus;* (2) endospores of blue-green algae or iron bacteria; (3) dinoflagellates, whose flagella have not survived entombment in the sediment; or (4) fungal spores.

The remarkable star-shaped organism (*Eoastrion* or "dawnstar") shown in Fig. 2-8a occurs throughout the fossil beds of the Gunflint formation. The organism consists of a central blob of organic material from which radiate a number of thin segmented filaments of equal length, the maximum linear extent of the star varying from 8 to 25 μ. In some instances the complex of filaments appears to lie at the center of a thin encapsulating spherical shell.

Another kind of complex microfossil found in the Gunflint chert in huge numbers, although so far almost exclusively at only one locale (near Kakabeka Falls, Ontario), is represented in Fig. 2-8b. These organisms, assigned to the new genus *Kakabekia,* may vary in diameter from 12 to 30 μ and are thus somewhat larger than the dawnstars. Although the overall morphology of *Kakabekia* resembles that of certain hydrozoans, it is probably much too small to be classed as a coelenterate. An example of one of the rarest, and perhaps the most bizarre, of the microfossils of the assemblage is shown in Fig. 2-8c. Individual specimens exhibit a relatively uniform diameter that ranges from 28 to 32 μ. Because of the spherical shape of the organism, it has been

named *Eosphaera* ("dawnsphere") *tyleri*. No clear phylogenetic relationships between this organism and any known living organism are
apparent.

Finally, by means of ingenious methods of sample preparation
coupled with electron microscopy, it has been possible to demonstrate
the presence of minute structures embedded in samples of the Gunflint
chert which resemble both rod-shaped and coccoid bacteria [30]. Typically, a sample of dense black chert secured from the Schreiber locality
of the formation was ground and polished and then subjected to mild
surface etching by hydrofluoric acid. The etched surface was then
shadowed with platinum in a vacuum evaporator and replicated with
a film of carbon. The replicas were floated onto the surface of a dilute
aqueous solution of HF and finally picked up onto electron microscope
sample grids. The method of preparation resulted in most cases in
the removal of the bacterial structures from the surface of the chert
and their incorporation into the replica.

Two examples of the resulting electron micrographs are presented
in Fig. 2-9. The rod-shaped structures in Fig. 2-9a have dimensions
(0.55×1.1 μ) similar to those of the smaller contemporary rod-shaped
bacteria. They occur either as isolated units or clumps, or even in
chains of varying length which may exhibit false branching. On other
electron micrographs, indications of an encapsulating sheath are present.
In some respects, such as apparent growth habit, the Gunflint remains
resemble certain modern iron bacteria, which is not particularly surprising
since the Gunflint formation is rich in iron ores. The spherical objects
(their approximate diameter is 0.35 μ) also resemble some genera of
contemporary iron bacteria (Fig. 2-9b).

That the bacterialike forms are actually indigenous to the black
cherts and are not contaminants introduced into the samples during
preparation is indicated by the fact that in many instances the forms
appear to pass into the plane of the polished surface of the mineral.

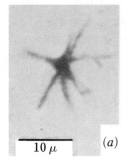

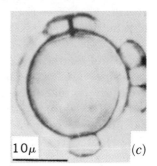

FIG. 2-8 Organic forms of extraordinary architecture present in the Gunflint chert.
(a) *Eoastrion;* (b) *Kakabekia;* (c) *Eosphaera tyleri* [28].

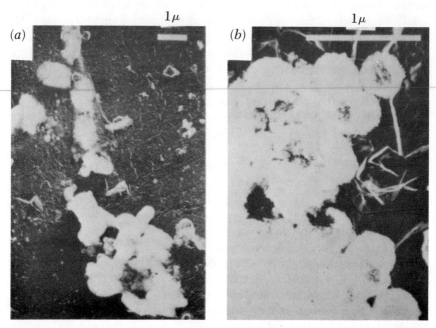

FIG. 2-9 Electron micrographs of carbon replicas of black chert samples from the Gunflint iron formation. The samples were ground, polished, and surface etched with HF. The etched surfaces were shadowed with platinum and replicated with a film of carbon (see text). (*a*) Structures resembling rod-shaped bacteria. Typical dimensions are 0.55 × 1.1 μ; (*b*) spherical objects resembling coccoid bacteria [30].

Southern Rhodesian and Saharan algal limestones

Until now we have been concerned almost exclusively with actual organic remains of once living organisms, with the notable exception of the sandstone fossil imprints of the Ediacara Hills deposit. We now turn to another kind of indication of very ancient Precambrian life which consists of characteristic traces of one aspect of the metabolic activities of primitive organisms preserved in two groups of African limestones.

In 1940, A. M. MacGregor read a short paper before the Geological Society of South Africa in which he described the occurrence of a remarkable undulatory pattern of closely spaced laminations in some Precambrian graphitic limestones exposed at a quarry of the Huntsman Lime Works near Bulawayo, Southern Rhodesia [31]. On the face of the quarry, occasional bands (with thicknesses ranging up to a few inches) of dark material with wavy upper boundaries could be seen running along the exposed surfaces of the rocks. Etching of the surface of such a band with dilute acid revealed a fine lamellar structure. The thin, ribbonlike, dark bands, which on the average are separated by intervals of 0.2 to 0.3 mm, are the cross sections of films of finely dispersed specks of graphite. The protuberances at the top of the band are vertical sections of elliptical cones and are typically spaced $\frac{1}{4}$ to 1 in. apart. No evidence of actual cellular remains is present in the limestone probably, as MacGregor suggested, because of the fact that the limestone is too coarse-grained to allow the preservation of delicate organic structures.

Similar patterns of concretionary lamellar deposition have been found at other sites in Africa and in North America as well [3,31,32]. That such patterns are not the result of solely inorganic geological processes, but on the contrary actually represent the combined effects of sedimentation and the vital activities of primitive lime-secreting algae, is strongly suggested by the fact that these formations closely resemble "structures being impressed at the present day on calcareous sediments in the Bahamas by the growth of plants belonging to the class Cyanophyceae, the simplest and most primitive of the algae" [32].

A minimum absolute age of 2.7 billion years has been assigned to the Southern Rhodesian algal limestones on the basis of $^{40}K-^{40}Ar$ and $^{87}Rb-^{87}Sr$ age determinations on granitic intrusions into the limestone beds [3,18].

Other types of algal limestones occur in profusion at many sites in central Africa. Most notable among these are the numerous algal reefs found in parts of the Sahara Desert [33]. Although it is very difficult to determine the absolute ages of these reefs with any degree of precision because of uncertainties in stratigraphic correlations in the area and the lack of any reliable absolute datings, Rutten has concluded that their ages lie somewhere between 1 to 2 billion years [3].

The Soudan iron formation

Among the oldest known carbon-rich sedimentary rocks are those of the Soudan iron formation of northeastern Minnesota [34]. A concordant age of 2.7 billion years has been obtained by both the uranium-lead and potassium-argon methods applied to individual mineral fractions of a granitic intrusion into the formation [35]. In addition to iron ores and carbon in the form of graphitic material, the Soudan rocks contain chert, various silicates, and pyrites, the latter occurring as spheres 1 to 3.5 cm in diameter. It is within these spheres that structures suggestive of primitive life forms have been found.

Pyrite-bearing samples of the rocks were obtained from the Soudan mine 545 m below ground level. Individual pyrite spheres were subjected to the following treatment in preparation for electron microscopy: first, a cut was made across the sphere to expose an internal planar surface. This surface was then polished and finally replicated by means of palladium and evaporated carbon. Examination of the replicas in the electron microscope revealed for the most part nothing but an occasional minute feature resembling characteristic surface imperfections in the nitrocellulose film used to remove any potentially interesting objects

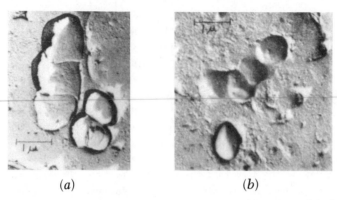

(a)   (b)

FIG. 2-10   Carbon replica electron micrographs of interior polished
surfaces of pyrite balls obtained from the Soudan iron formation.
Absolute age is 2.7 billion years [34].

from the pyrite surface.   A few of the replicas, however, exhibited structures whose detailed architecture differed considerably from the typically
circular imperfections in the nitrocellulose.   Examples of these forms
are shown in Fig. 2-10.   Their diameters range from 0.8 to 1.5 μ, which
together with the fact that they tend to occur in small clusters suggests
that the structures might conceivably correspond to the fossil remains
of ancient blue-green algae or bacteria.   However, as you will readily
appreciate, the evidence for this suggestion is very scant, as the investigators who made the discovery clearly realized: "Although they are
rather more persuasive than many putative Precambrian fossils, we are
not sure that these objects are not some pattern of abiogenic colloidal
material fortuitously incorporated in the pyrite" [34].

Even though the morphological evidence of organismic remains in
the Soudan formation is tenuous at best, chemical evidence to be mentioned below is consistent with the interpretation that much of the organic carbon imprisoned in the rocks is of biogenic origin.

The Fig Tree series

In our example of absolute age determination by the $^{87}Rb–^{87}Sr$ technique,
we discussed a granitic formation of enormous antiquity (3.2 billion
years) located in the central Transvaal region of South Africa.   A sedimentary formation of comparable age (3.1 billion years by the Rb–Sr
method [19]) containing carbon-rich bands of dense, black chert comparable to those of the Gunflint formation is situated in the eastern
portion of the Transvaal.   Samples of the black chert obtained from
an exposure of a particular sequence of strata known as the Fig Tree

series have been subjected to detailed micropaleontological examination for the possible presence of organic fossil remains [19].

Again the most reliable method of sample preparation proved to be surface replication of polished sections of the chert rather than treatment with HF, which typically results in considerable damage to very ancient microfossils. The detailed method of sample preparation was somewhat more elaborate than that discussed above in connection with the preparation of the bacterial specimens from the Gunflint chert, but the major features are similar and will not be repeated here. Electron microscopy of the surface replicas did indeed reveal the presence of a number of different kinds of organic microstructures. Compared with the rich profusion of forms in the Gunflint chert, however, the Fig Tree

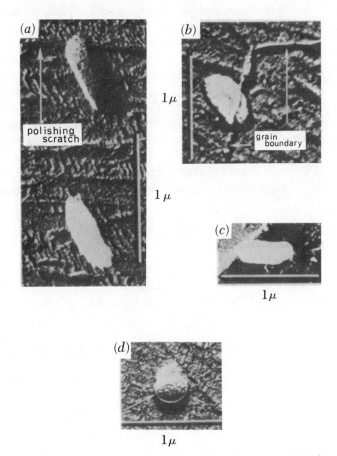

FIG. 2-11 Electron micrographs of carbon replicas of black chert samples from the Fig Tree series indicating the possible presence of primitive rod-shaped bacteria (*Eobacterium isolatum*). Arrow in (d) indicates possible cell wall (0.015 μ thick) in cross section. Absolute age is 3.1 billion years [19].

sediments appear to be grossly underpopulated. Nevertheless, some of the forms which do appear here and there as isolated units on the replicas bear a marked structural resemblance to contemporary rod-shaped bacteria. Several examples of these structures are shown in Fig. 2-11.

All of the structures shown in Fig. 2-11 are regarded as organic fossil remains of the same primitive bacterial species, which Barghoorn has named *Eobacterium isolatum*. The average dimensions of these microfossils are 0.56×0.24 μ, which place them near the lower limit of sizes of modern rod-shaped bacteria. The indigenous nature of *E. isolatum* is suggested by several lines of evidence, including the observation that chalcedony grain boundaries in the mineral matrix occasionally pass through the fossil structures and the fact that the bacterial structures are absent from glass microscope slides replicated in the same manner as the fossil-bearing chert surfaces.

Of course the possibility that *E. isolatum* is really some kind of colloidal organic artifact cannot be completely ruled out on the basis of the available evidence; further study is needed to settle the point. That they are not silicic inorganic artifacts is indicated by the fact that they survive etching with HF. In spite of this, since they are the oldest known possible traces of primitive terrestrial organisms, it is tantalizing to conclude, at least tentatively, that *E. isolatum* might in fact have been a not-too-distant relative of the hypothetical protobacterial organism whose primeval origins we are seeking in this inquiry.

The principal microfossils just discussed are summarized in Table 2-2.

Chemical fossils

Although the morphological evidence we have reviewed above, taken *in toto,* presents a rather impressive case for the immense antiquity of terrestrial life, there are, nevertheless, plausible reasons for serious

TABLE 2-2 Summary of major Precambrian microfossils examined

Age*	Sample	Remarks on findings
1.05	Nonesuch shale	Fragments of plant tissue
1.9	Gunflint chert	Structures resembling bacteria, blue-green algae, and spores, as well as miscellaneous forms
2.7	Southern Rhodesian lamellar limestone	Formed by lime-secreting algae
2.7	Soudan iron formation	Microscopic spheroids
3.1	Fig Tree series	Structures resembling rod-shaped bacteria

* Billions of years.

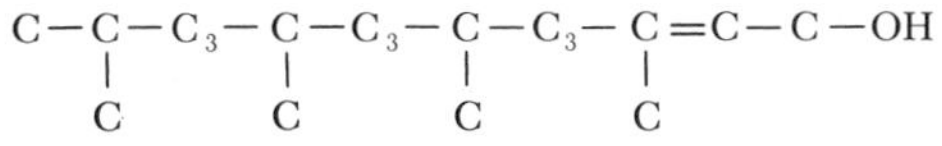

$$C-C-C_3-C-C_3-C-C_3-C=C-C-OH$$

$$\begin{array}{cccc} | & | & | & | \\ C & C & C & C \end{array}$$

Phytol

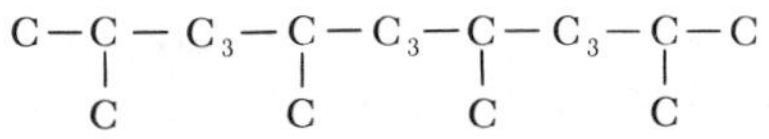

$$C-C-C_3-C-C_3-C-C_3-C-C \qquad C-C-C_3-C-C_3-C-C_3-C-C_2$$

$$\begin{array}{cccc} | & | & | & | \\ C & C & C & C \end{array} \qquad \begin{array}{cccc} | & | & | & | \\ C & C & C & C \end{array}$$

Pristane 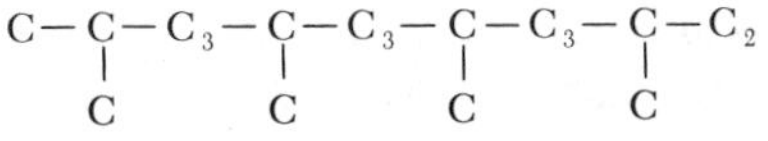   Phytane

FIG. 2-12 Structural relationships between phytol, pristane, and phytane. It is conceivable that phytol resulted from the hydrolytic degradation of chlorophyll. Hydrogenation and dehydration of the phytol could account for the appearance of phytane, and pristane could have been produced from phytol by hydrogenation and oxidation, followed by decarboxylation. See Ref. 36 for details.

doubts, such as we emphasized in connection with the organic microstructures of the Soudan formation and to a lesser extent in connection with *E. isolatum* of the Fig Tree series. Fortunately, most of the ancient sediments discussed above, and many other more recent sediments as well, have been subjected to detailed organic chemical investigation in an attempt to find unequivocal molecular traces of past biological activity. We shall not discuss the organic geochemical approach in detail here since several lucid and comprehensive accounts are available elsewhere [36,37,39]. It is sufficient to say that the method consists in extracting a portion of the organic matter imprisoned in the sediments by means of suitable solvents such as benzene, methanol, and hexane, or various mixtures of these. The extracted fractions are then subjected to a series of very sophisticated analytical procedures including molecular sieving, gas-liquid chromatography, and automated high-resolution mass spectroscopy. These procedures allow the determination of the intimate three-dimensional molecular architecture of closely related stereoisomers. In this way a large variety of normal, branched, and ring alkanes have been identified in the Nonesuch, Gunflint, Soudan, and Fig Tree sedimentary formations.

What is especially noteworthy about the array of hydrocarbons[*] recoverable from the sediments is the fact that some of them exhibit striking structural resemblance to certain molecules crucial to the operation of contemporary organisms. For example, the carbon skeletons of the hydrocarbons pristane, and phytane, which are prominent components of the isoprenoid fractions obtained from all the ancient sediments discussed above, closely resemble the carbon skeleton of the phytol side-chain of chlorophyll (see Fig. 2-12). Similarly, other hydrocarbons iden-

* Many other classes of organic substances have been identified in the ancient sediments. For detailed reviews, see Refs. 36 and 37.

tified in ancient sedimentary rocks, such as cholestane and β-carotene, closely resemble the biocompounds cholesterol and β-carotene [36]. On the basis of these close structural correspondences, it is a plausible assumption that the hydrocarbons might actually have been derived from analogous substances originally present in ancient organisms. We must point out, however, that the processes by which biological substances are imagined to undergo conversion to corresponding hydrocarbons in the sediments have not as yet been demonstrated to occur under laboratory conditions.

If we can regard the isoprenoid alkanes pristane and phytane as "biological markers" in the above sense, then the detection of these substances in the Soudan and Fig Tree sedimentary rocks considerably strengthens the tentative conclusion drawn from the scant morphological evidence—namely, that some simple forms of life existed on the Earth when the sediments were being deposited.

Although such confirmation is welcome, fundamental uncertainties remain. Whether or not such compounds as pristane and phytane can be regarded as unequivocal indicators of ancient life depends upon the answer to the following question: Can these hydrocarbons be formed from simple starting materials by purely nonbiological processes operating under natural geological conditions? Or alternatively, we might imagine the abiological production of the presumed biological precursor, such as chlorophyll, followed by its conversion in the sediment to the hydrocarbon. In neither case would the hydrocarbons qualify as biological markers.

So far, we have no direct evidence that pristane and phytane, or *any* isoprenoid alkane for that matter, can be *preferentially* formed abiologically under possible primitive Earth conditions. Complex mixtures of normal and branched hydrocarbons do result from relatively simple laboratory procedures such as the sparking of gaseous mixtures of simple alkanes. However, the distribution of products within such mixtures does not exhibit some of the most characteristic features of compounds in the hydrocarbon fraction of the extractable organic matter in ancient sediments [37]. Furthermore, some of these same features, such as an alternating distribution of n-alkanes in which the chains with odd numbers of carbons are relatively more abundant, are exhibited by unequivocally biogenic hydrocarbons extracted from relatively recent sediments.

The Fischer-Tropsch reaction (involving the metal-catalyzed reaction of CO and H_2 at elevated temperatures) results in the production of a variety of alkanes. Recent preliminary evidence [37] suggests that a homologous series of low-molecular-weight (C_9 to C_{14}) isoprenoids may be among the products of this reaction. However, the polyisoprenoids ($C > 14$), as well as the more complex and structurally specific steranes, triterpanes, and carotenoid derivatives, have not been identified as yet.

Another experiment of interest here is the polymerization of butadiene, 1,3-pentadiene, and isoprene (which can be produced in small yields by the thermal cracking of ethane-propane mixtures) [37]. This procedure leads to the synthesis of polymers with a linear 1,4-trans configuration (the structure found in natural polyisoprenoids) almost exclusively. However, the synthesis is successful only when carried out in the presence of highly specific catalysts in organic solvents. These requirements raise serious doubts as to the plausibility of such reactions having taken place on the primitive Earth. Nevertheless, the possibility of abiogenic formation of pristane and phytane, however remote, cannot be completely ruled out in view of the growing evidence of spontaneous ordering processes in possible chemical evolutionary reactions (see Chaps. 5 and 6).

Along these lines, direct evidence has been sought to show that chemical fossils may indeed have come from biological sources. The mass spectrometer has been employed in one such method [38]. The procedure is based on the observation that although carbon exists in nature as both ^{12}C and ^{13}C, biological systems selectively utilize the lighter isotope. To make comparisons between samples, the following equation, relating the ratio of ^{13}C to ^{12}C, is used (including data for a universal standard):

$$\frac{\delta^{13}C}{1,000} = \frac{^{13}C/^{12}C \ (\text{sample})}{^{13}C/^{12}C \ (\text{standard})} - 1$$

The more negative the value of $\delta^{13}C$, the greater the relative abundance of the lighter isotope in the given sample. For instance, atmospheric CO_2 has a $\delta^{13}C$ of -7 to -8. Plants, through photosynthesis, preferentially utilize the lighter isotope and exhibit a $\delta^{13}C$ of about -25.

A typical chemical fossil source that has been analyzed is the South African Witwatersrand system [38]. This system was laid down at least 2.15 billion years ago. Bacterialike structures have been observed under the microscope, and chemical study has revealed the presence of amino acids and monosaccharides. When analyzed by mass spectrometry, a $\delta^{13}C$ value averaging -28 was obtained, suggesting the carbon compounds in the samples were of biogenic origin.

A second difficulty encountered in the geochemical approach to the search for vestiges of ancient life concerns the indigenous nature of the imprisoned organic matter. Was this material originally present in some form at the time of deposition of the sediment, or did it seep into the sediment at some later time [36,37]? This question turns out to be especially relevant in the case of the Soudan shale since geological evidence indicates that at some time during its history the formation was subjected to temperatures (up to 400°C) at which pristane and phytane are unstable—yet these hydrocarbons are recoverable from the sediment today [34]. The evidence, including mass spectrometric data on $^{13}C/^{12}C$ ratios, is not conclusive, and clarification of the point, if it comes at all, must await further study.

The problem of possible contamination of the rock samples by laboratory dust and fingerprints also deserves careful consideration. Precautions must be taken at each step of the experimental procedures in order to avoid such contamination. A striking illustration of this possibility is provided by the finding that a distribution of biocompounds claimed to be indigenous to meteorites is also exhibited by human fingerprints [40]!

In spite of the above uncertainties, the geochemical approach to the problem of the antiquity of life is a valuable supplement to the micropaleontological approach. One very exciting additional possibility deserves mention here. The distribution of organic molecules recoverable from sedimentary rocks of increasing absolute age might conceivably be found to exhibit an interpretable set of changes as the ages pass through the epoch in Earth history during which the first life was emerging [37]. However, the most ancient known carbon-rich sediments (Fig Tree series) have already been found to contain the so-called biological marker compounds [36,37].

2.5   CONCLUSIONS

If we believe that the final consolidation of the mass of the Earth took place some 4.6 billion years ago and that the most ancient surviving traces of primitive life are at least 3.1 billion years old, then we can conclude that the first terrestrial life must have emerged during the interval between these two dates. On the basis of the available evidence, it is hazardous to attempt to circumscribe more narrowly the epoch of origin, especially since we know virtually nothing about the overall rates at which prebiological chemical evolution might have taken place. If further investigation provides convincing evidence that certain apparently filamentous organic structures observed at the electron microscope level in the Fig Tree black chert, for example, are in fact the residues of primitive blue-green algae, then it is likely that the simplest forms of life emerged considerably earlier than 3.1 billion years ago.

In Fig. 2-13 we summarize the probable absolute chronology of Precambrian terrestrial life on the basis of the evidence discussed in this chapter. In the next chapter we shall consider lines of evidence which provide clues about the chemical and physical setting in which the early stages of prebiological chemical evolution might have taken place.

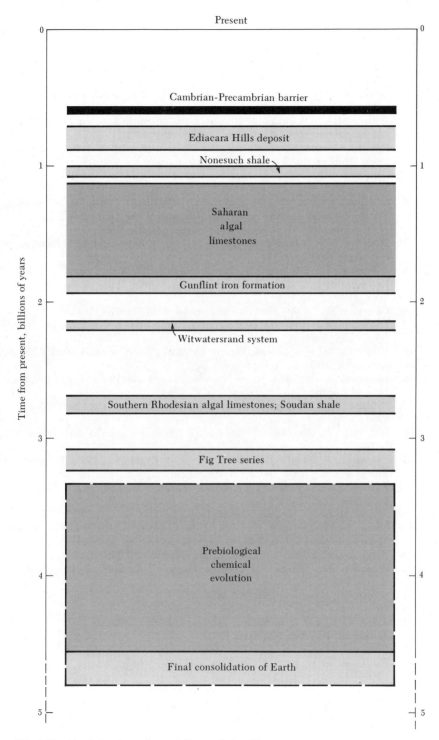

FIG. 2-13 Absolute chronology of Precambrian life.

REFERENCES

1. McNeill, W. H.: "History Handbook," University of Chicago Press, Chicago, 1958.
2. Zeuner, F. E.: "Dating the Past—An Introduction to Geochronology," Methuen & Co., Ltd., London, 1958.
3. Rutten, M. G.: "Geological Aspects of the Origin of Life on Earth," Elsevier Publishing Company, Amsterdam, 1962.
4. Croneis, C., and W. C. Krumbein: "Down to Earth," University of Chicago Press, Chicago, 1936.
5. Mason, B.: "Principles of Geochemistry," John Wiley & Sons, Inc., New York, 1958.
6. Gilluly, J., A. C. Waters, and A. O. Woodford: "Principles of Geology," W. H. Freeman and Company, San Francisco, 1959; Grabau, A. W.: "A Textbook of Geology," D. C. Heath and Company, Boston, 1921.
7. Pettijohn, F. J.: "Sedimentary Rocks," Harper & Row, Publishers, Incorporated, New York, 1957.
8. Hussey, R. C.: "Historical Geology," McGraw-Hill Book Company, New York, 1947; Dunbar, C. O.: "Historical Geology," John Wiley & Sons, Inc., New York, 1949.
9. Glaessner, M. F.: Biol. Rev. Cambridge Phil. Soc., 37:467 (1962).
10. Hurley, P. M.: "How Old Is the Earth?," Doubleday & Company, Inc., Garden City, N.Y., 1959.
11. Faul, H.: "Ages of Rocks, Planets and Stars," McGraw-Hill Book Company, New York, 1966.
12. Goldman, D. T.: "Chart of the Nuclides," Oak Knoll Atomic Power Laboratory, General Electric Co., Schenectady, N.Y., 1964.
13. Rankama, K.: "Isotope Geology," McGraw-Hill Book Company, New York, 1954.
14. Holmes, A.: "The Age of the Earth," Thomas Nelson & Sons, New York, 1937.
15. Tilton, G. R., et al.: Bull. Geol. Soc. Am., 66:1131 (1955); Tilton, G. R.: Trans. Am. Geophys. Union, 37:224 (1956).
16. Faul, H.: in H. Faul (ed.), "Nuclear Geology," p. 256, John Wiley & Sons, Inc., New York, 1954.
17. Alsopp, H. L.: J. Geophys. Res., 66:1499 (1961).
18. Nicolaysen, L. O.: in A. E. J. Engel, H. L. James, and B. F. Leonard (eds.), "Petrologic Studies," p. 569, Geological Society of America, 1962.
19. Barghoorn, E. S., and J. W. Schopf: Science, 152 (3723):758 (1966).*
20. Rankama, K.: "Progress in Isotope Geology," Interscience Publishers, New York, 1963.
21. Ulrych, T. J.: Science, 158:252 (1967).
22. Houtermans, F. G.: Z. Naturforsch., 2a:322 (1947).
23. Tilton, G. R., and R. H. Steiger: Science, 150:1805 (1965).
24. Brown, H.: Sci. Am., 80 (April, 1957).
25. Glaessner, M. F.: Sci. Am., 72 (March, 1961).
26. Barghoorn, E. S., W. G. Meinschein, and J. W. Schopf: Science, 148(3669):461 (1965).*
27. Tyler, S. A., and E. S. Barghoorn: Science, 119:606 (1954).
28. Barghoorn, E. S., and S. A. Tyler: Science, 147(3658):563 (1965).*
29. Hurley, P. M., et al.: J. Geol., 70:489 (1962).

30. Schopf, J. W., E. S. Barghoorn, M. D. Maser, and R. O. Gordon: *Science,* **149** (3690):1365 (1965).*
31. MacGregor, A. M.: *Trans. Geol. Soc. S. Africa,* **43**:9 (1940).
32. Young, R. B.: *Trans. Geol. Soc. S. Africa,* **43**:17 (1940); Black, M.: *Phil. Trans. Roy. Soc. Lond.,* **222B**:165 (1933).
33. Gravelle, M., and M. Lelubre: *Bull. Soc. Geol. France,* **7**:435 (1957).
34. Cloud, P. E., J. W. Gruner, and H. Hagen: *Science,* **148** (3678):1713 (1965).*
35. Anderson, D., Ph.D. thesis, University of Minnesota, March, 1965.
36. Bendoraitis, J. G., B. L. Brown, and L. S. Hepner: *6th World Petroleum Congress,* sec. 5, paper 15, Frankfurt-Main, 1963.
37. Calvin, M.: *Proc. Roy. Soc.,* **288A**:441 (1965); McCarthy, E. D., and M. Calvin: *Nature,* **216**:642 (1967).
38. Schidlowski, M.: *Nature,* **205**:895 (1965); Hoeps, J., and M. Schidlowski: *Science,* **155**:1067 (1967); Prashnowsky, A. A., and M. Schidlowski: *Nature,* **216**:560 (1967).
39. Abelson, P.: *Sci. Am.,* 83 (July, 1956).
40. Oró, J., and H. B. Skewes: *Nature,* **207**:1042 (1965).

* Copyright 1965, 1966 by the American Association for the Advancement of Science.

reconstructing the
primitive scenario

3-1   INTRODUCTION

In the last chapter we discussed evidence suggesting that some kind
of primitive microbial life was present on the Earth more than 3 billion
years ago. Other evidence was presented which suggested that the
Earth itself was formed some 4.5 to 5.5 billion years ago. Now we
must turn to a consideration of lines of evidence bearing on the physical
and chemical conditions which might have prevailed at the surface of
the Earth during roughly the first 1 billion years of its existence. We
hasten to point out, however, that the discussions in this chapter are
often highly speculative and consequently are subject to considerably
more uncertainty than those of Chaps. 2, 4, 5, and 6, which are largely
based on actual laboratory results. Nevertheless it is hoped that our
inquiry will lead us at least to tentative guidelines for laboratory simulation of parts of the primitive scenario of the origin of life.

Perhaps the most useful way of stating the problem to be considered
in this chapter is the following: The contemporary biosphere consists
primarily of carbon, nitrogen, oxygen, and hydrogen [1]. What were
the major chemical substances in which these elements were present
on the newly formed, prebiological Earth? Now, according to the
Oparin-Haldane scheme for biogenesis, which is our most general working hypothesis, the complexity of carbon compounds on the surface of
the primitive Earth is imagined to have increased gradually during the
course of prebiological chemical evolution. It would seem, then, that
the most suitable starting materials for simulation experiments would

be the simplest chemical combinations in which the above four elements could have occurred on the newly formed Earth. Since the simplest molecular combinations of these elements are gases at moderate temperatures, we are led to a consideration of the probable composition of the atmosphere of the primeval Earth.

If a mixture of simple gases made up of the elements C, O, N, and H is introduced into a closed glass system and allowed simply to stand at room temperature, chemical analysis of the reaction mixture would reveal essentially no change in composition, even after a period of years. The reason is that at room temperature the simple gases are not provided with sufficient free energy to overcome the activation barriers in order to react with each other, except at virtually undetectable rates. Thus we would not expect a simple mixture initially consisting of CO_2, N_2, and H_2O vapor, or CH_4, NH_3, and H_2O vapor, to reach thermodynamic equilibrium (with respect to the possible stable gaseous compounds of the elements involved) within periods comparable to the lifespan of man. If, however, suitable catalysts are present or if the mixture is heated (thus altering the equilibrium concentrations of the possible molecular species) sufficiently so that the average thermal energy per molecule is comparable to the reaction activation barriers, then equilibrium might be attained within laboratory times. Since activation energies for reactions between simple gases of the types mentioned above are typically of the order of 20 to 50 kcal/mole [2,3], compared with an average thermal energy of only 0.1 to 0.2 kcal/mole at $300°K$, temperatures as high as $1000°K$ may be required in order to ensure reasonably rapid reaction rates. More significantly, even if thermodynamic equilibrium were reached at such elevated temperatures, biochemically significant substances would not be present in the reaction mixture since they are all highly unstable under these conditions. We shall return to this point in Chap. 5.

On the basis of the above lines of reasoning, it is possible to suggest tentatively the following two general requirements for a primitive atmosphere simulation experiment:

1. A particular mixture of simple gaseous compounds of C, N, O, and H.
2. A continuously supplied source of free energy capable of promoting chemical reactions.

The free energy not only serves to raise individual reacting molecules above the activation barriers, but also may be stored in stable products having higher free-energy content than that of the initial gases. This is especially significant with respect to the possible formation of biologically important substances, since even the simplest of these, such as

TABLE 3-1 Standard free energies of formation of some
primitive gases and simple biological compounds

Primitive gas	Biocompound	$\Delta F°$, kcal/mole
CH₄	...	−12.14
NH₃	...	− 3.98
CO	...	−32.81
C₂H₆	...	− 7.86
...	D-Glucose	−219.22
...	L-Aspartic acid	−172.31
...	Succinic acid	−178.39
...	Glycine	− 89.26

the α-amino acids, may have higher standard free energies of formation
(per atom) than do the gaseous starting materials (see Table 3-1). In
addition, there must be regions within the reaction vessel in which the
temperatures are low enough to permit the survival of any biologically
important substances produced in the system. If heat is the only source
of free energy, then provision must be made in the experimental apparatus for temporary subjection of the reacting gases to high temperatures, followed by cooling of the resultant activated mixture to temperatures at which the reactive fragments could recombine to form stable
complex products.

Such an open system would, of course, never reach thermodynamic
equilibrium. At most, steady-state conditions might be attained, but
even this is by no means certain. Instead, one might expect the total
free-energy content and the chemical complexity of the substances in
the reaction mixture to increase with increasing reaction time. Such
a result would, of course, be entirely consistent with the Oparin-Haldane
hypothesis. In this sense, one major aspect of prebiogenic events
may be looked upon as nothing more than the capture of free energy
by molecular species for subsequent utilization.

However, before an actual simulation experiment can be performed
in the laboratory, it is necessary to decide which simple gases were
likely to have been present in the primeval atmosphere and which free-
energy sources might have been available for promoting chemical reactions. Other major features of the primitive scenario, such as the extent,
temperature, and average pH of the primitive oceans, will be reserved
for later discussion. In order to provide some basis for understanding
current concepts of the nature of the primitive atmosphere, we shall
again adopt an intuitive approach, this time beginning with an examination of the contemporary atmosphere for possible clues.

3-2 THE CONTEMPORARY ATMOSPHERE

In attempting to decide which gases to introduce into the reaction vessel of a simulation apparatus, one might simply assume that the composition of the primitive atmosphere was very similar to that of the present atmosphere (see Table 3-2). This assumption requires that the emergence of life on the primitive Earth did not result in significant changes in the composition of the primitive atmosphere; that is, the atmospheric gases presumably have not (and do not at present) participated in the chemical activities of the biosphere. On the contrary, however, it is well known that many of the gases of the contemporary atmosphere do in fact dynamically interact with the biosphere. Especially prominent in this regard are the crucial roles played by molecular oxygen in the life of both plants and animals. Oxygen is liberated from water by green plants during photosynthesis. In both plants and animals, oxygen is required for respiratory activity. The average time spent by an oxygen molecule in the atmosphere is about 2,000 years [4]. Also, atmospheric nitrogen is fixed by various soil bacteria and by some blue-green algae [5]. Although carbon dioxide is a minor constituent of the present atmosphere, it participates in a variety of fundamental biological processes. For example, in green plants it is converted to carbohydrates via the Calvin cycle [6]. Carbon dioxide is released from animal tissues as a result of respiration. It is also fixed by animal tissues through several carboxylation reactions [7]. The existence of this elaborate set of interactions between atmospheric gases and life processes strongly suggests that if the biosphere were not present, the composition of the atmosphere would be profoundly different from its present composition [8].

Another line of evidence suggesting that the prebiological atmosphere was considerably different from the present atmosphere is that the great bulk of the surface carbon of the Earth is currently incorporated either into the biosphere or into the massive carbonate sediments [9]. It is probable that an appreciable fraction of the carbon in these

TABLE 3-2 Composition of present atmosphere of the Earth [1]

Gas	Percent by volume
N_2	78.09
O_2	20.95
Ar	0.93
CO_2	0.03
Ne	0.002
He, CH_4, Kr, N_2O, H_2, O_3, Xe	<0.001

sediments is of biogenic origin [9]. Atmospheric carbon, primarily in the form of CO_2, makes up only a tiny fraction of the total. This suggests, but by no means proves, that the primeval atmosphere of the Earth was much richer in carbon than is the case at present. Of course, all of the organic carbon need not have been present initially in the atmosphere. It is likely that a substantial fraction of this carbon was gradually supplied in the form of CO and CO_2 from the interior of the Earth throughout geologic time. Evidence supporting this conclusion will be discussed in detail below.

A consideration of possible free-energy sources leads to a third difficulty with our initial assumption that the primitive atmosphere closely resembled the present atmosphere. The contemporary atmosphere is continuously (at least during daylight hours) being supplied with energy in the form of electromagnetic radiation from the sun. Does this input of energy result in chemical reactions between the simple atmospheric gases? In order for electromagnetic radiation to promote chemical reactions, it must first be absorbed by the reacting molecules. This requirement is the so-called *first law of photochemistry* [10]. In order to answer this question, we need to know three things:

1. The spectral intensity distribution of the solar radiation presently impinging on the Earth's atmosphere
2. The spectral intensity distribution of the solar radiation which reaches the surface of the Earth
3. The absorption spectra of the principal atmospheric gases

Before discussing the spectral evidence obtained from rocketborne spectrographs, let us briefly review the structure of the atmosphere. To do so, we shall make use of the simplified diagram shown in Fig. 3-1. Up to a height of about 15 km, the relative proportions of the major

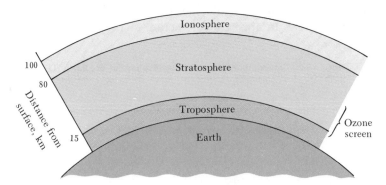

FIG. 3-1 Schematic diagram showing the major features of the structure of the Earth's contemporary atmosphere. The vertical scale is greatly exaggerated with respect to the curvature of the Earth.

gases remain constant due to thorough mixing by convection currents [1]. This region is known as the troposphere. Between 15 and 80 km above the surface, a number of distinct layers are present between which there is very little vertical circulation. This region of the atmosphere is called the stratosphere.

Throughout the troposphere and the stratosphere the predominant molecular species are N_2 and O_2. The region above the stratosphere is, however, rich in ionic species and is thus named the ionosphere. The presence of these ions suggests that either extremely high temperatures prevail in the ionosphere or that photochemical reactions, or at least photoionizations, are taking place there. As we shall see below, the ionization in this region is induced by short-wavelength solar ultraviolet radiation. It should be recalled that the overall density of the atmosphere decreases exponentially with increasing height above the surface because of a general balancing between the ordering influence of the Earth's gravitational field on the one hand and the disordering effects of random thermal motion of the light atmospheric gases on the other [1]. For similar reasons, there is some vertical separation of the atmospheric gases according to their molecular weights, but this is significant only above about 60 km.

Now, let us return to the question posed above, namely, is solar electromagnetic radiation a free-energy source for significant chemical transformations in the contemporary atmosphere? The spectral intensity distribution of the solar radiation field in the upper atmosphere has been determined both by means of rocketborne grating spectrographs and by extrapolation of the results of high-altitude Earthbound measurements to zero atmospheric pressure by the method of Langley [11]. The results of these studies indicate that appreciable amounts of short-wavelength ultraviolet radiation impinge on the upper atmosphere. In fact, the rocket data indicate that far-ultraviolet radiation of wavelengths as short as 200 Å is easily detectable at heights of 100 to 150 km above the surface of the Earth. The spectral data are summarized in Table 3-3.

Abundant data are available on the spectral intensity distribution of solar radiation incident on the surface of the Earth. Examination of a recent compilation of such data (Table 3-3) reveals that virtually no UV (ultraviolet) radiation of $\lambda < 2900$ Å reaches the surface, even though considerable radiation in the range of 200 to 2900 Å is incident on the upper atmosphere. Such a comparison indicates that short-wavelength UV radiation is somehow removed from the incident solar flux.

It can easily be shown that Rayleigh scattering cannot account for the loss of short-wavelength UV between the upper atmosphere and the surface of the Earth [12]. Therefore, some constituent of the atmosphere must be absorbing this radiation. However, the UV absorption spectra (see Fig. 3-2) of the two major components of the troposphere and ionosphere, namely, N_2 and O_2, show that these gases do not significantly absorb radiation of $\lambda > 2000$ Å [14]. Similarly, the corresponding absorption spectrum for carbon dioxide (Fig. 3-2), which so far in this discussion is the only candidate we have for a possible primeval source of atmospheric carbon, indicates that this gas also does not absorb an appreciable amount of light of $\lambda > 1900$ Å.

The data in Table 3-2 show that the noble gas argon is the third most abundant constituent of the present atmosphere. Might it be responsible for removing the short-wavelength UV from the incident solar radiation? Examination of its absorption spectrum reveals that, again, the answer is no. The fact that N_2, O_2, CO_2, and Ar do absorb UV radiation of $\lambda < 2000$ Å does, of course, account to some extent for the presence of ionic species in the ionosphere. However, we are still faced with the problem of accounting for the removal of 2000 to 2900 Å radiation.

A clue to the solution of the problem is provided by the absorption spectrum of the relatively rare atmospheric gas ozone (O_3). It is clear from the spectrum reproduced in Fig. 3-3 that ozone does absorb those

TABLE 3-3 Spectral intensity distributions of contemporary solar ultraviolet radiation at the top of the atmosphere and at sealevel (based on [12] and [13])
Visible wavelengths are included for comparison

Wavelength, Å	Incident intensity per 100 Å band, $\mu w/cm^2$	
	Top of atmosphere*	Sealevel†
5000	1,980	1,520
4500	2,200	1,470
4000	1,540	1,090
3700	1,330	590
3300	1,150	380
3150	820	180
3000	610	29
2950	630	8
2920	560	3
2800	240	
2600	130	
2400	58	
2200	30	
2000	3	
1808	0.007 ⎫ Solar line	
1657	0.018 ⎬ intensities	
1216	0.60 ⎪ ($\mu w/cm^2$)‡	
1026	0.02 ⎭	

* Mean solar spectral irradiance for zero air mass [13a].
† Tucson, Arizona; sun at zenith [13b].
‡ Ref. 13c.

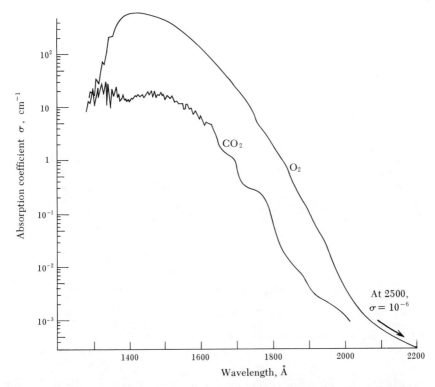

FIG. 3-2 UV absorption spectra of O_2 and CO_2. In this figure, the Schumann-Runge bands for O_2 between 1750 and 1950 Å have been deleted. At wavelengths between 2000 and 2900 Å, absorption coefficients are less than 10^{-3} cm^{-1}. (*After* [14a].)

UV wavelengths which are removed from solar radiation during its passage through the atmosphere [15]. It has been shown that there is in fact a diffuse layer of ozone in the lower stratosphere (Fig. 3-1) which accounts entirely for the absorption of solar radiation of wavelengths less than 3400 Å. The total amount of O_3 in this "ozonosphere" has been estimated from rocket spectrographic data to be equivalent to about 2 mm Hg [12]. Molecular oxygen present in the upper stratosphere and the ionosphere presumably gives rise to the ozone screen via the following photochemical transformation induced by the short-wavelength solar ultraviolet radiation impinging on the upper atmosphere:

$$O_2 + h\nu \; (\lambda < 1600 \text{ Å}) \rightarrow O\cdot + O\cdot$$
$$O\cdot + O_2 + M \qquad\qquad \rightarrow O_3 + M$$

where M is any third body [4].

Now, if the biosphere is a major source of the molecular oxygen in the contemporary atmosphere, as suggested already, then it is possible

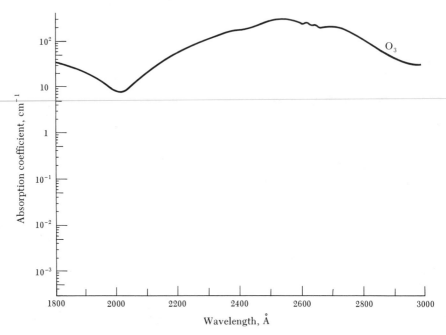

FIG. 3-3   UV absorption spectrum of ozone [15a].

that before the biosphere came into being, there was very little molecular O_2 in the atmosphere.   This in turn implies that the ozone screen might have been absent from the prebiological atmosphere, thus allowing the penetration of considerable amounts of short-wavelength solar UV radiation deep into the atmosphere.   Some radiation of wavelengths as short as 2000 Å conceivably could have reached the surface.   Thus the primitive atmosphere would have been abundantly supplied with a free-energy source for photochemical reactions.

These arguments would, of course, require modification if there were other sources (besides the biosphere) contributing molecular oxygen to the atmosphere.   It has been suggested that water vapor has undergone ultraviolet-induced photolysis in the upper atmosphere throughout geologic time, resulting in the production of O_2 and H_2 [16].   Implications of this possibility will be taken up later.   It is sufficient to say here that if the ozone screen was present very early in the Earth's history, before the earliest stages of chemical evolution had taken place, then the primitive atmospheric gases would have been deprived of a major source of free energy.   On the other hand, many simple metazoan forms of life probably could not have evolved during Darwinian evolution in the absence of an ozone screen since this screen protects these organisms from the lethal effects of short-wavelength solar UV radiation.

Other possible sources of free energy for chemical reactions in the present atmosphere are electric storms, cosmic radiation, and high-energy α and β particles, as well as γ rays emitted by terrestrial radioactive elements such as ^{40}K and ^{238}U. However, compared to the total solar ultraviolet energy impinging on the upper atmosphere of the Earth, these sources of energy are very small indeed. It has been estimated, for example, that the energy available from lightning and corona discharges from sharp objects is about 4 cal/(cm^2)(yr) compared to 570 cal/(cm^2)(yr) for the total incident UV flux for $\lambda < 2500$ Å [17]. These data are summarized in Table 3-4.

Even if the minor energy sources mentioned above are now in fact promoting, to a very limited extent, some chemical reactions among the atmospheric gases, it is highly unlikely that appreciable quantities of even the simplest biological substances are being supplied to the surface of the Earth. The principal reason for this is that the average state of oxidation of the carbon in biological materials is considerably lower than that of the principal carbon-containing gas of the atmosphere, namely, CO_2; that is, in order to synthesize a more reduced compound of carbon from, say, CO_2 and H_2O vapor, it is necessary to supply a large amount of free energy to the system in order to get the reaction to proceed. However, the natural sources of free energy discussed here promote chemical reactions primarily by breaking bonds in the reacting molecules. The new compounds which are then formed depend on how the resulting fragments recombine. In the presence of large amounts of molecular oxygen, it is likely that many of the fragments (among them, free-radical species) will combine directly with the oxygen [18]. In any case, even if trace amounts of carbon compounds more reduced than CO_2 are formed, they would be thermodynamically unstable in the present oxidizing atmosphere [17]. If a few molecules of these relatively more reduced compounds happen to be reaching

TABLE 3-4 Free-energy sources on the contemporary Earth [17]

Source	Energy, $cal/(cm^2)(yr)$
Total radiation from sun	260,000
Ultraviolet light	
$\quad \lambda < 2500$ Å	570
$\quad \lambda < 2000$ Å	85
$\quad \lambda < 1500$ Å	3.5
Electric discharges	4
Cosmic rays	0.0015
Radioactivity	0.8
$\quad$ (to 1.0 km depth)	
Volcanoes	0.13

the surface, they would be rapidly consumed by ubiquitous microorganisms. The main point is that in an atmosphere rich in molecular oxygen, it is highly unlikely that reduced carbon compounds will be formed in more than trace amounts; put another way, conditions prevailing at the surface and in the atmosphere of the Earth at present virtually preclude the possibility of any significant chemical evolutionary process of the type envisioned in the Oparin-Haldane hypothesis. This, in turn, strongly suggests that life is not originating at the present time from previously inanimate matter under natural conditions.

Thus far we have discussed the inadequacy of the contemporary atmosphere as a model of the prebiological atmosphere. The central difficulty is the presence of an appreciable partial pressure of molecular oxygen maintained almost exclusively by the activities of photosynthetic organisms. This dependence of O_2 partial pressure on photosynthesis suggests that the prebiological atmosphere might have contained much less molecular oxygen than does the present atmosphere. However, the situation is complicated by the fact that UV photolysis of H_2O vapor in the upper atmosphere may have provided appreciable amounts of O_2 *before* the emergence of life. More direct geochemical evidence indicating possible changes in the oxygen content of the atmosphere during Earth history would be very useful at this point. Let us move on, then, to a more detailed consideration of several lines of evidence bearing on the origin and evolution of the atmosphere.

3-3 THE PRIMITIVE ATMOSPHERE

Was molecular oxygen present?

Direct geological evidence bearing on the amount of O_2 in the primitive atmosphere is very scant indeed. The available information consists largely of mineral composition data for a few ancient igneous and sedimentary rock formations. For example, the gold-uranium deposits of the Dominion Reef and the Witwatersrand system in South Africa contain appreciable amounts of uraninite, UO_2 [19]. Isotopic datings of these and other similar sediments indicate absolute ages of 1.8 to 2.5 billion years [20]. In sediments of recent origin, uraninite is very rarely found [20]. Thermodynamic data on the various oxides of uranium, namely UO_2, U_3O_8, and UO_3, show that both uraninite and U_3O_8 are highly unstable even in the presence of only trace amounts of O_2 [21]. The surviving uraninite grains presumably have not been accessible to molecular oxygen since the time of their deposition. However, it is very probable that at the time of deposition, the UO_2 was accessible to the gases of the atmosphere and was in fact in thermodynamic equilibrium with the atmosphere. If this was the case, then the presence of UO_2 in the South African gold-uranium reefs points to the virtual absence of O_2 in the Earth's atmosphere around 2.0 billion years ago.

The South African gold-uranium reefs also contain appreciable amounts of the sulfides of iron, lead, and zinc [21]. These sulfides are thermodynamically unstable in the presence of even minute traces of molecular oxygen. For example, at 25°C the equilibrium pressure of O_2 for the oxidation of PbS to $PbSO_4$ is 10^{-63} atm [22]; that is,

$$PbS + 2O_2 \rightleftharpoons PbSO_4 \qquad \text{pressure of } O_2 = 10^{-63} \text{ atm at equil. (25°C)}$$

The thermodynamic data indicate that the equilibrium oxygen pressures for the oxidation of the sulfides to the corresponding sulfates are lower than the equilibrium pressure for the conversion of U_3O_8 to UO_3. The situation with respect to the iron oxides is somewhat less clear since the equilibrium O_2 pressure for the conversion of Fe_3O_4 to Fe_2O_3 is even less than the values for sulfide oxidations, implying that if sulfides are present, then whatever iron is present should be in the form of FeO or Fe_3O_4, rather than Fe_2O_3. The difficulty is that *all three* iron oxides are present in the sediment. Holland [21] has pointed out, however, that for oxygen pressures ranging from 10^{-72} to 10^{-21} atm, both UO_3 and Fe_2O_3 are thermodynamically stable.

In summary, the presence of metal sulfides instead of sulfates lends further weight to the conclusion that the Earth's atmosphere contained virtually no oxygen 2.0 billion years ago, provided, of course, that the sulfides were in equilibrium with the atmosphere during deposition of the sediment.

More evidence of the same kind is provided by an assemblage of Precambrian rocks (of age 2.0 billion years) located near Suodenniemi, Finland. These rocks exhibit a preponderance of FeO over Fe_2O_3. In addition, they contain native reduced carbon as a finely dispersed pigment [23]. Finally, a number of Precambrian iron formations have been shown to be relatively rich in SiO_2 instead of the more oxidized silicates [24].

Although this geological evidence is intriguing, it should be pointed out that it is by no means unequivocal. One of the difficulties is that the compositions of other Precambrian sediments point to a somewhat different conclusion about the composition of the atmosphere. For example, some sediments older than 2.5 billion years are known to contain hematite, and this has been interpreted to mean that free atmospheric oxygen was present during the formation of these sediments, although the point has been contested [21]. Also, there is no clear cut dependence of the oxidation state of sulfur on the age of the corresponding sediments. For example, $CaSO_4$ occurs in both ancient Precambrian limestones and in some recent sediments. Similarly, various sulfides, such as FeS and HgS, which have been taken as indications of an oxygen-free atmosphere occur in both recent and very ancient sediments [20].

In spite of the relative paucity and lack of conclusiveness of the direct geological evidence, it is nevertheless possible to construct some quite general arguments about the composition of the primitive atmosphere. These arguments depend upon some hypothesis about the origin of the solar system. The astronomical point of departure for the speculations is provided by the average relative abundances of the chemical elements in the cosmos as determined from spectroscopic data from the sun and other stars, comets, meteorites, interstellar dust clouds, planets in the solar system, and from geochemical data on the crust of the Earth. The most striking feature of the astrophysical data is the overwhelming preponderance of the element hydrogen in the spectra of virtually all stars and interstellar material [25].

It is important to note that the spectra give us information about the relative abundances of elements in different astronomical objects *at different times in the history of the universe* since the objects are at different distances from the Earth and since light propagates at a finite velocity. Therefore, the resulting overall abundance table (Table 3-5) represents a kind of space and time average of the composition of the universe.

A second kind of astronomical evidence providing support for current hypotheses about the origin of the solar system relates to the abundance of solar systems in the cosmos. The central point here is that if solar systems are very rare in the universe as a whole, then it is likely that some very rare occurrence was involved in the origin of

TABLE 3-5 Abundances of the elements (after [1])

Atomic number	Element	Gram-atoms/gram-atom of Si		
		Earth's crust	Sun's surface	Total universe
1	H	0.14	5.1×10^4	4×10^4
2	He	7.5×10^{-8}	1×10^4	3.1×10^3
3	Li	4.3×10^{-4}		1×10^{-4}
4	Be	2.2×10^{-5}		0.2×10^{-4}
5	B	3×10^{-5}		0.24×10^{-4}
6	C	2.7×10^{-3}	1	3.5
7	N	3.3×10^{-4}	2.1	6.6
8	O	2.9	2.8×10^2	21.5
10	Ne	$<5 \times 10^{-9}$		8.6
11	Na	0.12	0.1	4×10^{-2}
12	Mg	8.6×10^{-2}	1.7	0.91
13	Al	0.3	0.11	9.5×10^{-2}
14	Si	1	1	1
15	P	3.8×10^{-3}		1×10^{-2}
16	S	1.6×10^{-3}	0.43	0.38
18	A	4×10^{-7}		0.15
36	Kr	$<5 \times 10^{-9}$		0.51×10^{-4}
54	Xe	$<5 \times 10^{-9}$		0.4×10^{-5}

any particular system. In the case of our own planetary system, such a rare event might, for example, have been the passage of another star very close to our already-formed sun, resulting in the extraction of solar mass into the space between the sun and the passing star, as suggested in 1917 by Jeans and Jeffreys. This incandescent mass would later give rise to the planets [26]. We should point out that such a theory, although it was very popular among both scientists and laymen until quite recently, is subject to two very serious theoretical difficulties: (1) the kind of near collision between stars required by the theory has been estimated to occur in our galaxy at an average frequency of only 10 times per 5 billion years, and (2) the theory cannot account for the peculiar distribution of angular momentum in the solar system [16]. If, however, planetary systems are ubiquitous in the cosmos, then it is likely that some very general, relatively probable process underlies the origin of such systems.

The astronomical evidence strongly suggests the ubiquity of solar systems in the universe. Many stars have been shown to be multiple by direct telescopic observations of two or more individual masses revolving about a common point, as in the case of the visual binary star Xi Ursae Majoris [27]. Other stars which visually appear to consist of only a single mass exhibit patterns of motion indicative of the presence of one or more less massive planetary companions. A notable example here is Barnard's Star, which apparently consists of a massive luminous star plus one or more dark satellites, the most massive of which is somewhat larger than the planet Jupiter [16].

If we combine the relative abundances of the elements with the fact that planetary systems are common in the cosmos and suggest that solar systems arise by the gravitational condensation of originally highly rarefied clouds of interstellar dust of average elemental composition, then we have the major ingredients of the planetesimal hypothesis for the origin of the solar system [28,29]. Briefly, this hypothesis states that the matter constituting the present solar system was originally dispersed in a vast interstellar cloud of relatively cool dust and gas. Many such clouds have in fact been observed, and since they lie at different, very large distances from our solar system, the observational evidence indicates that such clouds were present at many different times in the past. Because of the mutual gravitational attraction of the constituent particles, the material in the cloud underwent a gradual compression. Vast quantities of material accumulated at the center of the system, giving rise to the nascent sun. This body eventually became incandescent due to the release of an enormous amount of gravitational potential energy as heat during the formation of the protosun. A particular pattern of turbulence somehow developed in the remainder of the dust cloud, resulting in the partial localization of matter into planetesimals which eventually gave rise to the present planets.

It is apparent that the Jeans-Jeffreys picture of the origin of the solar system was essentially a "hot" theory since the matter forming the planets was thought to have been originally incandescent ($T > 1000°C$). The currently popular planetesimal hypothesis, on the other hand, may be called the "cold" theory since the planetary and solar materials are thought to have been originally dispersed in a cold ($T < 0°C$) cloud of dust or gas [28]. The solar mass then eventually reached incandescent temperatures because of the release of gravitational potential energy upon contraction. This raises the problem of whether or not the surface of the Earth was ever entirely molten; this is a problem which the planetesimal theory does not resolve. We shall return to this question in our discussion of heat as a possible free-energy source for chemical evolution.

Finally, let us compare the relative abundances of the elements at the surface of the contemporary Earth with their average cosmic abundances (see Table 3-5). One obvious fact revealed by such a comparison is the marked deficiency of H and He at the surface of the Earth now. Even more significant for our purposes is the virtual absence of the rare gases Ne, Xe, and Kr from the present atmosphere. If we assume that the Earth was formed from an average sample of cosmic matter, then these gases must have been present in the original dust cloud. They have somehow been lost from the planetesimals giving rise to the Earth, but lost under physical conditions which permitted the retention of vast amounts of another volatile substance, namely the water of the present oceans. It is relatively easy to show that Ne, Xe, and Kr could not have escaped from the gravitational field of the fully formed Earth [28]. Therefore, these gases presumably escaped sometime before the Earth was fully formed, possibly very early in the accumulation process when the future terrestrial matter still consisted of relatively small planetesimals. However, since water was retained under these conditions, the temperature could not have been very high [28].

After this somewhat cumbersome but necessary excursion, we can now deal with the question of O_2 in the primitive atmosphere of the Earth. The central point is that if Ne, Xe, and Kr escaped into inter-protoplanetary space before the Earth was fully formed, then many other gases (lighter than Kr and not in some nonvolatile combination with other substances) must have escaped as well. In fact, it is likely that almost all of the gaseous phase (including, of course, any O_2 which might have been initially present) of the forming Earth was lost to interplanetary space before the Earth was formed [28]. Therefore, if the primitive fully-formed Earth had any atmosphere at all, it was probably of a "secondary" origin; that is, the gases in it presumably issued from the interior of the Earth under the influence of the heat generated in the final stages of gravitational collapse of the protoearth [4]. At present, gases such as CO_2, HCl, HF, and H_2S are issuing from the interior of the Earth via volcanic exhalations, fumaroles, and hot springs [21,30].

The extent to which molecular oxygen might have been present in the gaseous phase of material arising from volcanoes on the newly formed Earth has been considered in detail by Holland [21]. His argument begins with consideration of a hypothetical period in the early history of the Earth before the molten iron core was formed. Presumably during this period metallic iron was abundant in the Earth's mantle. The oxidation states of the gases in equilibrium with magmas formed as a result of local melting of the mantle could have been strongly influenced by the presence of the metallic (reduced) iron. Because virtually all of the metallic iron has since left the crust of the Earth and accumulated in the molten core, contemporary volcanic exhalations should be considerably more oxidized than the corresponding primitive gases.

On the basis of thermodynamic data for a melt consisting of FeO, Fe_2O_3, and SiO_2 in equilibrium with solid metallic iron at 1200°C, Holland concluded that the primitive equilibrium pressure of molecular oxygen was probably near $10^{-12.5}$ atm. This very low oxygen pressure has immediate implications with respect to the oxidation states of other primitive volcanic gases, but these will be discussed in succeeding sections. We need only point out here that Holland's arguments, although indirect and relying on some assumptions difficult to verify in any simple way, are completely consistent with the direct geological evidence already discussed. In order to bring all the possibly relevant information into focus here, it is significant to note in addition that molecular oxygen is not even detectable among the gases issuing from contemporary volcanoes (which presumably are in equilibrium with magmas not containing solid metallic iron), fumaroles, or hot springs, nor is it occluded in igneous rocks or in meteorites [21]. Thus, the primitive atmosphere of the Earth apparently contained, at most, only trace amounts of molecular oxygen.

Methane and ammonia

Now we must extend our inquiry to a consideration of the possible predominant molecular species in which the elements carbon and nitrogen might have been present in the earliest atmosphere of the fully formed Earth, as well as in the gas phase of the hypothetical planetesimals. Again, our point of departure is the table of relative abundances of the elements in the cosmos (Table 3-5). Reasoning from this table and from thermodynamic equilibrium data for a number of simple gas phase reactions (and from other lines of evidence to be discussed), Urey [28] has put forward the conclusion that carbon and nitrogen were present in the primitive atmosphere largely in the form of methane (CH_4) and ammonia (NH_3).

The salient features of Urey's argument can be briefly summarized as follows: since hydrogen is by far the most abundant element in the cosmos (Table 3-5), the gaseous phase of the planetesimals as well as the early atmosphere of the fully formed Earth contained excess molecular hydrogen. Carbon, nitrogen, and oxygen would therefore have been reduced to CH_4, NH_3, and H_2O if equilibrium were reached. Of course, H_2 was probably escaping into interplanetary space even before the Earth was formed, since the available evidence suggests that much heavier gases such as Ne, Xe, and Kr were lost during the hypothetical planetesimal stage. However, Urey estimates that the hydrogen pressure was at least 10^{-3} atm at the time of final consolidation of the mass of the Earth (compared to 10^{-6} atm at present) [17]. His conclusion rests on a synthesis of several lines of evidence including the contemporary rate of escape of H_2 from the upper atmosphere, an estimate of the total amount of H_2 which must have escaped throughout geologic time in order to account for the present partial pressure of O_2 (assuming that all of this O_2 was originally present in H_2O), and present oxidation states of C, N, and Fe. The problem of how long such a hydrogen pressure might have persisted is one of extreme difficulty and in fact represents an area of great uncertainty in our thinking about the time course of evolution of the atmosphere [9]. We shall return to this fundamental point later.

At any rate, working on the assumption that at least 10^{-3} atm of H_2 was available in the primitive atmosphere (either as a residue from the original dust cloud or as a result of outgassing of the interior, or due to contributions from both), it is possible to obtain some very rough estimates of relative partial pressures of simple carbon-containing gases. Urey considers the following equilibrium involving carbon dioxide [17]:

$$CO_2 + 4H_2 \rightleftharpoons CH_4 + 2H_2O \text{ (vapor)} \tag{1}$$

The equilibrium constant for this reaction at 25°C is about 10^{20} [17]. Urey argues that equilibrium might have been reached in the upper atmosphere where the short-wavelength solar ultraviolet flux was appreciable, and that the steady-state partial pressures of CO_2 and CH_4 at lower altitudes would be governed by this equilibrium. The methane pressure thus would depend on the carbon dioxide pressure. Urey suggests that the sea-level carbon dioxide pressure, which of course would have been considerably higher than the values for the upper atmosphere, was maintained at very low values due to the following reaction [17,28]:

$$CaSiO_3 + CO_2 \rightleftharpoons CaCO_3 + SiO_2 \tag{2}$$

At equilibrium, the CO_2 pressure is 10^{-8} atm [17], which is considerably lower than the contemporary value of 3.3×10^{-4} atm [1]. Assuming the present sea level CO_2 pressure as an upper limit for the corresponding primitive pressure, Urey concluded that CH_4 was the predominant molecular species in the primitive atmosphere and that its partial pressure exceeded that of carbon dioxide by several orders of magnitude.

Direct geologic evidence of the presence of CH_4 in the primitive atmosphere is virtually nonexistent. As Sagan has pointed out [16], the small traces of CH_4 in the contemporary atmosphere are due almost entirely to bovine flatulence and to the activities of certain marsh bacteria. It has been argued, however, that simple hydrocarbons could have been supplied to the primitive atmosphere by the reaction of metallic carbides with subterranean superheated steam during the differentiation of the mantle resulting in the formation of the crust of the Earth [31]. Evidence for the contemporary occurrence of such a process is provided by the observation that both gaseous and liquid hydrocarbons of presumably nonbiological origin are being formed beneath the Kola Peninsula in northern Russia [32].

Moving on to the question of the predominant molecular species in which nitrogen might have been present in the primitive atmosphere, we find again that the argument depends heavily on thermodynamic equilibrium data. Urey maintains that the following aqueous phase reaction was probably the principal factor controlling the relative amounts of molecular nitrogen and ammonia in the primitive atmosphere and oceans [17]:

$$\tfrac{1}{2}N_2 + \tfrac{3}{2}H_2 + H^+ \rightleftharpoons NH_4^+ \tag{3}$$

The equilibrium constant for this reaction at $25°C$ is 8×10^{13} times the hydrogen-ion concentration, provided the pH is less than 9. Assuming a pH of 8 (the average value for the contemporary oceans is 8.1 [33]; see Sec. 3-5) and a hydrogen partial pressure at the surface of the ocean of 1.5×10^{-3} atm as in the above argument for methane, Urey concludes that most of the volatile nitrogen was present as ammonium ion in the primitive oceans.

If direct geological evidence for CH_4 in the primitive atmosphere is virtually nonexistent, the corresponding evidence for ammonia, or ammonium ion in the primitive oceans, is even more so. Ammonium chloride has been found among the volatile materials issuing from some volcanoes, but only in very small amounts compared to the molecular nitrogen (N_2) in such emanations [9].

Another kind of evidence bearing on the possible presence of both CH_4 and NH_3 in the primitive terrestrial atmosphere has immediate intuitive appeal and has been cited very often in discussions of the origins of life, even though it is highly indirect. This evidence consists of spectroscopic data on the atmospheres of the planets Jupiter, Saturn, Uranus, and Neptune, collectively referred to as the *Jovian* planets, and on the composition of comets. Both methane and ammonia are present as major components in these planetary atmospheres [28]. Similarly, the available spectroscopic evidence on comets indicates that these bodies are made up largely of such molecular species as CH, CH_2, C_2, NH, NH_2, CO_2^+, N_2^+, and CN [34]. It seems plausible that many of these species might have arisen from CH_4 and NH_3 under the influence of short-wavelength solar UV and ionizing radiation.

It has been argued that the overall compositions of the Jovian planetary atmospheres have remained essentially unchanged throughout the history of the solar system [34]. This persistence in composition was presumably due to the coupling of the following two circumstances tending to prevent or retard the escape of H_2 into interplanetary space [35]: (1) the Jovian planets lie at very great distances from the sun and hence are much colder than the terrestrial planets (Mars, Earth, Venus, and Mercury), and (2) the enormous masses of the Jovian planets result in much higher escape velocities than the corresponding values for the relatively much less massive terrestrial planets. It is in this sense that the Jovian planets, and to a lesser extent, the comets, have been called "fossil" relics of the general reducing conditions prevailing in the cosmic dust cloud from which the solar system was presumably formed [34]. Reasoning in this way, it seems plausible to conclude that the earliest atmospheres of the terrestrial planets also contained methane, ammonia, and H_2, and hence were highly reduced [17]. The molecular hydrogen was subsequently lost to interplanetary space because of the high temperatures and low escape velocities relative to the Jovian planets. Escape of molecular hydrogen from the Earth was presumably a major factor in the transition of the primitive reduced atmosphere to the present oxidized atmosphere [21,28].

In this section we have summarized the major lines of evidence and conjecture which have been invoked in support of the view that the primitive atmosphere of the Earth was highly reduced and consisted primarily of methane and to lesser extent ammonia, molecular hydrogen, and water vapor. It is maintained by proponents of this view that such an atmosphere might have persisted for an appreciable time after the final consolidation of the mass of the Earth, perhaps until the origin of the first population of primitive cells [17]. As we have seen, the construction of the methane-ammonia position involves the synthesis of several different kinds of evidence and lines of reasoning ranging from direct observation of the production of methane on the Kola Peninsula to the presumed similarity of the primitive atmosphere of the Earth and the present atmospheres of the Jovian planets. In spite of the complexity of the evidence, the methane-ammonia view has an internal harmony which is perhaps responsible for its general appeal and widespread current acceptance. The position has, however, been seriously challenged on the basis of a simpler and relatively homogeneous body of geochemical evidence which suggests that carbon dioxide and molecular

nitrogen, rather than methane and ammonia, might have been the dominant gases in the primitive atmosphere.

Carbon dioxide and molecular nitrogen

The great bulk of the surface carbon of the Earth is presently locked
in massive sedimentary rock formations, such as limestone deposits
[1]. Much smaller amounts of carbon are present in the biosphere,
hydrosphere, and atmosphere. Rubey, to whose ideas this section is
largely devoted, estimates that the total amount of carbon (computed
as CO_2) contained in ancient sedimentary rocks is about 9.2×10^{22} gm,
whereas the corresponding amount for the three "spheres" is only about
1.5×10^{20} gm [9,36]. Similar calculations for H_2O yield estimates of
14.6×10^{23} gm for the combined hydrosphere, biosphere, and atmosphere and 2.1×10^{23} gm for the sedimentary rocks. Rubey also made
estimates for other volatile elements such as Cl, N, and S. With respect
to such data, one of the questions which Rubey posed was the following: Were the volatile materials derived entirely from crystalline
rocks by weathering processes operating throughout geologic spans
of time? On the basis of estimates of the current rates at which
such volatile materials are supplied to sites of sedimentary deposition,
together with some assumptions about the uniformity of such rates in
the past, Rubey concluded that only a very small part of the volatiles
could possibly have been contributed by weathering. The resulting inventory of excess (not attributable to rock weathering) volatiles is summarized in Table 3-6. It is of great interest to the origin of life problem
to account for the geologic origin of the excess volatile carbon in limestone and dolomite, since a substantial fraction of this carbon was
probably once present in living organisms [9].

In attempting to account for the above results, Rubey considers
two alternative hypotheses concerning the possible source of the excess
volatiles. The first hypothesis is simply that all of the excess volatile
material was originally partitioned between a dense primitive atmosphere (containing thousands of atmospheres of CO_2) and a primitive
hydrosphere containing a substantial fraction of the excess water.
Rubey concludes that this hypothesis would require an overwhelming
predominance of CO_2 and N_2 over CH_4 and NH_3 in the earliest stages
of the history of the atmosphere. However, the hypothesis also implies
that the primitive hydrosphere was highly acidic ($pH < 1$)—so much
so in fact that vastly more rock weathering would have taken place
in early Earth history than has been estimated to have taken place
throughout all of geologic time. Therefore, Rubey rejects this extreme
concept of the origin of the excess volatiles.

If the excess volatiles were not all originally present in a dense
primitive atmosphere, then it is reasonable to assume that they gradu-

TABLE 3-6 Excess volatile materials in
present atmosphere, hydrosphere, and
buried sedimentary rocks (after [9])

Materials	Amounts*
H_2O	16,000
Carbon as CO_2	910
Cl	300
N	42
S	22
H	10
B, Br, A, F, etc.	4

* In units of 10^{20} gm.

ally accumulated at the surface by outgassing of the interior, Rubey
maintains. Evidence for this view is provided by the observation that
contemporary volcanic exhalations are relatively rich in CO_2 and N_2,
and virtually devoid of CH_4 and NH_3 [9]. By far the most abundant
substance in contemporary volcanic exhalations is water [9,21]. This
fact also supports Rubey's argument since his table of excess volatiles
suggests that a substantial fraction of the water in the present hydrosphere issued from the interior of the Earth. Of course, the relevance
of this evidence depends upon the validity of the assumption that the
composition of contemporary volcanic exhalations resembles the composition of the gaseous mixtures reaching the surface of the primitive
Earth. Therefore, in evaluating Rubey's position, you should bear in
mind Holland's argument that the most primitive volcanic exhalations,
unlike their present counterparts, were in equilibrium with magmas containing large amounts of solid metallic iron and consequently were considerably more reduced than the contemporary emanations [21]. We
shall return to this point in the following section.

Several additional lines of evidence have been cited in favor of
the carbon dioxide–nitrogen view. You will recall that in the discussion
of the CH_4–NH_3 view, a number of thermodynamic equilibria were
considered. None of the equilibria involved molecular oxygen mainly
because of the presumed absence of O_2 due to the overwhelming excess
of H_2 [17]. Rubey argues, however, that minute traces of O_2 in the
primitive atmosphere would have had profound effects on the equilibrium pressures of methane [9]. The following reaction illustrates his
point:

$$CH_4 + 2O_2 \rightleftharpoons CO_2 + 2H_2O \qquad K_{eq} = 1.9 \times 10^{140} \ (25°C) \qquad (4)$$

A similar reaction can be written for the oxidation of NH_3 to molecular
nitrogen. It has been pointed out by many investigators, supporting
either the CH_4–NH_3 view or the CO_2–N_2 view, or a combination of

both, that small amounts of O_2 might well have been supplied to the primitive atmosphere by the UV photolysis of water vapor in the upper atmosphere [16]. Of course, the fact that the equilibrium constant for reaction (4) is many orders of magnitude larger than the corresponding constants for reactions (1), (2), and (3) discussed in the previous section does not in itself guarantee that the equilibrium was ever attained. The *rate* of the reaction must also be taken into account. Indeed, this consideration applies to all the reactions discussed in this chapter.

The possibility that one of the key geochemical equilibria used in the argument for the CH_4–NH_3 position might not have been attained or even approached on the primitive Earth has been considered in detail by Rubey [9]. The reaction in question is the so-called *Urey equilibrium* [see Eq. (2)]. It is argued that the operation of this equilibrium, together with the absorption of CO_2 into the hydrosphere to form HCO_3^-, maintained the partial pressure of CO_2 at very low levels on the primitive Earth and indeed throughout Earth history. However, both Urey and Rubey point out that the contemporary partial pressure (3×10^{-4} atm) of CO_2 is several orders of magnitude higher than the equilibrium value (10^{-8} atm), which suggests that the Urey equilibrium might not be the governing process on the contemporary Earth. This fact, in itself, is not particularly significant since CO_2 interacts much more rapidly with the biosphere than it does with the rock-forming minerals of the Urey equilibrium. In any case, CO_2 is only a minor constituent of the present atmosphere. The real difficulty arises when one attempts to assess the role of the Urey equilibrium on the prebiotic Earth. Rubey points out that the relationship expressed by Urey's equation is a vast over-simplification of the long series of processes which are actually involved in rock weathering and limestone formation in nature. Particularly important here is the fact that decaying organic matter derived from the biosphere participates in rock weathering by contributing carbonic acid to ground water. In the absence of such decaying organic material, the rate at which silicates are weathered is greatly reduced. In light of these facts Rubey concludes that Eq. (2) "cannot properly be used to estimate even approximately the maximum concentration of CO_2 in the early atmosphere before life had appeared on Earth" [19].

So far, very little has been said about the escape of molecular hydrogen from the atmosphere of the primitive Earth. You will recall that a major feature of the planetesimal hypothesis on the origin of the solar system is the assumption that the material of the forming planets was derived from an average sample of cosmic matter and hence was very rich in hydrogen. Evidence that much of the uncombined hydrogen escaped from the planetesimals which later formed the Earth is provided by the fact that the noble gases Ne, Xe, and Kr, which are much heavier than H_2, are markedly underabundant in the present atmosphere compared to their average cosmic abundances [28]. Now, much of the thermodynamic reasoning of the CH_4–NH_3 view depends on the presence of an appreciable amount (at least 10^{-3} atm) of residual H_2 in the primitive atmosphere. Rubey maintains, however, that even if the planetesimal hypothesis were correct, which he does not admit, the residual H_2 would have very rapidly escaped from the atmosphere into interplanetary space [9]. Assuming a kinetic temperature of $1500°K$ for the upper atmosphere, he estimates that virtually all the H_2 would have escaped within 300,000 years. Kuiper has also considered the hydrogen escape problem, and his estimate for the process is somewhat larger, namely, about 10^8 years [37]. In either case, CH_4 and NH_3 could have been abundant in the primitive atmosphere for only a very brief period at the beginning of Earth history, and this would be true only on the basis of an unverifiable assumption about the mode of origin of the Earth.

One additional point deserves mention here, if only for the sake of including all possibly relevant information. As Rubey points out, there are at present no convincing natural sources of juvenile* methane or ammonia [9]. Even the occluded gas phase of meteorites contains CO_2 and N_2, rather than CH_4 and NH_3, even though the rock-forming minerals of meteorites are considerably more reduced than contemporary terrestrial surface rocks. It is also of interest to note the recent space probe which has verified the presence of a large amount of CO_2 on the Earth's sister planet Venus.

In conclusion, then, the evidence and lines of reasoning discussed in this section point to a quite different composition for the primitive atmosphere than that postulated in the previous section, at least as far as the principal carbon- and nitrogen-containing gases are concerned.

Although the two positions are based on somewhat different kinds of evidence, they are in substantial agreement on at least the following point: the primitive atmosphere of the Earth contained at most only trace amounts of molecular oxygen. The extent to which the implications of an additional hypothesis, already alluded to above (namely, that there was a precore stage in the early history of the Earth), might resolve some of the points of conflict between the two positions will be discussed in the following section.

A synthesis of the two views

Rubey's thermodynamic equilibrium calculations on the primitive atmosphere do not take into account the possibility with the primitive magmatic gases might have been in equilibrium with a melt containing excess solid iron. Holland argues that the segregation of elemental iron

---

* "Juvenile" is used in the sense of never having been at the surface of the Earth before.

into the molten core might have taken place over a substantial period in the early history of the fully formed Earth [21]. He suggests that the process may have taken as long as 0.5 billion years.

We have already discussed the implications of this hypothesis on the equilibrium partial pressure of O_2 ($10^{-12.5}$ atm at $1200°C$) in the primitive volcanic emanations. Let us now turn to the question of the corresponding equilibrium pressures of other simple gases. On the basis of thermodynamic data for the reactions (assuming an oxygen partial pressure of $10^{-12.5}$ atm and a temperature of $1200°C$)

$$H_2 + \tfrac{1}{2}O_2 \rightleftharpoons H_2O \tag{5}$$

$$CO + \tfrac{1}{2}O_2 \rightleftharpoons CO_2 \tag{6}$$

Holland concludes that H_2 would be twice as abundant as water, and CO 5 times as abundant as CO_2 [21]. Similar considerations applied to the relevant reaction involving methane [Eq. (1)], however, yield the result that CH_4 was probably a minor constituent of the magmatic gases. It will be recalled that Urey concluded from the same equilibrium that CH_4 was a major gas of the primitive atmosphere [Eq. (1)]. The difference lies in the temperature dependence of the equilibrium constant. Urey made his calculation for the atmosphere as a whole assuming a temperature of $25°C$ at which $K_{eq} = 10^{20}$. Holland, on the other hand, is concerned at this point only with the partial pressure of methane in contact with highly localized high-temperature magmas. The assumed temperature of the melts is $1200°C$, at which the equilibrium constant for the methane reaction is $10^{-3.15}$ [21].

Thus far we have neglected to mention the possible molecular species in which the biologically crucial element sulfur might have been present in the primitive atmosphere. Urey [17] and Holland [21] have discussed this problem, and although there is some disagreement about the probable equilibrium partial pressures, there is general agreement that the predominant molecular species was probably H_2S and not SO_2. The relevant reaction is the following:

$$H_2S + 2H_2O \rightleftharpoons SO_2 + 3H_2 \tag{7}$$

Holland concludes that H_2S was a major constituent of the primitive magmatic gases, although its partial pressure was probably considerably less than 1 atm.

The composition of the primitive volcanic exhalations, however, was probably considerably different from the composition of the atmosphere as a whole since the average temperature of the latter, at least near the surface, must have been much lower than $1200°C$. Utilizing thermodynamic equilibrium data at $25°C$ for reactions involving CO, CO_2, CH_4, H_2O, and H_2, it is possible to estimate the equilibrium pressures of the carbon-containing gases, provided that some guesses are made about the pressure of hydrogen. As Holland points out, it is extremely difficult to estimate the primitive hydrogen pressure largely because even vague guidelines for estimating the temperature of the primitive upper atmosphere, which would determine the rate of escape of H_2 into interplanetary space, are not available [21]. Nevertheless, Holland maintains that the half-life (with respect to escape) of H_2 in the primitive atmosphere was most likely between 10^3 and 10^6 years, with the consequence that the primitive hydrogen pressure was probably somewhere between 2.5×10^{-5} and 0.77 atm. On the basis of these limits for the H_2 pressure, together with Rubey's numbers for the total amounts of excess volatiles, Holland estimated limits for the pressures of CO_2, CH_4, N_2, NH_3, and H_2S in the earliest stage in the history of the atmosphere, that is, during the period when large amounts of metallic iron were still present in the mantle (see Table 3-7).

After the formation of the molten core, the volcanic exhalations were presumably in equilibrium with subterranean melts devoid of excess metallic iron [21]. Under these conditions, Holland argues, the equilibrium pressure of O_2 would be about 10^{-3} atm instead of the $10^{-12.5}$ atm of the previous stage. This increased O_2 pressure implies a corresponding increase in the overall oxidation state of the magmatic gases, assuming again that thermodynamic equilibrium was reached in the melts. Thus, the principal volcanic gases during this second stage of the history of the atmosphere were probably water vapor, CO_2, and SO_2. Smaller amounts of N_2 and H_2 would also have been present, but methane and H_2S would have been virtually absent. The resulting suggested composition of volcanic exhalations during this stage turns out to be similar to the composition of contemporary emanations. In determining the probable equilibrium composition of the relatively cool atmosphere, Holland considers a number of gas phase and rock weathering equilibria in which several of the volcanic gases were likely to have participated. He concludes that even though CO_2 is abundant in the emanations, its atmospheric level would have been maintained low by reaction with rock-forming minerals, as Urey suggests [Eq. (2)], in spite of Rubey's contention [9] that the Urey equilibrium was probably not attained.

Finally, Holland considers the transition from this second stage atmosphere to the contemporary oxygen-rich atmosphere. The details of this phase of Holland's model need not concern us here. It is sufficient to say that the principal fact underlying this transition is the emergence of photosynthesis (following biogenesis) as a source of appreciable amounts of atmospheric oxygen. Table 3-7 represents an overall summary of Holland's conclusions about the composition of the Earth's atmosphere during the three stages of his model [21].

Holland's model incorporates features of both the methane-ammonia

TABLE 3-7 Summary of data on the probable chemical composition of the atmosphere during stages 1, 2, and 3* (after [21])

	Stage 1	Stage 2	Stage 3
Major components	CH_4	N_2	N_2
$P\dagger > 10^{-2}$ atm	$H_2(?)$		O_2
Minor components	$H_2(?)$		Ar
$10^{-4} < P < 10^{-2}$ atm	H_2O	H_2O	H_2O
	N_2	CO_2	CO_2
	H_2S	Ar	
	NH_3		
	Ar		
Trace components	He	Ne	Ne
$10^{-6} < P < 10^{-4}$ atm		He	He
		CH_4	CH_4
		$NH_3(?)$	Kr
		$SO_2(?)$	
		$H_2S(?)$	

* Stage 1 = 4.5 to 4.0 billion years ago; stage 2 = 4.0 to 2.0 billion years ago; stage 3 = 2.0 billion years ago to the present.
† P denotes partial pressure.

and the carbon dioxide–nitrogen positions discussed above. In particular, molecular oxygen is considered to have been virtually absent throughout the early history of the atmosphere. The synthesis, however, involves important modifications in each view. First of all, the two types of composition are not considered to be alternative possibilities for the earliest atmosphere of the fully formed Earth. Instead, one is thought to have preceded the other in the evolution of the atmosphere. Secondly, ammonia in stage 1 and carbon dioxide in stage 2 are considered to have been minor rather than major components of the atmosphere. Finally, even though a rapid rate of escape of H_2 is still assumed, the length of time allotted to an initial methane-rich stage is considerably longer than Rubey's estimate of 10^5 years because of the presumed presence of reduced (i.e., elemental) iron in volcanic melts.

3-4 FREE-ENERGY SOURCES ON THE PRIMITIVE EARTH

Solar ultraviolet radiation

Since the evidence discussed above strongly indicates that the primitive atmosphere was virtually devoid of molecular oxygen, it seems highly probable that there was no ozone screen either. The ozone screen of the contemporary atmosphere effectively absorbs the short-wavelength ($\lambda < 3000$ Å) component of solar ultraviolet radiation, as already discussed in detail. Therefore, it seems reasonable to conclude that in the absence of such a screen appreciable intensities of short-wavelength UV would penetrate the troposphere and reach the surface [4]. In order to estimate the absolute UV intensities which might have reached the surface of the primitive Earth, we must take into account the possible presence of small amounts of strong UV absorbers other than ozone in the primitive atmosphere. It is also necessary to have some idea of the UV emission of the primitive sun; that is, since all stars are presumably undergoing evolutionary change, we cannot assume at the outset that the intensity distribution of solar UV radiation incident on the upper atmosphere of the primitive Earth was the same as it is today [4,16].

Sagan has discussed the problem of primitive UV fluxes in detail and much of what follows is based on his arguments [4,16]. First of all, let us consider the probable course of evolution of the sun. Pathways of stellar evolution are conveniently represented on the so-called Hertzsprung-Russel diagram, which is a plot of the absolute bolometric magnitude (brightness referred to a standard distance from the solar system) versus the colors (and hence surface temperatures) of stars [38]. Such a representation of the evolution of the sun is shown in Fig. 3-4.

You will notice that for times earlier than 5 billion years ago, the point representing the sun is considered to have moved vertically downward on the diagram, with the consequence that the solar surface temperature remained approximately constant. The mass of the sun during this period was presumably contracting from an originally dispersed interstellar dust cloud [16]. Since the relative proportion of ultraviolet light in the solar emission spectrum depends upon the surface temperature, an implication of the model is that the primitive solar UV flux did not differ markedly from the present flux. Assuming that the distance between the sun and the Earth was about the same 4 to 5 billion years ago as it is today and that the values of certain fundamental physical constants, such as the speed of light, as well as Boltzmann's and Planck's constants, have remained constant, Sagan estimates the total primitive solar UV intensities at wavelengths less than some characteristic wavelength λ_0 by integration of the Planck black-body function [4]. A brief summary of his results, in units of photons per square centimeter per second incident upon the upper primitive atmosphere, is given in Table 3-8.

The amount of UV radiation which penetrated the primitive atmosphere and reached the surface depends upon how much of the incident flux was absorbed by atmospheric constituents. As we have already seen, the contemporary atmosphere, with the exception of the ozone screen, is essentially transparent to UV radiation down to about 1850 Å. Likewise, the molecular species in Holland's hypothetical primitive atmosphere (Table 3-7, stage 1) are all essentially transparent above

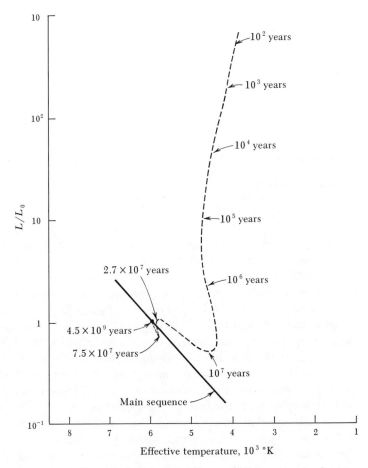

FIG. 3-4   A theoretical diagram of the evolutionary track of a star of solar mass, on its way toward the main sequence. The evolutionary track is shown as the dashed line beginning at very high luminosities and descending toward the inclined solid line which represents the main sequence. The point marked 4.5×10^9 years represents the present position of the sun. L = luminosity, and L_0 = present luminosity. (*After* [16].)

about 2000 Å. However, if chemical evolutionary reactions were in fact taking place in the primitive reducing atmosphere, then we might expect that some substances which did absorb UV of $\lambda > 2000$ Å were formed in appreciable yields. On the basis of results obtained in the kind of primitive atmosphere simulation experiments to be discussed in depth in Chap. 4, Sagan argues that compounds of intermediate oxidation state, such as aldehydes, were formed in substantial yields in the primitive atmosphere and that such substances contributed to the attenuation of solar UV [4]. By far, the aldehyde produced in greatest yield in simulation experiments is formaldehyde. This compound has a broad

TABLE 3-8 Estimated primitive UV intensities available at the top of the Earth's atmosphere [4]

λ_0, Å	Q^*
2900	7×10^{14}
2600	4×10^{14}
2400	9×10^{13}
2000	2×10^{13}

* Q = integrated photon flux in units of photons per square centimeter per second for $\lambda < \lambda_0$.

absorption band centered at about 2940 Å, but it is essentially transparent between 2400 and 2900 Å [39]. The only other likely candidate for a significant attenuating role in the primitive atmosphere is acetaldehyde, which exhibits appreciable absorption between 2400 and 2900 Å [40]. However, in spark experiments (see Chap. 4) acetaldehyde is not a major product [41]. In any case, we cannot rule out the presence of appreciable amounts of acetaldehyde and other UV absorbers in the primitive atmosphere solely on the basis of simulation experiments since we do not really know the extent to which the initial gaseous reactant mixtures accurately simulate the actual composition of the primitive atmosphere. Nevertheless, the available evidence allows the tentative conclusion that an appreciable fraction of the 2400 to 2900 Å solar radiation incident on the upper atmosphere did reach the surface of the oceans, and that smaller but significant fractions of the incident radiation between 2000 and 2400 Å and above 2900 Å penetrated deep into the troposphere [42].

The hypothetical constituents of the primitive atmosphere exhibit appreciable UV absorption only at wavelengths less than 1900 Å. For example, ammonia begins to absorb at about 1850 Å, whereas the absorption by water vapor begins around 1700 Å. Methane, however, absorbs strongly only at wavelengths less than 1450 Å. However, if ammonia and water vapor were only minor constituents of the earliest secondary atmosphere, then we can expect that substantial amounts of radiation were initially available for photoexcitation of methane. Molecular hydrogen absorbs only below 1000 Å [43].

Thermal energy

It is well known that chemical reactions are in general accelerated as a result of elevation of the temperature. However, in the absence of specific catalysts, most of the reactions of potential interest to prebiological chemical evolution proceed at virtually undetectable rates at room temperature. This is particularly true of reactions among the hypothetical constituents of the primitive atmosphere. A mixture of methane, water vapor, hydrogen, and ammonia enclosed in a hermetically sealed quartz vessel with a light-tight housing would remain at $300°K$ for millions of years without undergoing any appreciable chemical change. If, however, the mixture were heated to 1000 or $1500°K$, some small degree of chemical change would in fact occur within reasonable laboratory times, but the products would be predominantly free-radical species. The quartz walls of the heated vessel might in fact act as a weak catalyst for the process, with the consequence that in the absence of such walls even less chemical change would take place [44]. It is conceivable that some of the free radicals would recombine to form minute amounts of other simple gases. However, even the smallest of the organic molecules characteristic of living nature, such as sugars or amino acids, would be unstable at such elevated temperatures, as will be discussed in Chap. 5. Upon cooling of the mixture down to $300°K$, free-radical recombination would produce not only the original gases but a variety of other more complex substances as well. The yields of such compounds would presumably be increased by extension of the heating time, assuming that equilibrium had not been reached, or by prior exposure to even higher temperatures. The point is that only upon subsequent cooling would there be any chance of forming and preserving simple biological compounds.

On the basis of this argument, we can see that thermal energy might well have been a major source of free energy on the primitive Earth if the surface regions of the Earth passed through an early high-temperature phase. If, on the other hand, the average temperature of the surface was never appreciably greater than the contemporary value of about $300°K$, then the large-scale utilization of thermal energy for the promotion of chemical evolutionary reactions becomes less likely. It is of course possible that even though the average surface temperatures might have remained low throughout Earth history, localized hot spots such as volcanoes and fumaroles might have contributed significantly to chemical evolution [45]. We shall return to this possibility in the section on specialized microenvironments. At this point, let us consider lines of evidence which might bear on the *general* thermal history of the Earth.

It was once a commonly held belief that early in the history of the solar system the Earth was entirely molten. In fact, until relatively recently, many astronomers and astrophysicists accepted the theory that the mass of the Earth, and of the other planets as well, was originally torn from the incandescent surface of an already-formed sun during a near collision with another star [26]. Such a cataclysmic event exerts a very powerful force on the imagination. However, as we indicated in our discussion of the composition of the primitive atmosphere, a large body of evidence has been accumulated which suggests that the sun and the planets were formed simultaneously from an originally highly dispersed, *cold* cosmic dust cloud. Of course, the surface of the sun (and the interior as well) did eventually become molten and finally incandescent. This was presumably due to the release of astronomical quantities of gravitational potential energy as heat in the collapsing protosun, so that eventually the interior was hot enough to maintain thermonuclear reactions [46]. Release of gravitational potential energy on a much smaller scale is assumed to have resulted in heating and some melting of the interior of the nascent Earth as well. The questions we need to raise, then, are the following: Did the melting of the interior ever reach the surface of the Earth on a large scale? If not, what was the probable maximum average surface temperature? It is apparent that even though we abandon the stellar near-collision theory of the origin of the solar system, the possibility that the surface of the fully formed primitive Earth might have been hot requires careful consideraton.

At present there is great uncertainty concerning the early thermal history of the Earth's surface, and many conflicting ideas are currently at hand. There is fairly general agreement, however, that a considerable fraction of the interior of the Earth must have once been molten in order for the formation of the iron core (which presumably involved removal of metallic iron from the region of the mantle) to have taken place [1,21]. Some investigators maintain that the differentiation of the Earth into core, mantle, and crust required an originally entirely molten mass [47] and that the gradually cooling mantle first solidified at its base rather than at the surface and later on in progressively higher regions [48]. The timetable for solidification of the crust presents perhaps the greatest difficulty. Suggestions range from various highly speculative models of gradual crystallization to the possibility that the crustal material may never have been molten nor indeed even very much warmer than the present crust [1].

Direct geochemical evidence bearing on the probable temperatures of the primitive crustal materials is very sparse. Urey, however, has argued that the relative abundances of certain volatile elements in various kinds of materials in the contemporary crust might provide some clues [49]. We can illustrate the major features of Urey's reasoning by means of the following example: Chlorine and bromine are much more abundant in sediments and in the oceans than they are in igneous rocks or in meteorites. Fluorine, however, does not exhibit this marked concentration in the sediments. The problem is to account for this difference in distribution between Cl and Br on the one hand and F on the other. Urey argues that if the halogens were concentrated into sediments and oceans by means of a high-temperature volatilization process, then F should also have been concentrated since the vapor pressure of HF is comparable to those of HCl and HBr at elevated temperatures ($T > 500°C$). The lower the temperature, however, the greater the amount by which the vapor pressures of HCl and HBr exceed that of HF. Boron also exhibits a marked concentration in sediments and the oceans, but this element is volatile as H_3BO_3 only at relatively low temperatures ($T \approx 100$ to $200°C$). At higher temperatures (1000 to $1500°C$), B_2O_3 is formed, and this substance has relatively low volatility. Now, at temperatures as low as 100 to $150°C$, Cl, Br, and B are characteristically highly soluble in water as the anions of salts containing Na^+, K^+, Ca^{++}, and Mg^{++}. In this regard, they stand out from all other elements except iodine (about which the evidence is conflicting). Fluorine, however, forms the highly insoluble CaF_2. Therefore, if Cl, Br, and B were concentrated in sediments and in the oceans at low temperatures because of the high water solubilities of their salts rather than at elevated temperatures because of their high volatilities, then the virtual absence of F is readily understandable. Similar considerations apply to the elements Hg and As, both of which are volatile at temperatures above $500°C$, but neither of them is concentrated in sediments or the oceans. On the basis of this kind of evidence, Urey [17,49] concludes that the average surface temperature of the Earth may never have exceeded $150°C$, and that consequently thermal energy was not a significant source of free energy for chemical evolutionary reactions. Such conclusions are, of course, completely consistent with the low-temperature planetesimal theory of the origin of the solar system already discussed.

One of the underlying assumptions of Urey's argument is that the concentration of the various volatile elements into sediments and the oceans was occurring during the earliest phase of Earth history. If most of this concentration occurred during, say, the last 3.5 billion years, then the geochemical inventory data cited by Urey would provide little information on thermal conditions during the first billion years. Also, the hypothesis discussed above requires the presence of a hydrosphere, but as Urey himself points out, it is very difficult to determine whether standing bodies of liquid water were present on the primitive Earth [49]. If the temperature were much above $100°C$, the water would have boiled into the atmosphere. Finally, in evaluating Urey's argument, one should bear in mind the fact that he is discussing general geochemical conditions, rather than the possible existence of specialized, high-temperature microenvironments. The presence of volcanic activity on the contemporary Earth indicates that localized regions of the primitive crust could have been very hot, however, as will be considered in Chaps. 4 and 5.

Miscellaneous free-energy sources

There are no compelling reasons for concluding that the minor free-energy sources now available at the surface of our planet (see Table 3-4) were not also available on the primitive Earth. The amount of energy supplied by most of these sources in primeval times is, however, difficult to estimate. In the case of radioactivity in the uppermost kilometer of the Earth's surface, it is possible to estimate the corresponding amount of energy available 4.5 billion years ago from the rates at which the major long-lived radioactive species decay. Bullard has made the calculation for the unstable isotopes of uranium, thorium, and potassium, which emit α, β, and γ rays. His result suggests that 3 to 4 times more energy from this source was available in the crust per unit time than at present [50]. However, most of this energy was probably absorbed by the mineral lattices in which the radioactive isotopes were located and converted to heat before it could be utilized in promoting chemical reactions in the primitive atmosphere or oceans. Since all the conditions for electrical storms were probably met on the primitive Earth, it is likely that electrical discharge was a significant source of free energy for chemical evolution (see Table 3-4).

One additional source of energy for prebiological chemical evolution has recently been proposed, namely, the thermal and hypersonic energy produced upon passage of a meteor through the primitive atmosphere and upon impact with the surface of the hydrosphere [51]. It is well known that the surface of a meteorite is heated to incandescent temperatures (as high as 16,000°K) because of the frictional retarding force of the air. Also, pressures as high as 1,500 atm may be attained in the air space just forward of the infalling meteorite. Free radicals could be formed from constituents of the primitive atmosphere at these temperatures; these would recombine in the cooling wake of the meteorite. Many meteorites are completely vaporized before penetrating very deeply into the atmosphere. The larger ones, however, may survive all the way to impact with the surface. Such impacts on the primitive oceans would result in local regions of high temperature and pressure in which appreciable chemical change might have taken place.

The extent to which such processes might have contributed to chemical evolution depends on the probable frequency of meteoritic infalls on the primitive Earth. Such a number is very difficult to estimate. Rough guesses have, however, been offered [51]. It has been calculated that during the last 0.5 billion years of Earth history, 30,000 to 50,000 meteorites with diameters on the order of meters may have struck the surface. A single meteorite with a 1-km diameter moving at a hypersonic speed of 11 km/sec upon impact has a total kinetic energy of about 2×10^{27} ergs. Hochstim points out that this energy would be sufficient to completely vaporize 60 km^2 of ocean, 1 km deep, if it were all transferable to water as heat [51].

3-5   THE PRIMITIVE OCEANS

Many times throughout this chapter, and indeed throughout this book, the term "primitive ocean," or "primitive hydrosphere," is used. The assumption underlying this usage is that there were in fact standing bodies of liquid water on the surface of the primitve Earth either immediately following the final consolidation of the terrestrial mass or at least within the first 0.1 billion years. Due to the physical properties of water, this assumption requires that the earliest average surface temperatures did not exceed 110°C, allowing for an appreciable elevation of the boiling point by dissolved salts. However, as we have seen, there is some controversy about the earliest surface temperatures, so that even tentative conclusions about the presence or absence of liquid water are tenuous. Nevertheless, Rubey's geochemical inventory data (see Table 3-6) suggest that more than nine-tenths of the water in the present oceans was supplied by outgassing of the interior or was initially present at the surface in the form of water vapor. By means of estimates of the current rate of supply of juvenile water vapor to the surface by volcanoes, hot springs, and fumaroles, it has been suggested that the maximum volume of the oceans during the first 0.5 billion years of Earth history was approximately one-tenth the present volume [28]. However, there is considerable diversity of opinion concerning the rates at which the total volume of the hydrosphere might have increased [36]. There is substantially more agreement among geologists, however, that the overall inorganic *composition* of the oceans has remained essentially unchanged throughout Earth history [36].

Although the pH in different regions of the present hydrosphere varies from 1 to 10, the values for the open seas tend to cluster relatively tightly around 8.1 [1,33]. Apparently, many different mineral equilibria contribute to the control of pH, although it seems probable that several aluminosilicate clay minerals, such as kaolinite, montmorillonite, illite, and chlorite, play the principal roles [33]. Equilibria involving H_2CO_3, HCO_3^-, and CO_3^- are considered to be relatively unimportant in the maintenance of the slightly alkaline pH of the oceans, the major reason being that the buffering capacity of the carbonate ions is much smaller than the corresponding capacities of the aluminosilicate minerals.

On the basis of a nine-phase equilibrium model for the contemporary oceans, in which the atmosphere and the aqueous solution itself, as well as quartz, calcite ($CaCO_3$), and the zeolite mineral phillipsite, are added to the four clay minerals mentioned above, Sillén has concluded that the pH of the oceans has probably remained close to 8 throughout most, if not all, of the history of the hydrosphere [33]; that is, in Sillén's model, the composition of the atmosphere is not considered to have exerted a major influence on the average pH of the hydrosphere. For example, NH_4^+ ions, which you might expect on the basis of Holland's model for the earliest atmosphere (see Table 3-7) to have been considerably more abundant in the primitive oceans than at present, are assumed in Sillén's scheme to have been distributed between the aqueous and aluminosilicate phases in the same proportions as K^+ ions today, so that they would not have contributed appreciably to the elevation of pH.

Underlying Sillén's equilibrium model [33] is of course the fundamental assumption that the thermodynamic equilibria involving the clay minerals are in fact reached in the contemporary hydrosphere. As Sillén points out, all the relevant equilibrium data have not been obtained for the individual phases under laboratory conditions. In the context of biochemical origins, we also need to know whether or not the relevant clay minerals were likely to have been widespread on the surface of the primitive Earth. We should also point out that most of the thermodynamic equilibrium calculations upon which the above model of the ocean, as well as the other thermodynamic arguments relating to the primitive scenario, are based, assume a temperature of 25°C. The reason for this is that the most extensive tabulations of thermodynamic data conventionally refer to equilibria at 25°C.

3-6 SPECIALIZED MICROENVIRONMENTS

Thus far we have been primarily concerned with general or average geochemical and geophysical conditions which might have prevailed over vast areas of the primitive globe. However, as we have already seen in our discussion of the thermal history of the Earth, it is possible that the values of some physical parameters differed widely in particular localized settings from the mean terrestrial values. Indeed, the surface of the contemporary Earth exhibits a fantastic variety of specialized microenvironments in which, for example, the temperatures vary from the −71°C at Verkhoyansk [52] to the 645°C recorded in the Valley of the Ten Thousand Smokes [49]. If a comparable degree of variation occurred on the primitive Earth, then we are faced immediately with the following question: Must we limit our guidelines for primitive simulation experiments only to general geochemical conditions, or should we broaden our scope to include specialized conditions as well? Fox argues that the origin of life need not be considered to be a general geochemical phenomenon, but instead one which might have required a particular kind of localized environment [53]. He suggests that processes occurring in and around volcanic cinder cones might have been crucially involved. Urey, on the other hand, maintains that thermal energy supplied by volcanic activity played at most a negligible role in chemical evolution mainly because volcanoes are widely spaced, and eruptions are infrequent on the present Earth [17]. In partial reply, Fox argues that lava flows cover as much as 3 percent of the Earth's surface and that the temperatures a few inches below the surfaces of cinder cones are as high as 160°C, even if the volcanoes have not erupted for many years [54]. If this volcanic production of surface heat is integrated over geologic spans of time (like, for example, the first 0.5 billion years of Earth history, assuming with Holland [21] that magmatic activity occurred during this time), its cumulative effect in promoting chemical evolution might indeed have been very significant. Additional heat could have been contributed by other specialized thermal settings such as hot springs and fumaroles. In spite of these considerations, many investigators seem to favor the view that only continuous and relatively uniformly dispersed sources of energy are admissible in simulation experiments. The use of heat as a free-energy source will be considered in detail in Chaps. 4 to 6.

Local variations of conditions are also exhibited by the Earth's hydrosphere, although the extent of deviation from the mean is considerably less than that which occurs on the land masses. For example, the acidity of natural waters can vary from a pH of 1 in the case of some thermal springs, up to a pH of 10 for water in contact with alkali soils [1]. The local pH values around primitive oceanic volcanoes may have been considerably lower than the average values for the open seas because of the emanation of hydrogen halides [55]. In the majority of cases, however, the pH does not now differ by more than 1.5 units from neutrality [1]. Somewhat more variation is exhibited by terrestrial waters, where acidic pH values predominate, than by the open seas, where the average pH is slightly above 8 [1]. Temperatures range from slightly below 0°C as, for example, in Arctic and Antarctic waters, to near 100°C in hot springs. Again, greater variation is exhibited by terrestrial waters as compared to the open seas. Finally, the concentrations of dissolved salts can differ widely in various localized regions of the hydrosphere. The headwaters of terrestrial river systems, for example, may have very low salt concentrations, whereas waters in contact with evaporite deposits, such as are characteristic of the Great Salt Lake, are relatively very much richer in salt content. Thus, it seems plausible that a similar diversification of microenvironments was present in the primitive hydrosphere.

The greater diversification of specialized local settings on the solid land masses compared to that of the hydrosphere is correlated with the fact that random diffusion and mixing of materials is relatively unconstrained in water, whereas it is virtually prohibited in the rigid crystalline mineral lattices out of which the dry land is constructed; that is, the free diffusion of water molecules, and dissolved molecular species as well, together with the pattern of currents, contributes to the overall uniformity of the temperatures and salt concentrations in the open seas. Of course, some local variation is also maintained by the pattern of currents, the local prevailing intensities of solar radiation, and the influx of sedimentary materials at river deltas. The relatively greater range of physical and chemical parameters in terrestrial waters compared to open seas can be attributed to the fact that rivers, lakes, ponds, springs, etc. are often individually isolated from other bodies of water by intervening dry land, so that the averaging process accompanying mixing occurs to a lesser extent. In the atmosphere, at least at altitudes within the troposphere, the overall uniformity of physical and chemical conditions is even more marked than in the open seas, due to the virtually unimpeded random thermal motion of the atmospheric constituents [1].

In the context of our search for guidelines for primitive Earth simulation experiments, the above considerations are of quite fundamental significance because they considerably broaden our scope with respect to admissible experimental conditions. The diversity of specialized microenvironments in the different zones of the Earth's surface increases in the following order: atmosphere < open seas < terrestrial waters < solid land. Therefore, the requirement for adhering only to very general or average conditions in simulation experiments is progressively relaxed as we pass from purely gas-phase experiments to those containing solid phases. In fact, in the solid-phase category of experiment, virtually any plausible geochemical setting can be admitted as a possible candidate for part of the primitive scenario of the origin of life.

One implication of the random thermal motion of molecules dissolved in the hydrosphere deserves consideration here since it poses a serious difficulty in our thinking about biochemical origins. The difficulty, briefly stated, is as follows: Even the simplest forms of contemporary life consist of highly localized (i.e., within the small space bounded by the plasma membrane) interlocking reaction patterns. If we imagine that the constituents of the primeval atmosphere were undergoing simple chemical transformations resulting in the production of less volatile substances which were subsequently transported to the primitive hydrosphere, then once dissolved, such substances would tend to diffuse throughout the volume of the water, possibly making local concentrations exceedingly small. The probability of subsequent interaction between dissolved molecules of the same type to form more complex, polymeric substances would therefore be correspondingly low. Of course, in order to determine whether or not this difficulty is a serious one, we need to know something about the probable rates of production of various kinds of substances in the primitive atmosphere, their rates of transfer to the primitive oceans, and the volume of the primitive oceans. All of these quantities are exceedingly difficult to estimate even roughly,

although some imaginative attempts have been made.   Urey [28] estimates that the average concentration of dissolved organic substances
in the primitive hydrosphere may have been as high as 10 percent
(weight per unit volume), whereas Sagan [4] sets the figure at 1 percent.
At any rate, if some mechanism for concentrating organic substances into
relatively small regions of space were in fact operating somewhere in
the primitive scenario, then the probability of molecular interaction
would be considerably enhanced, and the difficulty partially overcome.

Because of their extraordinarily high surface adsorptive capacities,
the clay minerals have been suggested as concentrating agents in the
primitive oceans [56].   These minerals are exceedingly abundant on
the contemporary Earth and occur in a wide variety of geological settings
including mud flats, estuaries, river deltas, seashores, and the ocean
bottoms generally [57].   The characteristic crystal structure of clay minerals consists of stacks of relatively thin, flat sheets of various patterns
of silica tetrahedra and alumina octahedra.   Individual particles are
flat platelets typically 1 μ square and several hundred angstrom units
thick.   The external surfaces of such particles contain many adsorption
sites capable of binding organic substances by ionic and/or van der
Waal's interaction forces.   Some of the clay minerals are also capable
of adsorbing organic substances at sites on the internal faces of the
individual lattice sheets.   Notable in this regard is the clay mineral
montmorillonite which has a total adsorptive surface area of 430 m^2/gm
[58] compared with a value of only 2.8 m^2/gm for spherical SiO_2 particles 1 μ in diameter.   Montmorillonite has been shown to adsorb such
biologically important substances as adenosine, guanine, and nicotine
at its internal binding sites in highly stereoregular array, that is, with
the planes of the various organic ring systems oriented parallel to the
lattice surfaces [58].   Many other kinds of biocompounds, including
sugars, fatty acids, amino acids, and proteins, are known to interact
with montmorillonite [59].

Since the internal adsorption of organic substances involves the
displacement of originally adsorbed water molecules [57], the local submicroscopic environment at the binding sites is hypohydrous, a condition
which might favor the kind of reaction characteristic of contemporary
biological polymerization, namely, dehydration-condensation.   It has in
fact been suggested that simple polymerization reactions might have
been promoted by clay minerals on the primitive Earth [56].   However,
we should point out here that once organic molecules are internally
adsorbed by montmorillonite, they can be very difficult to remove, drastic
changes in pH often being required [59].   Therefore, in considering
the possible role of clays in prebiological chemical evolution, we should
not ignore the distinct possibility that these minerals might have exerted
a negative influence by *trapping* organic substances in almost inaccessi-
ble crystalline prisons.   We shall return to this point in Chap. 5.

3-7 CONCLUSIONS

In this chapter we have presented lines of evidence which constitute practically our only clues about the nature of the primitive setting of the origin of terrestrial life. Much of the evidence and reasoning is highly indirect, but wherever possible we have underscored the relevant direct geochemical data.

Let us summarize the major features of our hypothetical reconstruction. First of all, we saw that the present atmosphere, with its ozone screen and highly oxidizing conditions, is not a suitable guide for gas-phase simulation experiments. The primitive atmosphere probably consisted of some mixture of CO_2, CO, CH_4, NH_3, N_2, H_2O vapor, H_2S, and H_2. Although there is uncertainty concerning which of these simple gases predominated in the Earth's primitive atmosphere, the conclusion that molecular oxygen was at most only a trace constituent seems relatively well founded. An immediate consequence of the initial absence of O_2 is the likelihood that considerable amounts of short-wavelength UV radiation penetrated deep into the atmosphere and promoted photochemical reactions among the atmospheric constituents. The available evidence indicates that thermal energy probably also played a significant role in chemical evolution. Finally, a wide variety of specialized local environments, both on the land masses and in the hydrosphere, might have contributed to chemical evolution.

We have tried to emphasize that nearly every proposed feature of the primitive Earth has been deduced from the synthesis of many diverse kinds of evidence and arguments. Thus, in order to evaluate adequately the geochemical plausibility of the experiments discussed in the next three chapters, it is necessary to have some familiarity with astronomy, astrophysics, geochemistry, geophysics, atomic and molecular spectroscopy, chemical kinetics, and thermodynamics. However, a remarkable pattern is emerging from the experimental work to date which suggests that such a detailed evaluation, though fascinating, might in fact not be necessary. The long and short of this pattern is that the kinds of chemical evolutionary reactions which have been demonstrated in the laboratory exhibit an unexpected lack of dependence on the specific details of the experimental conditions (within limits, of course). For example, the α-amino acids characteristic of contemporary proteins are produced from a variety of starting gaseous mixtures supplied with a number of different free-energy sources. Similar statements can be made for other categories of biocompounds, as will be shown in Chaps. 4 to 6. At higher levels of complexity as well, the principal governing constraints on the course of the reactions appear to be engraved in the reacting elements themselves, rather than in the specific details of the environment or the free-energy source. Therefore, knowledge of the details of Earth history, which will probably remain hidden from us in any case, may not be required for a complete understanding of biochemical origins. The ramifications of this tantalizing conclusion will constitute a major theme of the following chapters.

REFERENCES

1. Mason, B.: "Principles of Geochemistry," John Wiley & Sons, Inc., New York, 1958.
2. King, E. L.: "How Chemical Reactions Occur," Benjamin, Inc., New York, 1963.
3. Williams, V. R., and H. B. Williams: "Basic Physical Chemistry for the Life Sciences," W. H. Freeman and Company, San Francisco, 1967.
4. Sagan, C.: in S. W. Fox (ed.), "The Origins of Prebiological Systems," pp. 207, 238, Academic Press Inc., New York, 1965.
5. Carpenter, P. L.: "Microbiology," W. B. Saunders Company, Philadelphia, 1967; Stewart, W. D. P., *Science*, 158:426 (1967).
6. Calvin, M., and J. A. Bassham: "The Photosynthesis of Carbon Compounds," Benjamin, Inc., New York, 1962.
7. Conn, E. E., and P. K. Stumpf: "Outlines of Biochemistry," John Wiley & Sons, Inc., New York, 1964.
8. Berkner, L. V., and L. C. Marshall: *Proc. Natl. Acad. Sci.*, 53:1215 (1965).
9. Rubey, W. W.: *Geol. Soc. Am. Spec. Papers No.* 62, p. 531, 1955.
10. Giese, A. C. (ed.): "Photophysiology," vol. I., Academic Press Inc., New York, 1964.
11. Method discussed in Ref. 12.
12. Dunkelman, L., and R. Scolnik: *J. Opt. Soc. Amer.*, 49:356 (1959); Wilson, N. L., et al., *Astrophys. J.*, 119:590 (1954).
13. (a) Johnson, F. S.: *J. Meteorol.*, 11:431 (1954); (b) from Koller, L. R.: "Ultraviolet Radiation," p. 132, John Wiley & Sons, Inc., New York, 1965 [data based on Pettit, E.: *Astrophys. J.*, 75:217 (1932)]; (c) Johnson, F. S.: in C. G. Goetzel, J. B. Rittenhouse, and J. B. Singletary (eds.), "Space Materials Handbook," p. 31, Addison-Wesley Publishing Company, Inc., Reading, Mass., 1965.
14. (a) Berkner, L. V., and L. C. Marshall: *J. Atmospheric Sci.*, 22:225 (1965) [based on data of Watanabe, K., M. Zelikoff, and E. C. Y. Inn: *Geophysical Research Papers*, A. F. C. R. C., No. 21, 1953; *Advan. Geophys.*, 5:153 (1958)]; (b) Heyroth, F. F.: "The Chemical Action of Ultraviolet Rays," Reinhold Publishing Corporation, New York, 1941.
15. (a) Ref. 14a [based on data of Vigroux, E.: *Ann. Phys.* (*Paris*), [12] 8:709 (1953)]; (b) Hartley, W. N.: *J. Chem. Phys.*, 111 (1881); Fabry, J.: *J. Math. Phys.*, 4:1 (1925).
16. Shklovskii, I. S., and C. Sagan: "Intelligent Life in the Universe," Holden-Day, San Francisco, 1966.
17. Miller, S. L., and H. C. Urey: *Science*, 130(3370):245 (1959).
18. Pryor, W. A.: "Free Radicals," McGraw-Hill Book Company, New York, 1966.
19. Ramdohr, P.: *Abhandl. Deut. Akad. Wiss. Berlin, Kl. Chem., Geol. Biol.*, 3:35 (1958).
20. Rutten, M. G.: "Geological Aspects of the Origin of Life on Earth," Elsevier Publishing Company, Amsterdam, 1962.
21. Holland, H. D.: in A. E. J. Engel, H. L. James, and B. F. Leonard (eds.), "Petrologic Studies," p. 447, Geological Society of America, 1962.
22. Kellogg, H. H., and S. K. Basu: *Am. Inst. Min. Met. Eng. Trans.*, 218:70 (1960).

23. Rankama, K.: *Geol. Soc. Am. Spec. Paper No.* 62, 651 (1955).
24. Lepp, H., and S. S. Goldich: *Geol. Soc. Am. Bull.*, **70**:1637 (1959).
25. Suess, H. E., and H. Urey: *Rev. Mod. Phys.*, **28**:53 (1956).
26. Page, T.: *Phys. Today*, **1**(6):12 (1948).
27. Struve, O., B. Lynds, and H. Pillans: "Elementary Astronomy," Oxford University Press, Fair Lawn, N.J., 1959.
28. Urey, H.: "The Planets," Yale University Press, New Haven, Conn., 1952.
29. Von Wiezsacker, C. F.: "The History of Nature," University of Chicago Press, Chicago, 1949.
30. Vinogradov, A. P.: in A. I. Oparin (ed.), "The Origin of Life on the Earth," p. 23, The Macmillan Company, New York, 1959.
31. Oparin, A. I.: "The Origin of Life on the Earth," Academic Press Inc., New York, 1957.
32. Oparin, A. I.: in S. W. Fox (ed.), "The Origins of Prebiological Systems," p. 96, Academic Press Inc., New York, 1965.
33. Sillén, L. G.: *Science,* **156**:1189 (1967).
34. Oró, J.: in S. W. Fox (ed.), "The Origins of Prebiological Systems," p. 137, Academic Press Inc., New York, 1965; *Ann. N.Y. Acad. Sci.,* **108**:464 (1963).
35. Urey, H.: *Handbuch Physik,* **52**:363 (1959).
36. Rubey, W. W.: in P. J. Brancazio and A. G. W. Cameron (eds.), "The Origin and Evolution of Atmospheres and Oceans," p. 1, John Wiley & Sons, Inc., New York, 1964.
37. Kuiper, G. P.: *Proc. Natl. Acad. Sci.,* **37**:383 (1951).
38. Payne-Gaposchkin, C.: "Introduction to Astronomy," Prentice-Hall, Inc., Englewood Cliffs, N.J., 1954.
39. Schou, S. A.: *Compt. Rend.,* **186**:690 (1928); also, Ref. 4.
40. American Petroleum Institute: *Ultraviolet Spectral Data, No.* 326, Carnegie Institute of Technology, Pittsburgh, 1967.
41. Miller, S. L.: in A. I. Oparin (ed.), "The Origin of Life on the Earth," p. 123, The Macmillan Company, New York, 1959.
42. Sagan, C.: *Radiation Res.,* **15**:174 (1961).
43. Terenin, A. N.: in A. I. Oparin (ed.), "The Origin of Life on the Earth," p. 136, The Macmillan Company, New York, 1959.
44. Grossenbacher, K. A., and C. A. Knight: in S. W. Fox (ed.), "The Origins of Prebiological Systems," p. 173, Academic Press Inc., New York, 1965.
45. Fox, S. W.: *Science,* **132**:200 (1960).
46. Fowler, W. A.: *Proc. Natl. Acad. Sci.,* **52**:524 (1964).
47. Latimer, W. M.: *Science,* **112**:101 (1950).
48. Jeffreys, H.: "The Earth: Its Origin, History and Physical Constitution," Cambridge University Press, New York, 1952.
49. Urey, H.: *Proc. Roy. Soc. (London),* **219A**:281 (1953).
50. Bullard, E.: in G. P. Kuiper (ed.), "The Earth as a Planet," p. 110, University of Chicago Press, Chicago, 1954.
51. Hochstim, A. R.: *Proc. Natl. Acad. Sci.,* **50**:200 (1963).
52. Petterssen, S.: "Introduction to Meteorology," McGraw-Hill Book Company, New York, 1958.
53. Fox, S. W.: *Nature,* **201**:336 (1964).
54. Fox, S. W. (ed.): "The Origins of Prebiological Systems," p. 197, Academic Press Inc., New York, 1965.
55. Steinman, G., D. H. Kenyon, and M. Calvin: *Biochim. Biophys. Acta,* **124**:339 (1966).
56. Bernal, J. D.: "The Physical Basis of Life," Routledge & Kegan Paul, Ltd., London, 1951; Akabori, S.: in A. I. Oparin (ed.), "The Origin of Life on the Earth," p. 189, The Macmillan Company, New York, 1959.

57. Grim, R. E.: "Clay Mineralogy," McGraw-Hill Book Company, New York, 1953.
58. Hendricks, S. B.: *J. Phys. Chem.,* **45**:65 (1941).
59. Greenland, D. J., R. H. Laby, and J. P. Quirk: *Trans. Faraday Soc.,* **58**:829 (1962); Steinman, G., D. H. Kenyon, and M. Calvin: *Nature,* **206**:707 (1965); Steinman, G.: *Science,* **154**:1344 (1966); Steinman, G.: unpublished results; Thompson, T. D., G. Lailach, and G. W. Brindley: personal communication; "Clays and Clay Minerals: Proceedings of the Sixteenth National Conference," Bailey, S. W. (ed.), pp. 285, 295, Pergamon Press, New York, 1968; McLaren, A. D., and G. H. Peterson: in W. V. Bartholomew and F. E. Clark (eds.): "Soil Nitrogen," chap. 6, American Society of Agronomy, Madison, Wis., 1965.

synthesis of biomonomers

4-1 INTRODUCTION

Oparin and Haldane suggested that laboratory experimentation could be used to duplicate primitive Earth events [1]. In other words, those phenomena which characterized primitive Earth events should also be observable in the laboratory. In this chapter we shall review the various approaches that have been taken to explain the course of chemical evolution, by which compounds essential for the appearance of living systems evolved. We shall discuss in detail the various approaches or schools of thought which have been formulated to elucidate and duplicate these phenomena. The chapter will review syntheses of the major classes of biomonomers under suggested primitive Earth conditions. The discussion will mainly be concerned with reported experimental data, rather than with speculative publications.

Because a given experiment is successful does not necessarily mean that it duplicates chemical evolution or has significance in explaining the course of chemical evolution, in the same sense as was discussed in Chap. 1. A given experiment, by being successful, may serve one of two possible functions. First of all, since many different approaches end up with the same significant biomonomers (as will be discussed in this chapter), it can be concluded that in fact chemical evolution took place under a number of different environments, all of which contributed to the same end. On the other hand, these results may indicate that only some of the experiments represent actual primitive Earth events and that the others merely demonstrate some interesting chemical phenomena. For example, it has been shown that it is possible to synthesize amino acids using a variety of starting reactant mixtures, and within a variety of environments. From such results general conclusions can be proposed.

The experiments we shall discuss are outlined around the transition from the simple to the complex. Such a transformation could have taken place by the application of high-energy sources (i.e., electrical discharge, UV, heat, and the like) to very simple reactants such as N_2, NH_3, CO, CH_4, H_2O, and H_2, whereby biomonomers were produced. On the other hand, some of these experiments begin with reactive compounds which in fact resulted from earlier syntheses. For example, when one passes an electrical discharge through a gaseous mixture of carbon monoxide, nitrogen, and hydrogen, hydrogen cyanide (HCN) is produced [2]. On the other hand, the reaction between hydrogen cyanide, ammonia, and various aldehydes (R—CHO) in water can lead to the production of amino acids [3]. Thus, the importance of HCN is emphasized. Taken as a whole, these experiments show overall trends, such as the central roles of cyanide and formaldehyde. By considering all the experiments that have been done in this field together, we see that such trends become evident.

It is true that we can never be certain that the conclusions drawn from these experiments do in fact have any bearing on the actual course of chemical evolution. However, by utilizing the information discussed in Chap. 3 on the probable nature of the primitive Earth, we can derive plausible models under which to carry out primitive Earth simulation experiments. The results of these experiments can point out to us that the transition from simple molecules to complex biologically significant compounds is a plausible occurrence within the framework of the knowledge of modern chemistry. With this in mind, the real importance of experiments designed to duplicate primitive Earth events is to point out which compounds and mechanisms were probably important in the evolution of biologically significant compounds, those compounds which were essential for the ultimate appearance of living systems.

It is not really essential for us to differentiate between the various forms of energy which could have promoted chemical evolution, for what these results have indicated is that chemical evolution itself would apparently be a probable series of events in any case. The greatest interest thus far has been in the production of amino acids. The syntheses of these compounds will therefore be used as examples to demonstrate the various approaches to elucidating the nature of chemical evolution. Nucleic acids have been of experimental interest only recently in the field of chemical evolution, most likely due to the newfound significance of these substances in general.

In summary, the intention of this chapter is to present a discussion reviewing the various approaches that have been taken in investigating possible modes of synthesis of biomonomers under hypothetical primitive Earth conditions. Each approach represents a particular kind of model for these abiotic events. A comprehensive study of the results of these approaches permits certain conclusions to be drawn and suggests the kinds of subsequent experiments which should be performed so as to consider the more advanced later stages of prebiotic events. The period preceding the appearance of biological systems, in which chemical evolution took place, undoubtedly was subject to the same chemical and physical laws which we experience today. This assumption is part of the doctrine of uniformitarianism discussed in Chap. 1. Without such a hypothesis (or data supporting another model) even the most elementary attempts to elucidate the nature of chemical evolution would be wholly unfounded. Thus, it is assumed that the syntheses which did take place on the primitive Earth were subject to known, well-defined laws and principles. The purpose of these investigations, therefore, is to determine which phenomena were most probably instrumental in primitive biogenesis.

This review describes the probable overall process by which simple reagents are thought to have become reactive intermediates and finally important biochemicals. The scheme begins with the application of energy to simple (primitive) compounds, such as methane (CH_4), ammonia (NH_3), and carbon monoxide (CO), that were probably available under primitive Earth conditions, as discussed already in Chap. 3. These substances were then transformed into reactive compounds, such as nitriles (R—CN) and aldehydes (R—CHO), from which biomonomers ultimately evolved. This discussion will seek to give both arguments that support and dispute the conclusions drawn from these results. It will be left to you to decide how well the experiments in fact duplicate primitive Earth events. Although it is true that many compounds of general chemical interest can be produced by the methods to be described, the discussion will be centered around prebiological chemical evolution* and those results which bear plausible significance to biogenesis.

4-2   ELECTRON BOMBARDMENT OF SIMPLE GASEOUS MIXTURES

As mentioned in Chap. 3, one theory maintains that the molecules constituting the primitive atmosphere were largely in the reduced form [4]. This would make methane (CH_4) the carbon source, ammonia

---

* The use of the word "evolution" in this book should not be taken in the restricted sense used by zoologists and geneticists involving information development by mutation and modification of nucleic acids. Rather, it is used here more generally to denote any event or series of events involved in the appearance of biologically important compounds or systems, either prebiogenetic (Chemical) or postbiogenetic (Darwinian).

(NH_3) the nitrogen source, and water (H_2O) the oxygen source. With the idea that electrical discharges served as an important source of free energy in prebiological reactions, an experiment was set up to test the hypothesis that biologically important compounds can be synthesized from reduced gaseous reagents upon the application of free energy in the form of electrical discharge [5]. First of all, an apparatus was constructed to simulate phenomena occurring in the primitive atmosphere. This apparatus is pictured in Fig. 4-1. A gaseous mixture containing methane, ammonia, and hydrogen was admitted into the apparatus. The lower sphere contained liquid water. In the upper sphere (5 liters) two tungsten electrodes were connected to high-frequency tesla coils and were separated by a gap of around 10 mm. The water in the lower sphere was heated during the sparking process, causing water vapor to pass up the left stem and through the sparking sphere; it liquefied again in the vicinity of the condenser below the sparking sphere. In this manner, a cyclic system was maintained so that the products formed in the sparking sphere were washed down into the aqueous phase. Similarly, this permitted water to serve as one of the reactants of the system. One could view this experimental setup as representing syntheses taking place in the upper atmosphere, with rain water washing the products out of the gaseous phase into the oceans. The apparatus in Fig. 4-1 permitted volatile products to be recycled through the spark gap several times.

This system was intended to serve as a model for events occurring on the primitive Earth. The temperature, except that in the immediate vicinity of the spark itself, was maintained at 100°C or less in accordance with the low-temperature model of the formation of the Earth discussed earlier in Chap. 3. It was believed that such a model represents general

FIG. 4-1 Apparatus used in the sparking of simple gaseous mixtures consisting of a large sparking chamber A, a boiling flask B, a water-cooled condenser C, and a U tube F. Gases were initially admitted through stopcock D. By boiling the water in flask B during the experiment, a circulating system was maintained. Condenser C helped to collect distillates in the U tube after they had passed through sparking chamber C. Using tesla coils, a spark was made to jump between the two electrodes E in flask A. (*After* [5*b*].)

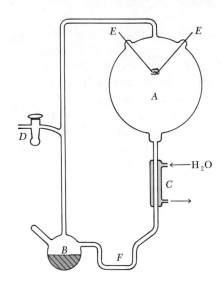

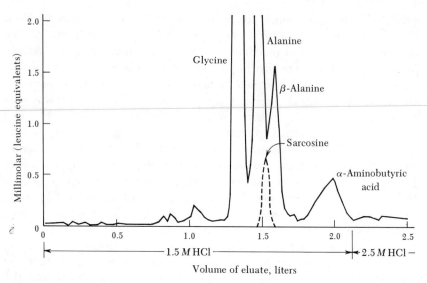

FIG. 4-2 Column chromatographic separation of the water-soluble compounds produced by the sparking of methane, ammonia, hydrogen, and water. (*After* [5b]).

geochemical and geophysical phenomena rather than a selection of specific conditions in particular environments.

In a typical experiment, the apparatus was filled with hydrogen at 10 cm Hg pressure, methane at 20 cm Hg, and ammonia at 20 cm Hg [5]. Minor variations on this apparatus were also attempted, although the general principles remained the same. A high-frequency tesla coil supplied a spark discharge of 60,000 volts. Usually the sparking was carried on for a period of 1 week, in which 1.5×10^3 kcal was supplied to the reactant mixture.

After 1 week of sparking, the aqueous phase was generally yellow. A yellow-brown material collected around the electrodes during the sparking process. The products in the aqueous phase, consisting of about 1 gm of organic material, were analyzed by a combination of anion- and cation-exchange chromatography. Certain amino acids were identified in the spark products by comparison of chromatographic elution rates with known standards.* A typical pattern is shown in Fig. 4-2. Paper chromatography was also used to identify the amino acid products. The products thought to be glycine and alanine were treated with

---

* Amino acids are organic compounds characterized by a carboxyl group (COOH), an amino group (NH₂), and a side chain (R) which distinguishes one amino acid from another. One example of an amino acid would be alanine, whose structure is

$$NH_2—CH—COOH$$
$$|$$
$$CH_3$$

where $R = CH_3$.

TABLE 4-1 Yields of amino acids by sparking a mixture of CH_4, NH_3, H_2, and H_2O for 1 week [5c]

Compound	Yield, moles $\times$ 10^5	Percent yield*
Glycine	63	2.1
Alanine	34	1.7
Sarcosine	5	0.3
β-Alanine	15	0.8
α-Aminobutyric acid	5	0.3
N-Methyl alanine	1	
Aspartic acid	0.4	
Glutamic acid	0.6	

* Based on initial carbon.

p-toluene sulfonyl chloride. The resulting derivatives were collected. Their melting points were compared with those of authentic samples and thus corroborated the identity of the spark products. Similar means were used to identify β-alanine and α-aminobutyric acid. Typical yields of amino acids are shown in Table 4-1.

A number of organic acids were also identified in the product. These are listed in Table 4-2. These acids were primarily identified through the derivatives analyzed following conversion to aldehydes. Actual product yields varied from experiment to experiment because of the variability of the spark itself. In addition to the compounds already noted, evidence of iminodiacetic acid, iminoacetic-propionic acid, α-hydroxybutyric acid, succinic acid, urea, and methylurea was obtained. A typical experiment in which the sparking was carried on over a period of 1 week gave an overall yield of about 15 percent in terms of the organic compounds noted, based on original carbon as methane.

The possibility that the compounds identified were produced by microorganisms was eliminated through runs with the same gaseous reactants but without sparking, whereby only microgram amounts of

TABLE 4-2 Yields of organic acids by sparking a mixture of CH_4, NH_3, H_2, and H_2O for 1 week [5b]

Compound	Yield, moles $\times$ 10^5	Percent yield*
Formic acid	23.3	3.9
Acetic acid	15.2	0.5
Propionic acid	12.6	0.6
Glycolic acid	56	1.9
Lactic acid	39	1.8

* Based on initial carbon.

amino acids were produced. The lack of optical activity in the amino acids produced similarly helped to reject this possibility.

In view of the presence of nitriles, such as HCN, and aldehydes, such as HCHO, identified in the product solutions and the fact that ammonia was also available as one of the initial reactants, it was deduced that the means by which amino acids were produced involved a Strecker-type mechanism; thus

$$\text{RCHO} + \text{NH}_3 \rightleftharpoons \underset{\text{Aldimine}}{\text{R}-\overset{\displaystyle \overset{\text{NH}}{\|}}{\text{C}}\text{H}} \xrightarrow{\text{HCN}} \underset{\text{Aminonitrile}}{\text{R}-\overset{\displaystyle \overset{\text{NH}_2}{|}}{\text{C}}\text{H}-\text{CN}} \xrightarrow{\text{H}_2\text{O}}$$

$$\underset{\alpha\text{-Amino acid}}{\text{R}-\overset{\displaystyle \overset{\text{NH}_2}{|}}{\text{C}}\text{H}-\text{COOH}} + \text{NH}_3$$

$$\text{RCHO} + \text{CH}_3\text{NH}_2 + \text{HCN} \rightarrow \text{R}-\overset{\displaystyle \underset{\displaystyle \underset{}{\text{NH}-\text{CH}_3}}{|}}{\text{C}}\text{H}-\text{CN} \xrightarrow{\text{H}_2\text{O}}$$

$$\underset{\substack{N\text{-Substituted} \\ \alpha\text{-amino acid}}}{\text{R}-\overset{\displaystyle \underset{\displaystyle \underset{}{\text{NH}-\text{CH}_3}}{|}}{\text{C}}\text{H}-\text{COOH}}$$

Also, it was suggested that the production of β-alanine involved a Michael addition as follows:

$$\text{CH}_2\text{=CHCN} + \text{NH}_3 \rightarrow \text{NH}_2-(\text{CH}_2)_2-\text{CN} \xrightarrow{\text{H}_2\text{O}} \underset{\beta\text{-Alanine}}{\text{NH}_2\text{CH}_2\text{CH}_2\text{COOH}}$$

To test the hypothesis that a Strecker synthesis was involved, the apparatus noted in Fig. 4-1 was slightly modified by adding stopcocks to the U-tube to permit withdrawal of samples and was then filled with hydrogen, ammonia, HCN, HCHO, acetaldehyde, propionaldehyde, and water. After boiling the mixture for a week, the nonvolatile compounds noted in Table 4-3 were found.

With this in mind, it is possible to speculate on the location of the various reactions taking place in the apparatus of Fig. 4-1. The production of HCN and aldehydes presumably occurred in the gaseous phase in the vicinity of the spark. Condensation of these products in the aqueous phase, followed by hydrolysis, would lead to the production of amino acids. Formic acid was also identified as a product, and this is believed to be the result of the hydrolysis of HCN. The partial hydrolysis of nitriles could have accounted for the appearance of amino acid amides.

Evidence tending to corroborate the suggested mechanism was also obtained by following the change of the concentration of HCN, alde-

TABLE   4-3   Yields of compounds from the boiling of H_2, NH_3, HCN, HCHO, CH_3CHO, C_2H_5CHO, and H_2O for 1 week [5c]

Acid	Yield, moles $\times$ 10^5	Percent yield*
Glycine	98	16
Alanine	129	35
α-Aminobutyric	27	23
Glycolic	72	12
Lactic	42	12
α-Hydroxybutyric	15	13
Iminodiacetic	56	18
Iminoaceticpropionic	45	

* Based on total aldehyde reactant.

hydes, amino acids, and ammonia in the reaction system during the sparking process. This was done by withdrawing samples at various times during sparking and analyzing them for the components of interest. The resulting kinetic data are shown in Fig. 4-3. This figure shows the appearance of amino acids accompanied by the decrease of ammonia, HCN, and aldehydes. These results would be consistent with a Strecker mechanism since in such a system, HCN and the aldehydes would serve as the intermediates ultimately leading to the amino acids themselves. The reaction may indeed proceed through α-amino nitriles since these compounds have been identified in the first hours of the sparking, even before amino acids are present in detectable amounts [6]. Water is an important reactant in such a system.

In the methane-ammonia-hydrogen-water reaction, it has been suggested that the first step involves the formation of a methyl radical [7]. This was concluded from the fact that if methanol is substituted for methane, a 50 percent greater yield is observed. It is known that it takes 20 percent less energy to form a methyl radical from methanol than from methane [8]. Once a methyl radical is formed, the overall reaction would proceed as if methane had been employed.

When ethane was substituted for methane in the initial gaseous mixture, valine and leucine were also obtained upon sparking. The addition of ferrous ammonium sulfate as a possible reducing agent had little effect on the total yield [5,6,9]. When nitrogen was substituted for ammonia in the initial gaseous mixture, the total yield was diminished by about one-half, and the distribution of products varied somewhat. Thiocyanate was also synthesized when hydrogen sulfide was added to the reactant mixture [10]. Related experiments employing a variety of reactant mixtures are summarized in Table 4-4. The results in this table clearly demonstrate the point made earlier; i.e., even though very different gaseous mixtures have been subjected to electrical discharge,

Biochemical Predestination

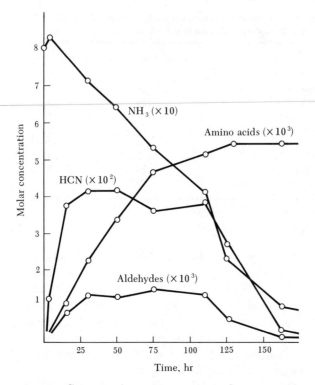

FIG. 4-3 Concentrations of ammonia, hydrogen cyanide, aldehydes, and amino acids formed by sparking a mixture of methane, ammonia, water, and hydrogen in the apparatus pictured in Fig. 4-1 [5c].

very similar products have resulted (amino acids). This would suggest that amino acid production could have occurred in various environments or at different stages of the Earth's development.

In these experiments, the importance of cyanide and aldehydes has

TABLE 4-4 Production of amino acids with electrical discharge excitation of mixtures of simple reactants

Reactants	Reference
$CH_4 + NH_3 + H_2 + H_2O$	5, 10–12
$CH_4 + NH_3 \quad + H_2O$	13
$CH_4 + NH_3 + CO + H_2O$	12
$CO \ + NH_3 \quad + H_2O$	14
$CO \ + N_2 \ + H_2 + H_2O$	13
$CO_2 + NH_3 + H_2 + H_2O$	13
$CO_2 + N_2 \quad + H_2 + H_2O$	13

been emphasized. In order for a suggested model of prebiological development to be taken seriously, it must result in the production of compounds of biochemical significance. This of course follows from the principle of biochemical similarity discussed in Chap. 1, whereby we assume that compounds of contemporary general biochemical significance were important during the period of primordial biogenesis as well. The experiments just noted have produced such compounds in that amino acids were identified in the products. Also, the results of this approach have been confirmed. The experimental setup employs simple reagents and conditions which could very well have been found on the primitive Earth. However, yields generally were not very great even though the energy input was rather high (see Tables 4-1 and 4-2). It is not certain if electrical discharge was a significant contributor to the promotion of chemical evolution, although one would expect similar results (as will be discussed in the next section) with the employment of ultraviolet light. The main model discussed thus far depends on the argument of reducing conditions. The validity of such a model depends on the strength of the evidence provided in Chap. 3 for such conditions.

Although certain experiments have been successful in terms of the types of compounds produced, speculation on the plausibility of such events must be tempered by the laws of nature (assuming they are the same now as then). For example, the degree of authenticity can be influenced by the thermodynamics of the reaction under consideration. A thermodynamic calculation was performed, and it was found that the reaction of methane, ammonia, and water to produce alanine has a free-energy change of 62 kcal [12]. On the other hand, the reaction of carbon monoxide with methane and ammonia to produce alanine has a change of free energy of -5.9 kcal; thus,

$$CH_4 + NH_3 + H_2O \rightarrow \text{Alanine} \qquad \Delta F = 62 \text{ kcal}$$
$$2CO + NH_3 + CH_4 \rightarrow \text{Alanine} \qquad \Delta F = -5.9 \text{ kcal}$$

The second reaction was demonstrated by carrying out the spark experiment for 80 hr in an apparatus similar to the type just described. In addition to alanine, aspartic acid, glutamic acid, glycine, β-alanine, and α-aminobutyric acid were observed in the reaction product. In this system, HCN was also found after sparking, suggesting that this reaction also followed a Strecker mechanism. That molecular hydrogen is not necessary for such a reaction to take place was clearly pointed out by its omission in this work (also see Table 4-4). Such an observation would suggest that the early stages of chemical evolution leading to the production of amino acids could have taken place after molecular hydrogen had been lost from the Earth's atmosphere.

It has been suggested that cyanoacetylene ($HC\equiv C-CN$) may have served as a major intermediate in the production of aspartic acid from

$$CH_4 + N_2 \xrightarrow{e^-} H-C\equiv C-C\equiv N \xrightarrow{NH_3} NH_2CH=CH-CN$$

$$NH_2CH=CH-CN \xrightarrow{HCN} NC-\underset{\underset{NH_2}{|}}{CH}-CH_2CN \xrightarrow{H_2O} HOOC-\underset{\underset{NH_2}{|}}{CH}-CH_2-CONH_2$$

Asparagine

$$Asparagine + H_2O \longrightarrow HOOC-\underset{\underset{NH_2}{|}}{CH}-CH_2-COOH$$

Aspartic acid

FIG. 4-4 Scheme for the synthesis of aspartic acid and asparagine from simple reagents using cyanoacetylene as intermediate [15].

methane, ammonia, and water in the sparking experiments [15]. First of all, cyanoacetylene is produced by sparking a mixture of methane and nitrogen. When cyanoacetylene was heated in the presence of ammonia, HCN, and water for 24 hr at 100°C, a yield of 10 to 15 percent of aspartic acid and 5 to 10 percent of asparagine appeared. The suggested overall scheme is pictured in Fig. 4-4. This scheme is in contradistinction to the mechanism proposed earlier in which hydrogen cyanide and ammonia reacted with acrolein (CH_2=CH—CHO) to produce aspartic acid [5].

Thus far it has been shown that electrical discharge can readily serve as a source of free energy for promoting the synthesis of amino acids from primitive gaseous reactants. Other experiments have been carried out to demonstrate that β particles can also supply the needed energy for these reactions. In a typical experiment, a gaseous mixture was prepared containing methane, ammonia, and hydrogen [16]. The apparatus employed is pictured in Fig. 4-5. Water was placed in the lower reservoir and refluxed during irradiation so as to wash away prod-

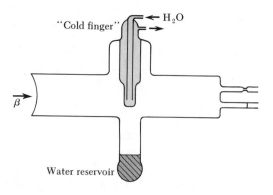

FIG. 4-5 Apparatus used in the β-particle bombardment of a mixture of CH_4, NH_3, H_2, and H_2O. Water contained in the reservoir was shielded from the radiation and was boiled during the experiment. Products were removed from the gaseous phase by condensation on the water-cooled "cold finger" and collection in the reservoir. The β radiation passed through the gaseous phase from left to right. (*After* [16].)

ucts of the gaseous phase with the aid of the "cold finger" water-cooled condenser and also to supply H_2O as one of the reactants. The methane employed was ^{14}C-labeled to aid in the identification of reaction products. Six-microsecond pulses of 5-Mev electrons from a linear accelerator were employed as the energy source. The total dose (delivered to the gas mixture) was approximately 1×10^{11} ergs/2 hr. By cooling the exterior chamber with an air stream, the average temperature inside remained around 30°C. The nature of the gaseous products was determined by mass spectrometry. The water-soluble products which were collected in the reservoir below the cold finger were analyzed by paper chromatography. In a typical experiment, glycine (0.19 percent yield), alanine (0.39 percent), and lactic acid were identified as products of the reaction. Small amounts of aspartic acid were also found. The identification of urea in the reaction mixture suggested that the mechanism of formation is similar to that concluded for the electrical discharge experiments. The production of urea was thought to involve a cyanate intermediate like that employed in the Wöhler synthesis. Over 90 percent of the initial reagent material could be accounted for on paper chromatograms as discrete products of the reaction. The primordial source of high-energy β particles on the primitive Earth was believed to be unstable elements like potassium 40.

The synthesis of cysteic acid, taurine, and cystamine was effected by including H_2S in the reactant mixture in the type of experiment just described [17]. Yields on the order of 0.01 percent were obtained when 10^9 rads of radiation was applied through the use of an electron accelerator. No cysteine, cystine, methionine, homocysteine, or homocysteic acid was identified in the product, but the presence of cysteine was inferred from the appearance of cysteic acid, its oxidation product. Since the irradiation itself was carried out in the absence of air, such oxidation could have taken place later, possibly during the paper-chromatographic analysis of the product.

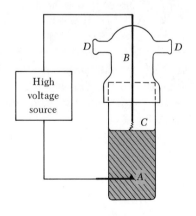

FIG. 4-6 Schematic drawing illustrating sparking vessel with submerged electrode A, suspended electrode B, solution surface C, and ventilation ports D. The nonvolatile reactants were dissolved in the aqueous phase. A visible spark passed between electrode B and the aqueous solution surface C. Nitrogen (or air) was blown through the chamber by way of the ventilation ports D. Mechanism [19] suggested for glycine synthesis (see Table 4-5):

$$N_2 \rightarrow 2N$$
$$CH_3COOH \rightarrow CH_2COOH + H$$
$$N + 3H_2O \rightarrow HNO_3 + 2H_2O + H$$
$$N + 2H \rightarrow NH_2$$
$$CH_2COOH + NH_2 \rightarrow NH_2CH_2COOH$$

TABLE 4-5 Additional syntheses of amino acids employing electrons as a free-energy source

Reactants*	Products	Reaction phase	Remarks	Reference
1. $NH_4OAc + H_2O$ (β, 2 Mev)	Gly, Asp	Aqueous	Probably radical reaction	18
2. $CH_3COOH + N_2 + H_2O$ (e^-)	Gly, Asp	Aqueous	Occurs in presence of O_2; apparatus pictured in Fig. 4-6	19

* $\beta = \beta$ particles from accelerator; $e^- =$ electrical discharge.

4-3   UV IRRADIATION OF SIMPLE GASEOUS MIXTURES

In the chapter on geochemistry we noted that solar ultraviolet radiation was probably the major source of free energy on the primitive Earth. Although the first experiments to test models of chemical evolution involved electrical discharge (largely because of convenience), further work was carried out to determine if ultraviolet radiation could also promote the synthesis of biomonomers.

A gaseous mixture of ethane, ammonia, and water was subjected to mercury-sensitized UV radiation [20]. In this case the principal wavelength maxima occurred at 2537 and 1849 Å. The apparatus used in this experiment is pictured in Fig. 4-7. Through the use of the pump, a circulating system was maintained. Thermal convection was aided by the heating coil (D) on the left arm and the water-cooled condenser on the right arm. The light source, a 1-m-long low-pressure mercury arc lamp with a quartz envelope (emission maxima at 2537 and 1849 Å), supplied 3×10^{18} quanta/sec to the reaction mixture, as determined by the photodissociation of chloroacetic acid. Prior to irradiation a drop of mercury was heated in the evacuated lamp jacket. The boiling flask (A) was then filled with water. The gaseous mixture involved in the reaction was added and circulated as indicated by the arrows in the figure. In this manner, products of the irradiation accumulated in the aqueous phase of the boiling flask for further reaction. In a typical experiment, 40 cm Hg of ethane and 20 cm Hg of ammonia were employed. The irradiation was generally carried out for 1 week in each case.

When ethane, ammonia, and water were irradiated in this manner, amino acids were produced. Analysis was carried out by paper chromatography. When methane replaced the ethane, no amino acids appeared. This result is apparently due to the fact that methane absorbs virtually no light at wavelengths greater than 1470 Å [20].

Mercury sensitization was employed so that higher wavelengths

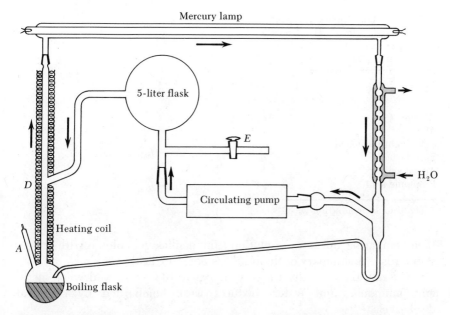

FIG. 4-7   Apparatus used for the mercury-sensitized synthesis of amino acids from simple gases by ultraviolet irradiation.   The circulation of the gases was promoted by the boiling water in the lower flask A, the heating coil D, the water-cooled condenser, and the circulating pump.   Irradiation of the gases took place as they flowed past the mercury lamp.   Nonvolatile products collected in the U tube below the condenser and passed into the boiling flask.   Gases continued to circulate by way of the pump [20a].

could be used.   For example, water normally absorbs at less than 2000 Å [21].   However, when irradiated in the presence of mercury, radiolysis of water is observed at wavelengths above 2100 Å; thus

$$Hg + h\nu \rightarrow Hg^*$$
$$Hg^* + H_2O \rightarrow H + OH + Hg$$

It was suggested that the amino acid synthesis involves the production of radicals, at least in part.

$$Hg + h\nu \rightarrow Hg^*$$
$$Hg^* + C_2H_6 \rightarrow Hg + H + C_2H_5$$

A xenon lamp with resonance wavelengths at 1296 and 1470 Å was used as the radiation source to produce glycine with methane as the carbon supply [20].   Since glycine is synthesized, it was concluded that the C—C bond of the amino acid is formed by radicals produced in the reaction.   Ethane was also effective.

Carboxylic acids were also produced by UV irradiation of these simple gaseous mixtures [20].   This was determined by isolating the acid fraction of the product with ion-exchange chromatography and

TABLE 4-6 Compounds produced by the
Hg-sensitized ultraviolet irradiation of
gaseous mixture of C_2H_6 (40 cm), NH_3 (20
cm), and H_2O [20a]

Product	Yield, $\mu moles$*
Glycine	32.0
Alanine	23.0
α-Aminobutyric acid	0.5
Formic acid	72
Acetic acid	203
Propionic acid	17

* The time of irradiation was 1 week.

then comparing the rates of elution from a silica gel column with known standards. A summary of the results is noted in Table 4-6.

Overall, these results are very similar to those observed when methane, ammonia, and water mixtures were bombarded by electrical discharge.

4-4 HEATING OF SIMPLE GASEOUS MIXTURES

A third possible source of free energy would be heat. Although it is now believed that the surface of the Earth was, in general, not very hot at any phase of its development (see Chap. 3), the environment around volcanoes, for example, could provide the heat necessary for the reactions to be discussed here. A more detailed consideration of this thermal model will be found in the discussion of condensation reactions (Chap. 5).

It has been shown that the heating of methane and ammonia in the presence of Al_2O_3 or SiO_2 produces HCN [22]. Similarly (as will be discussed later), the heating of ammonium cyanide is known to produce amino acids [23]. Therefore, it was postulated that the heating of methane, ammonia, and water should lead to the production of a number of amino acids [24]. Since absorption lines attributable to cyanide are present in the spectra of comets, it is believed that this thermal-type system would serve as a model for reactions taking place in these bodies [25]. Another suggestion is that such heating might duplicate primordial conditions around volcanoes [24]. One observation prompting this model is that some primitive algae are thermophilic [24]. To test the possible role of the model, the apparatus diagramed in Fig. 4-8 was employed. The style of this apparatus is very similar to that used in the electrical discharge experiments discussed earlier. The electrodes in the sparking experiment have now been replaced by a furnace. The products of the heating reaction can thus recycle

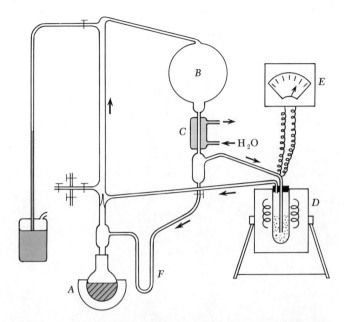

FIG. 4-8 Apparatus used for the pyrogenesis of amino acids from simple gases. The water in flask A was boiled, aiding in the flow of the gaseous reactants through sphere B, water-cooled condenser C, and oven D. Products collected in U tube F and passed into flask A. The remaining gases continued to pass through the apparatus for further reaction. The temperature in the oven was followed by thermocouples attached to gauge E. Stopcocks have been omitted. (*After* [24b].)

through the system several times. The water contained in the lower vessel is heated by refluxing, and thus convection is maintained by cooling with the condenser in the right stem. A chromel-alumel thermocouple attached to a calibrated potentiometer measured the temperature in the furnace, which was of the Hoskins combustion type. The tube in the furnace contained either alumina (Al_2O_3) or silica (SiO_2). The apparatus was made of Pyrex glass. Usually, furnace temperatures of 950 to 1050°C were employed. The aqueous phase in the lower boiling flask initially contained 2 N ammonium hydroxide. It was hoped that the ammonia and methane in the apparatus would react by heating in the furnace to produce NH_4CN. Further reaction of this compound in the liquid reservoir would then produce the amino acids.

Typical results are noted in Table 4-7, and these should be compared with results obtained by electrical discharge.

This experiment is of course based on the hot-surface theory. The primordial source of such energy could have been gravitational contraction or volcanoes (this will be discussed in greater detail in Chap. 5). The mechanism of amino acid synthesis is probably again of the

TABLE 4-7   Results of heating methane, ammonia, and water at 950°C using quartz sand catalyst [24b]

Amino acid*	Percent yield
Aspartic acid	3.4
Threonine	0.9
Serine	2.0
Glutamic acid	4.8
Proline	2.3
Glycine	60.3
Alanine	18.0
Valine	2.3
Alloisoleucine	0.3
Isoleucine	1.1
Leucine	2.4
Tyrosine	0.8
Phenylalanine	0.8
α-NH_2-Butyric acid	0.6
β-Alanine	?
Sarcosine	
N-Methylalanine	

* Basic amino acids were not fully studied. The pyrosynthesis of amino acids has been independently confirmed [69.] Yield is based on percent of total amino acid product.

Strecker type since it was shown that the heating of ammonium formate or formamide also produced amino acids [24]. The possibility of microbial contamination was eliminated by blank runs where the reactants were not heated. When no heating was applied, only traces of the amino acids were detected. The products of the reaction were resolved and identified with an automatic amino acid analyzer.

It was pointed out that the distribution of amino acids in the heating experiment more nearly approximated the proportions of these residues found in contemporary proteins than did the corresponding distribution in the sparking experiment. Such differences could suggest a possibility of slightly different mechanisms in the two procedures. The Strecker mechanism may explain only part of the overall synthetic process. This point will be brought up again later.

In summary, we have seen that amino acid synthesis from simple reactants can be promoted by a number of free-energy sources, such as electrical discharge, ultraviolet light, and heating. In the sparking experiments it is not certain if the reactions were brought about by the spark itself or by the heat and/or UV light emitted by it. What these results have shown, however, is that given any of these forms of energy and any of a number of possible combinations of simple reagents, the production of amino acids (and other biomonomers to be discussed) appears to be probable. In other words, with the conditions that are thought to have been present on the primitive Earth, the production of compounds essential for the ultimate appearance of living systems would have been the result of comprehensible physical and chemical phenomena. Whether or not this is universal remains to be determined by extraterrestrial exploration.

4-5 SYNTHESIS OF BIOMONOMERS FROM REACTIVE REAGENTS

It has been pointed out repeatedly in the experiments discussed thus far that nitriles and aldehydes apparently played an important role in the progress of chemical evolution. For example, in the sparking experiments in which amino acids were produced from methane, ammonia, and water, the intermediate appearance of nitriles and aldehydes suggested that this process proceeded by the Strecker mechanism [5]. That amino acids could be produced directly from aldehydes and nitriles was demonstrated in that experiment as well. On a simpler level, the reaction of aqueous KCN and HCHO can produce glycine [26].

A number of syntheses have demonstrated that these reactive compounds (for example, HCN and HCHO) could have been produced from very simple reagents with energy sources that were probably available on the primitive Earth. Several of these syntheses are summarized in Table 4-8. Although the majority of experiments listed in this table were not carried out with the intention of elucidating the probable course of chemical evolution, they are summarized here to indicate that the products of interest could have arisen under very simple conditions. Thus, it can be assumed that these reactive compounds could very likely have appeared on the primitive Earth under the conditions that are believed to have existed during chemical evolution.

By *reactive compounds* we mean reagents that are prone to react by themselves and with other reagents with little or no energy input to give products at a much faster rate than the simpler compounds from which they were originally produced. As will be shown, mild heating of ammonium cyanide readily leads to the production of amino acids. Table 4-8 shows that cyanide is produced from methane and ammonia at high temperatures. The reaction of ammonium cyanide to give amino acids proceeds at a much faster rate at a given temperature than the reaction of methane and ammonia to give these biomonomers. Thus, one would classify ammonium cyanide as a reactive reagent. Many of these procedures employ methods proposed by the various schools of thought discussed earlier in this chapter.

With this in mind, a number of experiments have been carried out in an attempt to employ these reactive compounds in order to pro-

TABLE 4-8   Production of reactive compounds from simple gaseous reagents

Reactive products	Starting materials	Energy source*	Reference
1. HCN	$CH_4 + NH_3$	e^- or Δ	22, 28
	$CH_4 + N_2$	e^-	29
	$C_2H_2 + N_2$	e^-	30
	Hydrocarbons $+ N_2$	e^-	31
	$CO + N_2 + H_2$	e^-	32
2. $HC \equiv CH$	CH_4	e^-	33
3. NH_3	$N_2 + H_2$	Glow	34
	$N_2 + H_2O$	UV	35
4. NH_2NH_2	NH_3	e^-	36
5. NH_2OH	$NH_3 + H_2O$	e^-	37
6. HNO_3	$N_2 + H_2O$	e^-	38
7. HCHO	$CH_4 + H_2O$†	e^-	39
	$CH_4 + CO_2$†	e^-	40
	CH_3OH‡ $+ N_2$	e^-	41
	$CO + H_2$	e^-	42
	$CO_2 + H_2O$	e^-, α, UV, γ	39, 43, 44
8. $HCONH_2$	$NH_3 + CO$	e^-	45
9. Aromatic hydrocarbons	CH_4	Δ	46

* e^- = electrical discharge; Δ = high temperature ($\sim 1000°C$); α = alpha particles; glow = glow discharge; γ = gamma rays.
† CH_3CHO also identified as a product.
‡ Aqueous medium; see experiment 2 in Table 4-5.

duce biomonomers essential for primitive biogenesis. A few of these experiments will now be discussed. This review is not meant to be comprehensive, but rather it will consider selected examples illustrating the production of the various classes of biomonomers from reactive compounds.

Amino acids

One synthesis of amino acids employs hydroxylamine hydrochloride (see Table 4-8 for possible primordial origin) and paraformaldehyde [27]. In a typical experiment, aqueous solutions containing the two reactants (0.25 M each) were prepared and heated in Pyrex tubes. Such variables as temperature, pH, time, concentration, relative proportions of reactants, and the possible role of inorganic catalysts were investigated. Ion-exchange column chromatography was used to resolve product mixtures. Identification of the amino acids was achieved by determining the melting points of their paratoluenesulfonates and by their characteristic chromatographic behavior. The best yields of amino acids were achieved when the reaction was carried out at pH values less

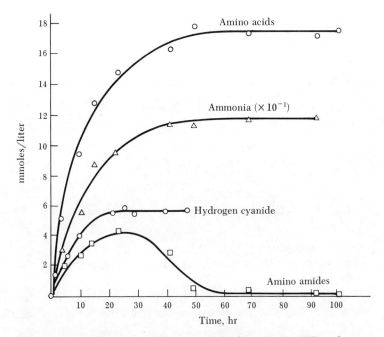

FIG. 4-9   Kinetics of the reaction between hydroxylamine·HCl and paraformaldehyde producing amino acids [27].

than 2.   Similar results were obtained when formaldehyde replaced the
paraformaldehyde.   The time variation of the concentrations of certain
reactants, intermediates, and products of the reaction is noted in Fig.
4-9.

Yields of amino acids decreased as the temperature of reaction was
lowered.   Enhanced yields were achieved when sodium molybdate and
sodium vanadate were added as catalysts.   In addition to glycine, acetic
acid, formic acid, lactic acid, and glycolic acid were identified as products of the reaction.   Alanine, β-alanine, serine, aspartic acid, and
threonine were also obtained.   However, glycine was by far the predominant amino acid in the product solution.   The mechanism in Fig.
4-10 was proposed for this reaction on the basis of experimental observations [27].   A number of points can be considered which tend to support
this mechanism:

1. When the reaction was carried out at lower temperatures in a
less polar solvent (methanol), the reaction rate decreased, permitting
closer analysis of the reaction steps.   Glycinamide was the first ninhydrin-positive product to be observed under these conditions; later glycine
appeared (see Fig. 4-10, steps 1 and 5).

2. Formaldoxime·HCl reacted to form HCN on long standing at
room temperature (step 2).

3. As the concentration of ammonia, HCN, and the product amino

1. $HCHO + NH_2OH \rightleftharpoons H_2O + CH_2NOH$

      Hydroxylamine   Formaldoxime

2. $CH_2NOH \xrightarrow{-H_2O} HCN$

3. $HCHO + NH_3 + HCN \cdot \longrightarrow CH_2(NH_2)CN$

                          Aminoacetonitrile

FIG. 4-10 Mechanism proposed for the synthesis of glycine from formaldehyde and hydroxylamine [27].

4. $CH_2(NH_2)CN + H_2O \longrightarrow CH_2(NH_2)CONH_2$

                           Glycinamide

5. $CH_2(NH_2)CONH_2 + H_2O \longrightarrow CH_2(NH_2)COOH$

                           Glycine

acids increased, the concentration of hydroxylamine and formaldoxime decreased.

4. The following reaction had previously been reported [47] and apparently explains the source of ammonia in the above reactions:

$$CH_2NOH \xrightarrow{R} HCONH_2 \xrightarrow{H_2O} HCOOH + NH_3 \text{ (source of NH}_3\text{)}$$

with $\xrightarrow{-H_2O}$ and $\xrightarrow{H_2O}$

Also possible: $HCN \xrightarrow{H_2O} HCONH_2$

5. Step 3 is a Strecker reaction.

It was suggested that the synthesis of serine in particular proceeds through glycinamide with the addition of formaldehyde [27]. Thus

$$HCHO + NH_2CH_2CONH_2 \longrightarrow NH_2-\overset{\displaystyle CH_2OH}{\underset{\displaystyle |}{CH}}-CONH_2$$

$$\downarrow H_2O$$

$$NH_2-\overset{\displaystyle CH_2OH}{\underset{\displaystyle |}{CH}}-COOH + NH_3$$

This is similar to the production of polyserine to be discussed in Chap. 5. The synthesis of amino acids from hydroxylamine occurs even at room temperature. The suggestion was made that these observations could also explain the previously reported reaction in which aqueous formaldehyde and formhydroxamic acid were irradiated by ultraviolet light and amino acids were produced [48].

A related experiment involved irradiation of an aqueous solution of formaldehyde and ammonium ion by ultraviolet light from a PRK-2 quartz lamp by which amino acids were produced [12]. These amino acid products, resolved and analyzed by paper and column chromatography, included glycine, serine, alanine, glutamic acid, valine, isoleucine, phenylalanine, and a number of unidentified basic amino acids. The source of the ammonium ion was either ammonium nitrate or ammonium chloride. The irradiation was carried out in quartz cuvettes for 20 hr, in which approximately 2.7×10^6 ergs/$(cm^2)(min)$ was supplied. The formaldehyde concentration was 2.5 percent, and the ammonium-ion concentration was 1 to 1.5 percent. The volume of the reaction medium was 20 ml, and the temperature was maintained between 40 and 45°C. In certain cases the temperature was lowered and ranged from 1 to 2°C. The initial pH was 1.5 to 5. In some experiments chalk ($CaCO_3$) was added, and in this case the initial pH was 5 to 6.2, although the best amino acid yields were obtained at low pH values. Isoleucine, phenylalanine, and the basic amino acids were produced only if the lower temperatures were employed. It is worthy of special note that the aromatic amino acid phenylalanine was identified in this experiment. Since benzenoid amino acids were also produced in the heating experiment discussed earlier, it would appear that the production of these more complex residues is not as difficult as might have been supposed. The mechanism of their production, however, is not clear.

In another experiment, an aqueous solution of ammonium cyanide was heated at 70°C for 25 days [23]. Analysis of the resulting mixture by paper chromatography revealed the presence of alanine, glycine, and aspartic acid in the product. The experiment was repeated, and the results were confirmed and extended [49]. A number of additional amino acids were detected when aqueous ammonium cyanide was heated at 90°C for 18 hr, followed by hydrolysis of the product in 6 N HCl (see Table 4-9). Since the product mixture gave a positive

TABLE 4-9 Ninhydrin-positive compounds produced by the heating of 1.5 M aqueous ammonium cyanide [49]

Product	Yield, $\mu moles/liter$
Aspartic acid	504
Threonine	2
Serine	184
Glycine	868
Alanine	84
Isoleucine	2
Leucine	2
Urea	15,800
Unidentified components	
Amino acid c	221
Amino acid d	186

TABLE 4-10 Additional syntheses of amino acids under simple conditions

Reactants	Products	Free-energy source	Reaction phase	Footnote	Reference
1. $KCN + HCHO + H_2O$	Gly	...	Aqueous		26
2. $HCHO + NH_2NH_2 + H_2O$	Amino acids	...	Aqueous		55
3. $(CH_2O)_n + KNO_3 + H_2O$	Val, His, Pro, Lys, Ser, Asp, Gly, Asn, Arg, Orn	Sunlight (80 hr)	Aqueous	*	56
4. $(CH_2O)_n + N_2 + H_2O$	Gly, Ala, Val, His, Glu, Asp, Orn, Leu	500-watt electric bulb	Aqueous, atmospheric N_2	†	57
5. $CH_4 + NH_3 + CO + H_2O$	Ala + other amino acids	UV	Gaseous	‡	58
6. NH_4^+ or NH_3 + succinic, maleic, or propionic acid	Gly, Ala, Asp	UV	Aqueous	§	59
7. Mixtures of CH_4, C_2H_2, H_2, H_2O, N_2, NH_3	Ninhydrin (+) products	x-rays	Gaseous		10
8. $(NH_4)_2CO_3$	Gly, Ala (?)	γ rays	Solid (under vacuum)	¶	60

* $T = 18$ to $23.5°C$; $FeCl_3$ catalyst added; final pH $= 1$ to 0.8; no amino acids if reactants kept in dark; $(CH_2O)_n = $ paraformaldehyde; nature of products varies with concentration of KNO_3; able to obtain crystals of Asp, Ser, Gly, and Asn for chemical analysis.

† MoO, $CuSO_4$, $FeCl_3$, or $CoCl_2$ used as catalysts; distribution of products varies with time of irradiation; also able to use NH_4 carbaminate, KNO_3, or NH_4NO_3 as nitrogen source; mechanism suggested for glycine synthesis:

$$CH_2O + 2H \rightleftharpoons CH_3OH$$
$$CH_2O + O \rightleftharpoons HCOOH$$
$$O + 2CH_2O \rightleftharpoons HOCH_2—COOH$$
$$HOCH_2—COOH \rightleftharpoons CHO—COOH + 2H$$
$$CHO—COOH + 2NH_3 \rightleftharpoons NH=CHCOONH_4$$
$$NH=CHCOONH_4 + 2H \rightleftharpoons NH_2CH_2COONH_4$$
$$NH_2CH_2COONH_4 + H_2O \rightleftharpoons NH_2CH_2COOH + NH_3$$

‡ Suggest use of mineral oxides on which to absorb reactants and thus be able to use longer wavelengths.

§ Hydroxy and keto acids are also effective.

¶ Propose radioactive minerals served as primordial source of γ rays.

Sakaguchi reaction, it was concluded that arginine and/or guanidine was also present among the products.

In earlier experiments, HCN oligomer treated with aqueous base produced glycine [50]. It was suggested that the pyrogenesis of amino acids from NH_4CN might involve HCN tetramer [51]. This was concluded from the fact that

$$4HCN \rightarrow 2(HN{=}CH{-}C{\equiv}N) \rightarrow \underset{NC}{\overset{H_2N}{\diagdown}} C{=}C \underset{CN}{\overset{NH_2}{\diagup}} \rightarrow amino\ acid$$

In the experiment in which amino acids were produced by heating ammonium cyanide, a black polymer was also produced [23]. Base-catalyzed polymerization of HCN also produces a black polymer; HCN tetramer (diaminomaleonitrile) has been clearly observed during the reaction [52]. This tends to support the suggested involvement of the tetramer in the amino acid synthesis.

In a related investigation, anhydrous HCN and liquid ammonia were mixed and held at room temperature for 48 hr [53]. After hydrolysis, lysine, histidine, aspartic acid, threonine, serine, glycine, and isoleucine were identified, as well as diaminomaleonitrile (before hydrolysis). Apparently, amino acid and peptide precursors had been produced in the initial phase of the procedure. Similarly, when a dilute, aqueous solution of cyanide (pH 8 to 9) was irradiated with ultraviolet light, glycine, serine, aspartic acid, and glutamic acid were recovered after hydrolysis of the product [54]. This could be taken to mean that a Strecker mechanism, involving aldehydes, is not the only means by which amino acids could have arisen under the simple conditions of the primitive Earth. In a related study, UV irradiation of aqueous NH_4SCN has yielded methionine after hydrolysis [41].

In conjunction with the results discussed thus far, the experiments listed in Table 4-10 further emphasize the suggestion that the primordial synthesis of biomonomers may well have been promoted by a variety of free-energy sources such as heat, UV light, x-rays, sparking, α particles, etc.

Sugars

Most sugars are reducing polyhydroxyl compounds by virtue of their aldehyde function ($R{-}CHO$). One example would be ribose whose structure is: $CH_2OH(CHOH)_3CHO$. The possibility that sugars might be synthesized simply from formaldehyde ($H{-}CHO$) was investigated some time ago [62]. If formaldehyde is dissolved in a basic solution, sugars are produced [63]. A number of experiments were carried out to establish just which sugars are synthesized by this method. In particular, fructose, cellobiose, xylulose, and glycolaldehyde were identified [64]. Later investigations also indicated the presence of galactose, fructose, mannose, arabinose, ribose, ribulose, xylose, and lyxose [65]. In addition, glyceraldehyde, dihydroxyacetone, and a number of tetroses were found [66].

Studies of the mechanism of this reaction indicated that the initial step is very slow and involves an induction period in which two formaldehyde molecules react to give glycolaldehyde [67]. This is followed by a fast reaction in which another formaldehyde condenses with glycolaldehyde, giving glyceraldehyde. The induction period was found to disappear if one added glyceraldehyde, glycolaldehyde, or dihydroxyacetone to the initial solution. It was believed that the second step of the reaction is fast because it is autocatalytic [67]:

$$
\begin{array}{c}
& & \overset{\displaystyle OH}{\underset{\displaystyle |}{}} & & \overset{\displaystyle OH}{\underset{\displaystyle |}{}} \ \ \overset{\displaystyle OH}{\underset{\displaystyle |}{}} \\
2HCHO \ \xrightarrow[\text{induction period}]{\text{very slow}} \ & CH_2\!-\!CHO & \xrightarrow[\text{fast}]{HCHO} & CH_2\!-\!CH\!-\!CHO \\
& \text{Glycolaldehyde} & & \text{Glyceraldehyde}
\end{array}
$$

$$
\underset{CH_2\!-\!CH\!-\!CH\!-\!CHO}{\overset{OH \ \ \ OH \ \ \ OH}{| \ \ \ | \ \ \ |}} \ \rightleftharpoons \ \underset{CH_2\!-\!CH\!-\!C\!-\!CH_2OH}{\overset{OH \ \ OH \ \ O}{| \ \ | \ \ \|}} \ \xleftarrow{HCHO} \ \underset{CH_2\!-\!C\!-\!CH_2}{\overset{OH \ \ O \ \ OH}{| \ \ \| \ \ |}}
$$

Dihydroxyacetone

$$
\longrightarrow \underset{CH_2\!-\!CHO}{\overset{OH}{|}} + \underset{CH_2\!-\!CHO}{\overset{OH}{|}}
$$

By this process, glycolaldehyde is regenerated, and 2 moles of formaldehyde are used up. Under suitable conditions it is possible to convert up to 50 percent of the formaldehyde to glycolaldehyde [68]. Further condensation of the four-carbon aldehyde with HCHO would lead to the production of pentoses and hexoses.

Although the experiments just discussed were not carried out with the intention of elucidating the possible course of chemical evolution, the findings from them may well have a bearing on this problem. It has already been pointed out that aldehydes could have been readily produced under possible primitive Earth conditions (see Table 4-8). With this in mind, an investigation was carried out to determine conditions by which pentoses and hexoses could have been produced on the primitive Earth. Aqueous solutions were prepared containing formaldehyde (HCHO) and acetaldehyde (CH_3CHO), or glyceraldehyde ($CH_2OH(CHOH)CHO$) and acetaldehyde [6,69]. Calcium oxide served as the base catalyst. The temperature was maintained at 50°C or less. A 3 percent yield of deoxyribose, in particular, was observed (as will be seen, this observation is very important in the context of the primitive synthesis of nucleic acids). Ammonia, as ammonium hydroxide, can replace the calcium oxide as catalyst. This is significant to chemical evolution since many observers feel that much ammonia was available. The reaction was more easily controlled with ammonia than with calcium oxide. With ammonia as the catalyst, products appeared continuously when the reaction was run at room temperature for a 2-month period. Thus, a gradual buildup of product was observed (as one might expect to occur during chemical evolution).

Other experiments were carried out to determine if ultraviolet light could replace the base catalyst in producing sugars in aqueous solutions of formaldehyde. Under appropriate conditions it was found that by using ultraviolet light or γ radiation from a cobalt 60 source, pentoses and hexoses are produced from formaldehyde [70]. In particular, ribose and deoxyribose were specifically identified among the products. Carbon 14-labeled formaldehyde was used in these reactions. The solutions to be irradiated by ultraviolet light were placed in Vycor tubes, whereas for γ irradiation glass tubes were employed. Oxygen was removed prior to the irradiation. Formaldehyde normally absorbs around 2880 Å. Vycor transmits light of this wavelength. In the experiments utilizing cobalt 60 γ radiation, 5×10^6 rads/hr was supplied. Products were identified by paper chromatography. Although pentoses and hexoses were the main products, other sugars were observed. Since the reaction was carried out at a pH of 4.5, it is evident that in this case the production of sugars was not a base-catalyzed reaction.

It was previously noted that formaldehyde was produced in a gaseous mixture of methane, ammonia, and water bombarded by an electrical discharge [5]. By using ^{14}C-labeled methane in this experiment, it was now also possible to identify ribose and 2-deoxyribose as products of the reaction [70].

Heterocyclic bases

Components essential for nucleic acids are the heterocyclic bases. One example would be adenine, whose structure is:

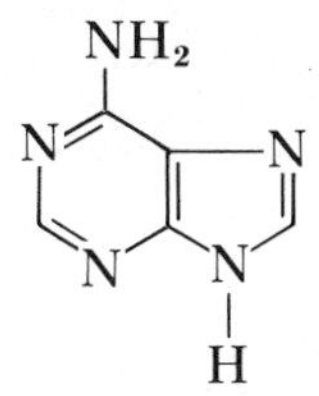

With the use of ammonium cyanide, success has been achieved in the synthesis of adenine, the base common to ATP, nucleic acids, and other compounds fundamental in the maintenance of biological systems [49,71]. In this synthesis as well, the probable role of cyanide in chemical evolution has again been emphasized. The aqueous solutions of ammonium cyanide were normally heated for 1 or more days. The production of adenine by this process was found to be linear with time when the reaction was carried out at room temperature. In a typical experiment involving this reaction, a solution of ammonium cyanide was prepared by passing freshly generated HCN into an aqueous solution of ammonium hydroxide. The resulting NH₄CN solution was then heated for a selected period of time.

The products of the reaction were identified by paper chromatography [71]. In addition to adenine, 4-aminoimidazole-5-carboxamide (AICA), 4-aminoimidazole-5-carboxamidine (AICAI), formamide, and formamidine were identified. When 9.9 M NH₄CN was heated at 90°C for 1 day, 60 mg/liter of adenine was obtained, for example. The gain of the adenine paralleled the loss of HCN. The yield of the adenine rose if the product mixture was treated with HCl after heating. It was possible to confirm the identity of the products, as well as the identity of the intermediates of the reaction, by means of UV spectrophotometry. Also, a picrate derivative was made of the adenine product, and its melting point compared well with that of a known standard of adenine picrate. The heating of NH₄CN also produced glycinamide, glycine, alanine, and aspartic acid, as noted earlier. The black amorphous polymer of HCN was again obtained as a side product.

UV light can also stimulate the production of adenine from HCN [70]. In this experiment, ¹⁴C-labeled HCN was dissolved in aqueous solution in 10^{-3} molar concentration. UV light from Hg lamps with quartz envelopes was supplied for seven days. No oxygen was present during the procedure. At the end of the irradiation, 6 percent of the starting material was isolated as nonvolatile products. Adenine represented 1 percent of this, guanine 0.5 percent, and urea 10 percent. In other words, a 0.06 percent yield of adenine from HCN was obtained.

It was previously noted in this chapter that HCN is produced by the electron bombardment of a gaseous mixture of methane, ammonia, hydrogen, and water [5]. Although heterocyclic bases were not observed in the original experiments [5], the procedure was repeated using ¹⁴C-labeled methane [16,72]. This time adenine was clearly identified among the products of the reaction by cochromatography (Fig. 4-11). The energy source was a 4.5-Mev electron beam. It was found that increasing yields of adenine were obtained by decreasing the initial hydrogen concentration. This suggested that molecular hydrogen prevented the oxidation of methane, which was needed for the purine synthesis. The net production of hydroxyl radicals and methyl radicals was apparently inhibited by the presence of hydrogen. This also indicated that adenine production could have continued long after hydrogen had disappeared from the Earth's atmosphere (compare with Table 4.4). Adenine seems to be the only base formed under these conditions.

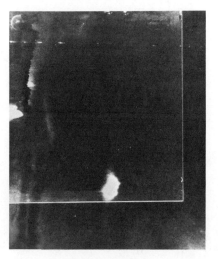
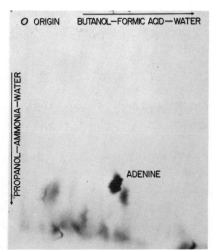

Standard   Product

FIG. 4-11   Identification by cochromatography of adenine produced by electron-beam irradiation of NH_3, CH_4, and H_2O. Both pictures are different representations of the same chromatogram—the "product" is an autoradiogram showing the location of radioactively labeled products of the irradiation; the "standard" is a picture showing the position of all UV-absorbing compounds on the chromatogram, in this case the compound being a known sample of adenine added to the reaction product prior to chromatography [72].

This may be partly because adenine has the greatest resonance energy of all the heterocyclic bases found in nucleic acids [73]. When no hydrogen was present, the production of approximately 0.014 percent adenine was observed. At 50 mm Hg pressure of hydrogen, a yield of 0.002 percent was observed, and at 100 mm Hg pressure, 0.001 percent was obtained.

Detailed studies of the synthesis of adenine from cyanide have suggested the mechanism for this reaction, and it is pictured in Fig. 4-12 [71]. The overall reaction apparently involves the condensation of a three-carbon compound with a one-carbon compound to form a 4,5-disubstituted imidazole or 4,5-disubstituted pyrimidine (step 5). The second part of the reaction involves cyclization with a one-carbon compound to form the bicyclic system of adenine (step 6). The first step consists of the production of iminoacetonitrile (NC—CH=NH). This then leads to the synthesis of aminomalonodinitrile [NC—CH-(NH_2)—CN], the trimer of HCN. Steps 3 and 4 incorporate the ammonolysis of HCN and HCN trimer to formamidine (NH_2—CH=NH) and aminocyanoacetamidine (and the latter to aminomalonodiamidine), respectively. In step 5 (Fig. 4-12) the imidazoles are produced. Here, 4-aminoimidazole-5-carboxamidine (AICAI) appears. If the semi-

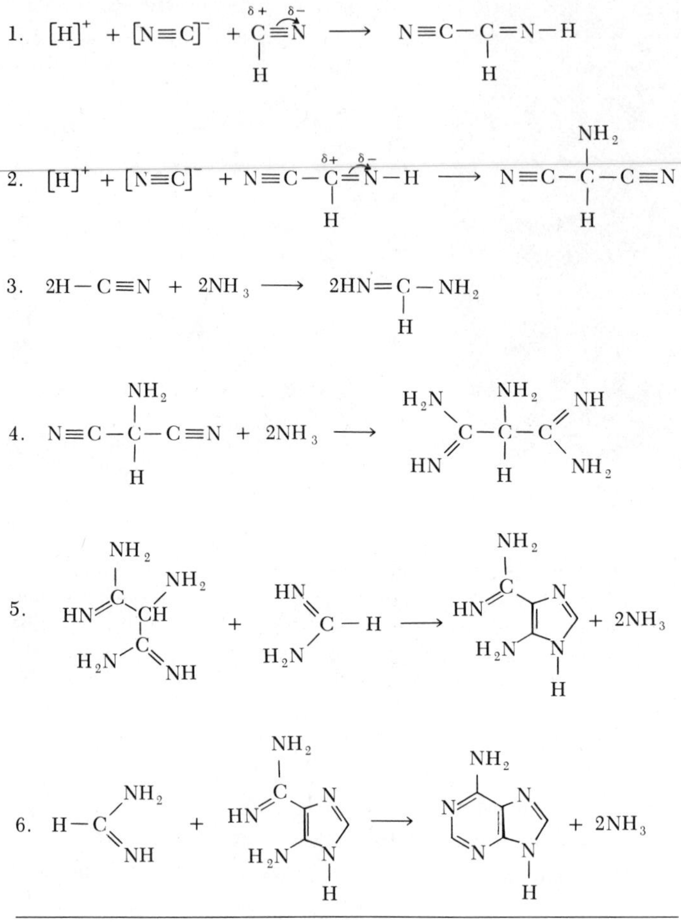

1. $[H]^+ + [N\equiv C]^- + \overset{\delta+}{C}\overset{\delta-}{\equiv}N \longrightarrow N\equiv C-C=N-H$
   (with H below C on left, H below C on right)

2. $[H]^+ + [N\equiv C]^- + N\equiv C-\overset{\delta+}{C}\overset{\delta-}{=}N-H \longrightarrow N\equiv C-C-C\equiv N$
   (with H below C; product has NH_2 above central C and H below)

3. $2H-C\equiv N + 2NH_3 \longrightarrow 2HN=C-NH_2$
   (with H below C)

4. $N\equiv C-\underset{H}{\overset{NH_2}{C}}-C\equiv N + 2NH_3 \longrightarrow$ (product: $\overset{H_2N}{\underset{HN}{}}C=C(\overset{NH_2}{\underset{H}{}})-C\overset{NH}{\underset{NH_2}{}}$)

5. $+$ $\longrightarrow$ $+ 2NH_3$

6. $+$ $\longrightarrow$ $+ 2NH_3$

Overall reaction: $5HCN \longrightarrow$ adenine

FIG. 4-12 Mechanism suggested for the synthesis of adenine from HCN [71b].

amide of aminomalonodinitrile is used in this step, one would get 4-aminoimidazole-5-carboxamide (AICA), whose structure is:

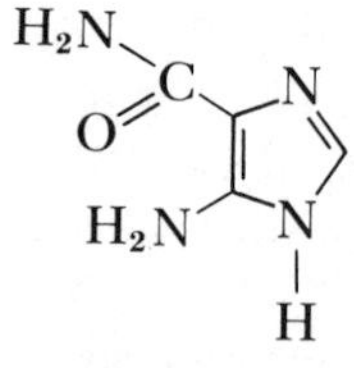

In the actual experiment, both imidazoles were observed. It had previously been shown that the reaction between formamidine (NC—CH=

NH) and aminocyanoacetamide [NH$_2$—CO—CH(NH$_2$)—CN] would produce AICA [71]. A kinetic study demonstrated that AICAI was found early in the reaction and slowly disappeared as the concentration of adenine increased. In step 6 adenine is produced. This observation has been confirmed by other workers [49]. Step 6 is apparently not pH-dependent. It was shown independently that the reaction between formamidine and AICAI could produce adenine [71]. Theoretically, the reaction would appear to work by the condensation of a three-carbon compound such as aminomalonodinitrile (NC—CH(NH$_2$)—CN), amino-cyanoacetamidine (NH=C(NH$_2$)—CH(NH$_2$)—CN), or aminomalono-diamidine (NC=C(NH$_2$)—CH(NH$_2$)C(NH$_2$)=NH) with a one-carbon compound, such as HCN, formamidine (NH$_2$—CH=NH), or formamide (HCONH$_2$). However, the reaction of formamide and AICAI does not produce adenine.

The production of 4-amino-5-cyanoimidazole (I) was found to occur in the reaction of the aminomalonodinitrile and formamidine [74]. Thus

$$\underset{\substack{|\\ \text{NH}_2}}{\text{NC—CH—CN}} + \text{NH=CH—NH}_2 \longrightarrow \underset{\underset{\text{I}}{}}{\begin{array}{c}\text{NC}\diagdown\text{N}\\ \diagup\diagdown\\ \text{H}_2\text{N}\quad \underset{\text{H}}{\text{N}}\end{array}}$$

When the product was reacted with more HCN and ammonia, adenine was produced. This would suggest that it probably first goes to AICAI and then to adenine. This is in agreement with the suggestion that aminomalonodinitrile is the intermediate. A yield of 50 percent of 4-amino-5-cyanoimidazole (I) was obtained from 0.01 M aminomalono-dinitrile and 0.1 M formamidine after 1 day at 50°C. Thus, compound I could also have been important in the synthesis of adenine from HCN.

The following alternative mechanism has been proposed [75]:

$$\underset{\substack{|\\ \text{NH}_2}}{\text{NC—CH—CN}} + \text{HCN} \longrightarrow \underset{\underset{\text{II}}{}}{\begin{array}{c}\text{NC}\diagdown\qquad\diagup\text{CN}\\ \text{C=C}\\ \text{H}_2\text{N}\diagup\qquad\diagdown\text{NH}_2\end{array}} \longrightarrow \text{Adenine}$$

By this system, diaminomaleonitrile (II), the tetramer of HCN, is produced. The reaction noted in this scheme is much faster than that between aminomalonodinitrile and formamidine to give 4-amino-5-cyanoimidazole (I). If the HCN tetramer is irradiated at 350 mμ, a 77 to 82 percent yield of 4-amino-5-cyanoimidazole appears. This reaction apparently involves a photochemically induced rearrangement. Without the UV irradiation, the reaction does not proceed.

Hydrolysis to formamide predominates if the concentration of

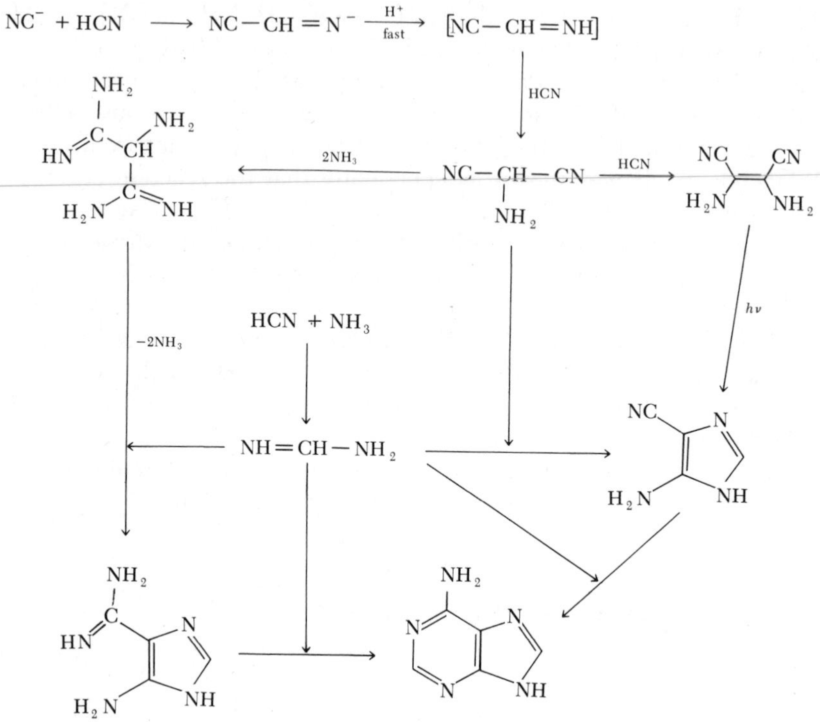

FIG. 4-13　Summary of mechanisms suggested for the synthesis of adenine from cyanide. (*Based on Refs. 71 to 76.*)

aqueous HCN is 0.01 M, whereas polymerization to adenine predominates if the concentration of HCN is 1 M [76]. Therefore, the production of adenine is favored if the concentration of HCN is raised. This suggested that one might enhance the production of adenine from HCN by concentration of the reactant. Freezing is one possible method for doing this. (This is similar to the method employed for the production of thymine dimer [77]. In this case, the production of the dimer is observed only if the solution of the reactant is frozen, thus raising the reactant concentration locally.) Other possibilities for enhancing the production of adenine might be evaporation or adsorption of the reactant to a solid surface. It was found experimentally that polymerization to adenine could occur in the HCN–water system at its low-temperature eutectic point [76]. It is interesting to note that this phenomenon is in direct contradistinction to Oparin's original suggestion that chemical evolution probably occurred at very high temperatures [1].

The overall reactions of cyanide to produce adenine are summarized in Fig. 4-13. This diagram illustrates the different mechanisms suggested for these reactions.

In summary, what the experiments just discussed have indicated is that cyanide and nitrile derivatives were undoubtedly key intermediates in the primordial synthesis of the base adenine. With the conditions that are now believed to have existed on the primitive Earth, the production of adenine would seem to have been a likely event.

Criticism has been raised in the past that experiments concerned with elucidating the course of chemical evolution do not appear to have any application to other chemical problems. However, it is interesting to note that the production of adenine from HCN has now been developed as an industrial process [78]. This is not to say that the purpose of experiments related to chemical evolution should be explicitly concerned with the application to specific problems outside this area of interest. However, as with any other area of research involved with basic theoretical problems, the possible future application of findings from them may be unanticipated when the initial experiments are carried out.

Porphyrins

Experiments have shown that aldehydes may have been involved in the primordial synthesis of porphine-like compounds. Such compounds represent the fundamental structures found in cytochromes, chlorophyll, hemoglobin, and the like. It was originally demonstrated that when pyrrole and benzaldehyde are heated together at 180°C, they condense with each other to form $\alpha,\beta,\gamma,\delta$-tetraphenylporphine and $\alpha,\beta,\gamma,\delta$-tetraphenylchlorin [79]. Thus,

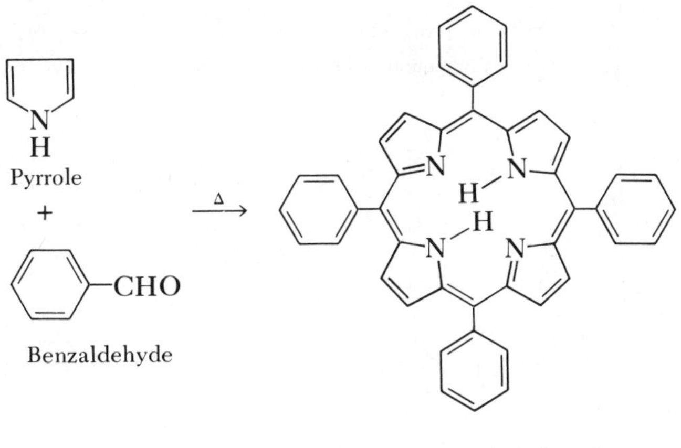

Pyrrole
+
Benzaldehyde

$\alpha,\beta,\gamma,\delta$ – tetraphenylporphine

The primordial production of aldehydes has been discussed in detail here already. Since pyrroles can be synthesized by means of electrical discharge in a mixture of acetylene (see Table 4-8) and ammonia [1] as well as UV-irradiation of δ-aminolevulinic acid [80], it is believed that compounds essential for the production of porphines could very possibly have been present on the primitive Earth.

To study the synthesis of porphines, pyrrole and benzaldehyde were dissolved in pyridine; zinc acetate was included as a catalyst [80]. The solution was contained within a Pyrex tube and irradiated in the presence of O_2 with a cobalt 60 γ-ray source for 10 hr. The dose rate was approximately 0.5 Mr/hr. Solvent extractions and chromatographic separations isolated the desired product.

A similar experiment was carried out using water as the solvent. The pyrrole-benzaldehyde solution was irradiated with ultraviolet light at an incident intensity of 1.5×10^{15} quanta/(sec)(cm^2). The light was filtered so as to transmit 45 percent of the radiation at 2500 Å. Porphine products were isolated by column chromatography. When the same mixture of reactants was stored without irradiation, porphines were also produced. If pyridine replaced the water as solvent, only traces of porphines were observed after several days in storage. In this case, no porphine-like products were observed after 2 hr of irradiation by ultraviolet light (under the conditions given above). The porphine product synthesized from pyrrole and benzaldehyde is compared by

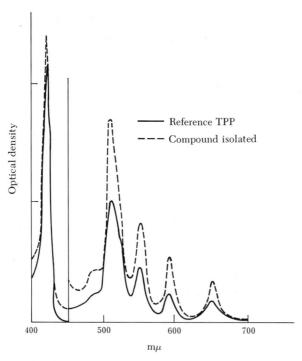

FIG. 4-14 Spectrum of the product from the reaction of pyrrole with benzaldehyde compared with reference tetraphenylporphine (TPP). The synthetic compound was prepared by irradiating a solution of the reactants with ultraviolet light [80a].

spectrophotometry with standard tetraphenylporphine in Fig. 4-14. Using 3 to 6 ml of each reagent (13 ml total), product yields were generally obtained in the 0.001 to 1.0 mgm range. The yields of porphine products following irradiation generally increased upon standing. It was previously suggested that the abiotic synthesis of porphyrins might involve autocatalysis [81] (also see Chap. 6). Such a suggestion could serve to explain the aging phenomenon just noted in this experiment.

The role of porphyrins in the structure and function of hemoglobin, chlorophyll, cytochromes, and other biological compounds is well known. It is not clear if the presence of porphyrins was essential for the initial appearance of living systems. However, in order for oxidation and reduction processes to have become more efficient, the appearance of porphyrins and porphyrin-utilizing compounds at some stage of evolution was certainly important.

A number of other syntheses of biomonomers under simple conditions are summarized in Table 4-11. Although many of these experiments were not carried out with the intention of working under primitive Earth conditions, they have been included here to further point out that various types of biocompounds could have resulted from simple processes employing uncomplicated reactants and energy sources. The range of conditions is also interesting and will be discussed again later in this chapter.

4-6 CONCLUSIONS

The purpose of this chapter has been to review the various approaches that have been employed in attempting to explain the nature of the chemical evolution by which compounds essential for the appearance of biological systems arose. Each approach, first of all, has been outlined in accordance with a particular model of the primitive Earth, including types of reactants available, free-energy sources on hand, etc. In the case of the synthesis of amino acids, for example, successful experiments have been carried out through the employment of a variety of initial reactant mixtures and energy sources. Through a knowledge of the intermediates and products of these reactions, an overall picture is derived. The recurrence of nitriles and aldehydes (HCN and formaldehyde, in particular) in a number of syntheses of amino acids starting with very different reactants and using different energy sources suggests that these compounds played prominent roles in chemical evolution. With such conditions available for reaction, essentially all of the major classes of biomonomers would apparently have been produced. This overall scheme is illustrated in Fig. 4-15.

TABLE 4-11 Additional syntheses of biomonomers other than amino acids under simple conditions

Class	Reactants	Products	Free-energy source	Reaction phase	Footnote	Reference
A. Fatty acids	1. $CO_2 + C_2H_4$	Long-chain fatty acids ($C \rightarrow 40$)	γ, pressure (1,000–7,500 lb/in.)	Gaseous	a	82
	2. $CO_2 + H_2O$	$HCOOH$	α	Aqueous	b	43
	3. $CO_2 + H_2O$	$HCOOH$	γ (^{60}Co) (57×10^{10} Mev/ml)	Aqueous	c	44
	4. $HCOOH + H_2O$	$(COOH)_2$	α (40 Mev)	Aqueous	d	83
	5. $CH_3COOH + H_2O$	Malonic acid, malic acid, tricarballylic acid, capric acid, $(CH_2COOH)_2$	α	Aqueous	e	83
B. Carbohydrates	$HCHO + H_2O$	Hexoses and hydroxy acids	UV	Aqueous	f	84
C. Purines	1. Guanidine salts + AICA	Guanine	Heat	Aqueous NH_3	g	69
	2. Urea + AICA	Guanine and xanthine	Heat	Aqueous NH_3	h	69, 71, 76
	3. Aspartic acid + glutamic acid + mixture of 16 other amino acids	Guanine	Heat (180°C)	Dry solid	i	85
D. Pyrimidines	1. Malic acid + urea + polyphosphoric acid	Uracil	Heat (100°–140°C)	Anhydrous liquid	j	86
	2. Malic acid + urea + strong mineral acid	Uracil	Heat	Concentrated acid	k	87
	3. Urea + $CH_2{=}CH{-}CN$, $NH_2{-}CH_2{-}CH_2{-}CN$, or $NH_2{-}CH_2{-}CH_2{-}\overset{\displaystyle O}{\overset{\|}{C}}{-}NH_2$	Uracil	Heat (130°C)	Aqueous NH_3	l	6
	4. $KCNO + C_2HCN + H_2O$	Cytosine	Heat (100°C, 1 day)	Aqueous	m	15
E. Miscellaneous	1. $CH_4 + NH_3 + H_2 + H_2O$	Unidentified organic compounds	Hypersonics	Gaseous + aqueous	n	88
	2. $CH_4 + NH_3 + H_2O$	Urea, acetone, acetamide	Accelerated protons	Gaseous		61
	3. Pyrrole + paraformaldehyde + cations	Porphyrin	Heat	Concentrated reactants	o	90
	4. $CO + H_2O$	$HCHO + (HCO)_2$	Xenon lamp ($\lambda_{max} = 1295, 1470$ Å)	Gaseous		91

^{a} IR suggests linear chains; some unsaturation; when $T = 125°C$, average MW as high as 1150; radical reaction; NMR ruled out polyester; model for reactions taking place under sea at high pressures.

^{b} One of first to test Oparin hypothesis; postulate unstable isotopes were primordial source of α particles; 4 percent yield of HCOOH; 10^{-7} HCHO molecules produced per ion pair supplied.

^{c} HCHO, CH$_3$CHO, and (COOH)$_2$ also obtained; HCOOH yield pH-dependent [G(HCOOH) = 0.25 at pH of 2.0); yield increases if one adds FeSO$_4$; yield decreases if one adds O$_2$; radical reaction.

^{d} Also get HCHO; assumes HCOOH already available; bubble H$_2$ through solution during irradiation; G((COOH)$_2$) = 0.025 (average); no air present. Aqueous carbonates (or bicarbonates) $+ \beta$ (or α) also yield (COOH)$_2$ [89].

^{e} Works if O$_2$ present; no product if O$_2$ absent and FeSO$_4$ present; succinic and tricarballylic acids predominant at low dose levels.

^{f} Hg quartz lamps used; reducing product; appeared to lack pentoses and trioses.

^{g} Small yield; guanidine production detected in work discussed earlier in this chapter [5,49].

^{h} Urea production detected in work discussed earlier; AICA = 4-amino-imidazole-5-carboxamide.

^{i} Means for prebiotic synthesis of malic acid and urea discussed in earlier experiments; the details of thermal model to be discussed in chapter on polymerization; 3×10^{-3} percent yield; labeled reagents used; products identified by chromatography, spectrophotometry, color tests, and melting points.

^{j} Use of polyphosphate to be discussed in greater detail in chapter on polymerization; urea and malic acid synthesis already discussed.

^{k} Known: malic acid $\xrightarrow{\text{strong mineral acid}}$ malonic semialdehyde $\xrightarrow{\text{urea}}$ uracil [87].

^{l} Product characterized by chromatography and UV spectrophotometry; on the basis of relative yields, suggest following mechanism:

$$CH_2=CH—CN \xrightarrow{NH_3} NH_2—CH_2—CH_2—CN \xrightarrow{H_2O} NH_2—CH_2—CH_2—\overset{\displaystyle O}{\overset{\|}{C}}—NH_2$$

^{m} 5 percent yield; when run at room temperature for 7 days get 1 percent yield; identified by chromatography and UV spectrophotometry.

^{n} Impact of fired bullet was source of hypersonic energy; simulates meteorite impact.

^{o} Pyrrole has been synthesized from acetylene and ammonia by thermal activation [92]. Formaldehyde [5], pyrroles [90], and porphyrin-like compounds [93] have appeared upon electrical discharge bombardment of methane-ammonia-water mixtures. As noted earlier in the text, pyrroles can be synthesized by UV irradiation of δ-aminolevulinic acid [80], and the latter compound has been identified following attack by accelerated electrons on a methane-ammonia-water atmosphere [94].

^{p} Nucleosides, nucleotides, lipids, and sugar phosphates will be discussed in chapter on condensation reactions.

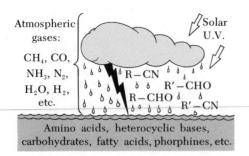

Atmospheric gases:
CH₄, CO, NH₃, N₂, H₂O, H₂, etc.

Solar U.V.

R—CN R'—CHO R—CHO R'—CN

Amino acids, heterocyclic bases, carbohydrates, fatty acids, phorphines, etc.

FIG. 4-15 Overall schematic picture of the hypothetical synthesis of biomonomers during prebiotic chemical evolution.

This scheme suggests to us a general theme for the course of chemical evolution. Such a molecular phylogeny begins with simple reagents which were undoubtedly part of the primitive atmosphere. From these were produced the reactive compounds, such as nitriles and aldehydes. Subsequent reaction of these latter compounds would produce the essential biomonomers. The application of the approaches outlined in this chapter to the investigation of possible modes of further evolution of the biomonomers just noted will be considered in detail in the chapter on condensation and polymerization reactions (Chap. 5).

The experiments discussed in this chapter indicate that a rich variety of biologically important molecules could have been synthesized on the primitive Earth by simple means. Although some of the products of these reactions may not have been involved in biogenesis, it is important to note that biomonomers essential to contemporary life could have arisen in this way. In the next chapter we shall see that the nature of the products of these simple reactions will have much to do with the evolution of more complex compounds and biogenetic processes. The initial reactions probably involved simple components of the gaseous phase, or upper atmosphere. Through the application of energy, reactive intermediates were produced. These then became dissolved in the aqueous phase, or oceans, and participated in reactions yielding biomonomers. Since it is practically impossible to establish which of the models of the primitive Earth is correct, the demonstration that chemical evolution could have taken place in any of a number of them reduces the necessity to ascertain which is correct.

Since it now appears that the reactivity of nitriles and aldehydes in particular could have been instrumental in the promotion of the earliest stages of chemical evolution, it would be of interest for us to consider what it is that makes these compounds participate in the reactions of interest. A comparison of their general structures first of all indicates that each bears a double or triple-bonded carbon atom, that is, R—CH=O and R—C≡N. This imparts to these compounds the ability to add other groups into their structure. For a simple example consider the acid hydrolysis of an olefin. This begins with the nucleophilic attack of a proton across the electron-rich double-bond system to form a π

complex, followed by conversion to a carbonium ion and then addition of water.

$$\begin{array}{c} \diagdown \\ \diagup \end{array}C\!=\!C\begin{array}{c} \diagup \\ \diagdown \end{array} + H^+ \;\rightleftharpoons\; \begin{array}{c} \diagdown \\ \diagup \end{array}C\begin{array}{c} + \\ \vdots \\ H^+ \end{array}C\begin{array}{c} \diagup \\ \diagdown \end{array} \;\rightleftharpoons\; \underset{H}{\overset{|}{-\overset{+}{C}\!-\!C-}}\begin{array}{c} | \\ | \end{array} \;\underset{-H_2O}{\overset{+H_2O}{\rightleftharpoons}}\; \overset{\displaystyle H\diagdown\overset{+}{\underset{|}{O}}\diagup H}{-\underset{|}{\overset{|}{C}}\!-\!\underset{H}{\overset{|}{C}}-}$$

$$\qquad\qquad\qquad \pi\,\text{complex} \qquad\qquad \text{Carbonium ion}$$

An additional factor with aldehydes and nitriles is that oxygen, in the first case, and nitrogen, in the second case, are more electronegative than carbon. As a result, the electrons linking the appropriate atoms will not be symmetrically distributed with respect to the two centers but rather will be drawn more toward the noncarbon atom. Therefore, the bond between them is polarized with an electron-dense region around the nitrogen or oxygen, forming a negative site. In the same sense, a positive center is formed around the carbon, thus promoting directed interactions. In the case of acid hydrolysis of a nitrile to an amide, for example, the positively charged proton (hydronium ion) would attach to the negative site of the nitrogen, leaving the positive carbon susceptible to attack by the negative pole of the water. Thus

$$R\!-\!C\!\equiv\!N \leftrightarrow R\!-\!\overset{+}{C}\!=\!\overset{-}{N} \underset{-H^+}{\overset{H^+}{\rightleftharpoons}} R\!-\!\overset{+}{C}\!=\!NH$$

$$\overset{\displaystyle H\diagdown\underset{O}{+}\diagup H}{R\!-\!\overset{+}{C}\!=\!NH} \underset{-H_2O}{\overset{+H_2O}{\rightleftharpoons}} R\!-\!\underset{\displaystyle O}{\overset{|}{C}}\!=\!NH \overset{-H^+}{\longrightarrow} R\!-\!\underset{\displaystyle OH}{\overset{|}{C}}\!=\!NH \rightleftharpoons R\!-\!\overset{\displaystyle O}{\overset{\|}{C}}\!-\!NH_2$$

Base (B)-catalyzed aldol condensation, involved in the synthesis of pentoses and hexoses from formaldehyde discussed earlier, similarly depends on the polarity of the carbonyl group of the aldehyde. Thus

$$R_2\!-\!C\!=\!O \leftrightarrow R_2\!-\!\overset{+}{C}\!-\!\overset{-}{O}$$

$$R'\!-\!\underset{|}{\overset{|}{C}}\!-\!H \overset{B}{\rightleftharpoons} R'\!-\!\underset{|}{\overset{|}{C}}{}^- + BH^+$$

$$R'\!-\!\underset{|}{\overset{|}{C}}{}^- + R_2\!-\!\overset{+}{C}\!-\!\overset{-}{O} \rightleftharpoons R'\!-\!\underset{|}{\overset{|}{C}}\!-\!\underset{|}{\overset{\displaystyle O^-}{\overset{|}{C}}}\!-\!R_2 \overset{BH^+}{\rightleftharpoons} R'\!-\!\underset{|}{\overset{|}{C}}\!-\!\underset{|}{\overset{\displaystyle OH}{\overset{|}{C}}}\!-\!R_2 + B$$

The addition of one HCN molecule across the triple-bond system of another is undoubtedly involved in the synthesis of HCN tetramer mentioned earlier in this chapter in connection with the production of adenine from cyanide. It will be seen in the next chapter that the ability of nitriles to add compounds across their C≡N bond system is utilized in one model designed to explain the primordial synthesis of peptide bonds.

> . . . the beginning of organic life . . . is to be found to a very much larger degree in cyanogen . . . cyanogen and its compounds had plenty of time and opportunity to follow their great tendency to transformation and polymerization . . . to a labile protein, which constitutes living matter.

E. Pflüger, 1875

REFERENCES

1. Oparin, A. I.: "The Origin of Life," Dover Publications, Inc., New York, 1953; Haldane, J. B. S.: Rationalist Ann., 3 (1929).
2. Briner, E., and H. Hoefer: Helv. Chim. Acta, 23:826 (1940).
3. Fieser, L. F., and M. Fieser: "Introduction to Organic Chemistry," p. 305, D. C. Heath and Company, Boston, 1957.
4. Urey, H. C.: Proc. Natl. Acad. Sci., 38:351 (1952).
5. (a) Miller. S. L.: Science, 117:528 (1953); (b) Miller, S. L.: J. Am. Chem. Soc., 77:2351 (1955); (c) Miller, S. L.: Biochim. Biophys. Acta, 23:480 (1957); (d) Miller, S. L., and H. C. Urey: Science, 130:245 (1959); (e) Miller, S. L.: Ann. N.Y. Acad. Sci., 69:260 (1957).
6. Oró, J.: Ann. N.Y. Acad. Sci., 108:464 (1963).
7. Franck, B.: Chem. Ber., 93:446 (1960).
8. Pitzer, K. S.: J. Am. Chem. Soc., 70:1140 (1948).
9. Oró, J.: Nature, 197:862 (1963).
10. Heyns, K., W. Walter, and E. Meyer: Naturwiss., 44:385 (1957).
11. Hough, L., and A. F. Rogers: J. Physiol., 132:28 (1956).
12. Pavlovskaya, T. E., and A. G. Pasynskii: in A. I. Oparin (ed.), "The Origin of Life on the Earth," p. 151, Pergamon Press, New York, 1959; Kolomiychenko, M. A.: Ukr. Biokhim. Zh. SSR., 36:216 (1964), trans. in Fed. Proc., 24, (2) T199 (1965).
13. Abelson, P. H.: Science, 124:935 (1957); Ann. N.Y. Acad. Sci., 69:274 (1957).
14. Lob, W.: Chem. Ber., 46:684 (1913).
15. Sanchez, R. A., J. P. Ferris, and L. E. Orgel: Science, 154:784 (1966).
16. Palm, C., and M. Calvin: J. Am. Chem. Soc., 84:2115 (1962).
17. Choughuley, A. S. U., and R. M. Lemmon: Nature, 210:628 (1966).
18. Hasselstrom, T., M. C. Henry, and B. Murr: Science, 125:350 (1957).
19. Steinman, G. D., and H. A. Lillevik: Arch. Biochem. Biophys., 105:303 (1964).
20. (a) Groth, W. E., and H. V. Weyssenhoff: Planet. Space Sci., 2:79 (1960); (b) Angew. Chem., 69:681 (1957); Ann. Phys., 4:69 (1959); Naturwiss., 510 (1957).
21. Hoffman, M. Z., and A. Sher: Nature, 210:1039 (1966); Anbar, M., S. Guttman, and G. Stein: J. Chem. Phys., 34:703 (1961).
22. Kotake, M., M. Nakagawa, T. Ohara, K. Harada, and M. Minomia: Kagaku Zasshi, 59:121, 151 (1956).
23. Oró, J., and S. S. Kamat: Nature, 190:442 (1961).
24. (a) Harada, K., and S. W. Fox: Nature, 201:335 (1964); (b) in "Origins of Prebiological Systems," p. 187, Academic Press Inc., New York, 1965; (c) Harada, K.: Nature, 214:479 (1967).

25. Oró, J.: *Nature,* 190:389 (1961).
26. Polstorff, K., and H. Meyer: *Chem. Ber.,* 45:1905 (1912); Franzen, H.: *J. Prakt. Chem.* [2], 86:133 (1912).
27. Oró, J., A. Kimball, R. Fritz, and F. Masters: *Arch. Biochem. Biophys.,* 85:115 (1959).
28. Peters, K., and H. Keister: *Brennstoff-Chem.,* 10:108 (1929).
29. Briner, E., and A. Baerfuss: *Helv. Chim. Acta,* 2:663 (1919).
30. Berthelot, M.: *Compt. Rend.,* 67:1141 (1869).
31. Evans, H. G. V., G. R. Freeman, and C. A. Winkler: *Can. J. Chem.,* 34:1271 (1956).
32. Briner, E., and H. Hoefer: *Helv. Chim. Acta,* 23:826 (1940).
33. Berthelot, M.: *Ann. Chim. Phys.* [4], 30:431 (1873).
34. Brewer, A. K., and J. W. Westhave: *J. Phys. Chem.,* 34:153 (1930).
35. Getoff, N.: *Nature,* 210:940 (1966).
36. Hickling, A., and G. R. Newns: *Proc. Chem. Soc.,* 368 (1959).
37. Bessen, A.: *Compt. Rend.,* 152:1850 (1911).
38. Berthelot, M.: *Compt. Rend.,* 142:1367 (1906).
39. Lob, W.: *Chem. Ber.,* 37:3593 (1904).
40. Finlayson, D., and J. Plant: *CA,* 29:1201 (1935).
41. Steinman, G., "Protobiochemistry," Michigan State University, East Lansing, Mich., 1963; unpublished results.
42. Lob, W., *Z. Elektrochem.,* 12:282 (1906).
43. Garrison, W. M., D. C. Morrison, J. G. Hamilton, A. A. Benson, and M. Calvin: *Science,* 114:416 (1951).
44. Getoff, N., G. Scholes, and J. Weiss: *Tetrahedron Letters,* 18:17 (1960); Groth, W., and H. Suess: *Naturwiss.,* 26:77 (1938).
45. Bessen, A.: *Compt. Rend.,* 152:1850 (1911).
46. Oró, J., and J. Han: *Science,* 153:1393 (1966).
47. Duvstan, W. R., and A. L. Bossi: *J. Chem. Soc.,* 73:353 (1898).
48. Baly, E. C. C., I. M. Heibron, and D. P. Hudson: *J. Chem. Soc.,* 121:1078 (1922).
49. Lowe, C. V., M. W. Rees, and R. Markham: *Nature,* 199:219 (1963).
50. Wippermann, R.: *Chem. Ber.,* 7:767 (1876).
51. Kliss, R. M., and C. N. Matthews: *Proc. Nat. Acad. Sci.,* 48:1300 (1962).
52. Volker, T.: *Angew. Chem.,* 72:379 (1960); Webb, R. L., S. Frank, and W. C. Schneider: *J. Am. Chem. Soc.,* 77:3491 (1955); Long, D. A., and W. D. George: *Proc. Chem. Soc.,* 285 (1960).
53. Matthews, C. N., and R. E. Moser: *Proc. Natl. Acad. Sci.,* 56:1087 (1966).
54. Abelson, P. H.: *Proc. Natl. Acad. Sci.,* 55:1365 (1966).
55. Master, H.: M. S. thesis, University of Houston, 1957.
56. Bahadur, K.: *Nature,* 173:1141 (1954).
57. Bahadur, K., S. Ranganayaki, and L. Santamaria: *Nature,* 182:1668 (1958); Santamaria, L., and L. Fleischmann: *Experientia,* 22:430 (1966); Bahadur, K.: in A. I. Oparin (ed.), "The Origin of Life on the Earth," p. 140, Pergamon Press, New York, 1959.
58. Terenin, A. N.: in A. I. Oparin (ed.), "The Origin of Life on the Earth," p. 136, Pergamon Press, New. York, 1959.
59. Deschreider, A. R.: *Nature,* 182:528 (1958); Cultrera, R., and G. Ferrari: *Ann. Chim. (Rome),* 49:1639 (1959); *Gazz. Chim. Ital.,* 90:1637 (1960).
60. Paschke, R., R. Chang, and D. Young: *Science,* 125:881 (1957).
61. Bergen, R.: *Proc. Natl. Acad. Sci.,* 47:1434 (1961).
62. Butlerow, A.: *Compt. Rend.,* 53:145 (1861); *Ann.,* 120:295 (1861).
63. Loew, O.: *J. Prakt. Chem.,* 33:321 (1886); *Chem. Ber.,* 22:470 (1889); Fischer, E., and F. Passmore: *Chem. Ber.,* 22:359 (1889).

64. Euler, H., and A. Euler: *Chem. Ber.*, **39**:45 (1860); Schmitz, E.: *Chem. Ber.*, **46**:2327 (1913).
65. Mariani, E., and O. Torraca: *Intern. Sugar J.*, **55**:309 (1953).
66. Mayer, R., and L. Jaschke: *Ann.* **635**:145 (1960); Pfeil, E., and H. Ruckert: *Ann.*, **641**:121 (1961).
67. Breslow, R.: *Tetrahedron Letters*, **21**:22 (1959).
68. Langenbeck, W.: *Angew. Chem.*, **66**:151 (1954).
69. Oró, J., and A. C. Cox: *Federation Proc.* **21**:80 (1962); Oró, J.: in S. W. Fox (ed.), "Origins of Prebiological Systems," p. 157, Academic Press Inc., New York, 1965.
70. Ponnamperuma, C., and R. Mariner: *Rad. Res.*, **19**:183 (1963); Ponnamperuma, C.: in S. W. Fox (ed.), "Origins of Prebiological Systems," p. 221, Academic Press Inc., New York, 1965.
71. (*a*) Oró, J.: *Biochem. Biophys. Res. Comm.*, **2**:407 (1960); Oró, J., and A. P. Kimball: *Arch. Biochem. Biophys.*, **94**:217 (1961); Oró, J.: *Federation Proc.*, **20**:352 (1961); Oró, J., and A. P. Kimball: *Arch. Biochem. Biophys.*, **96**:203 (1962); (*b*) Oró, J.: *Nature*, **191**:1193 (1961).
72. Ponnamperuma, C., R. M. Lemmon, R. Mariner, and M. Calvin: *Proc. Natl. Acad. Sci.*, **49**:737 (1963).
73. Pullman, B., and A. Pullman: *Nature*, **196**:1137 (1962).
74. Ferris, J. P., and L. E. Orgel: *J. Am. Chem. Soc.*, **87**:4976 (1965).
75. Ferris, J. P., and L. E. Orgel: *J. Am. Chem. Soc.*, **88**:1074 (1966).
76. Sanchez, R., J. Ferris, L. E. Orgel: *Science*, **153**:72 (1966); *J. Mol. Biol.*, **30**:223 (1967).
77. Setlow, R. B.: *Science*, **153**:379 (1966).
78. *Chem. Eng. News*, p. 39, Aug. 8. 1966; Wakamatsu, H., et al.: *J. Org. Chem.*, **31**:2035 (1966).
79. Ball, R. H., G. D. Dorough, and M. Calvin: *J. Am. Chem. Soc.*, **68**:2278 (1946); Rothemund, P.: *J. Am. Chem. Soc.*, **58**:625 (1936).
80. (*a*) Szutka, A.: in S. W. Fox (ed.), "Origins of Prebiological Systems," p. 243, Academic Press Inc., New York, 1965; (*b*) Szutka, A.: *Nature*, **212**:401 (1966).
81. Calvin, M.: *Science,* **130**:1170 (1959).
82. Stoops, C. E., and C. L. Furrow: *Science,* **134**:839 (1961).
83. Garrison, W. M., et al.: *J. Am. Chem. Soc.*, **74**:4216 (1952); **75**:2459 (1953).
84. Baly, E. C. C.: *Ind. Eng. Chem.*, **16**:1016 (1924); Irvine, J. C., and G. V. Francis: *Ind. Eng. Chem.*, **16**:1019 (1924).
85. Ponnamperuma, C., R. S. Young, E. F. Munoz, and B. K. McCaw: *Science,* **143**:1449 (1964).
86. Fox, S. W., and K. Harada: *Science,* **133**:1923 (1961).
87. Davidson, D., and O. Bandisch: *J. Am. Chem. Soc.*, **48**:2379 (1926).
88. Hochstim, A. R.: *Proc. Natl. Acad. Sci.*, **50**:200 (1963).
89. Hasselstrom, T., and M. C. Henry: *Science,* **123**:1038 (1956).
90. Hodgson, G. W., and B. L. Baker: *Nature,* **216**:29 (1967).
91. Groth, W.: *Z. Physik. Chem.*, **37**:3071 (1937); Groth, W., and H. Suess: *Naturwiss.*, **26**:77 (1938).
92. Chichibabin, A. E.: *J. Russ. Phys. Chem. Soc.*, **47**:703 (1965); *Chem. Abst.*, **9**:2512 (1915).
93. Hodgson, G. W.: *Third Western Reg. Meeting Am. Chem. Soc.*, 1967; *Chem. Eng. News*, p. 20, Nov. 6, 1967; *Proc. Natl. Acad. Sci.*, **59**:22 (1968).
94. Choughulay, A. S. U.: cited in Ref. 80*b*.

dehydration condensation and polymerization

5-1 INTRODUCTION

The previous chapter indicated that several methods have been proposed and experimentally tested in an attempt to explain the primordial appearance of biomonomers. This discussion has shown us that essentially all of the classes of required monomers could have appeared under the conditions that were believed to have existed on the primitive Earth. Many biological operations utilize polymers composed of these compounds. Therefore, the next aspect of chemical evolution that we shall consider is the means by which monomer association reactions could have taken place.

Most condensations occurring in contemporary organisms involve the removal of a molecule of water. A number of such reactions are illustrated in Fig. 5-1. It can be seen from this diagram that the major problem involved in condensations of biochemical significance is the removal of that molecule of water. Such a phenomenon involves a positive change of free energy; in other words, it is thermodynamically an unfavorable event. For example, in forming a peptide bond, $\Delta F^0_{298} = 3$ to 4 kcal at the dipeptide level [1]. There are a number of ways of overcoming this difficulty. The formation of dehydration condensation products would be favored if the water by-product of the reaction is somehow removed. One way of doing this (see Fig. 5-2) is to carry out the process at temperatures above the boiling point of water, in which case the water produced would boil away. A decrease in the concentration of H_2O (e.g., it boils away) for a particular value of ΔF would be counteracted by an increase of the desired product, A–B. Another possibility [(b) in Fig. 5-2] is for the water to enter into the chemical structure of another compound. Thus, dehydration leading to the condensation of one set of reactants would be accompanied by the hydrolysis of another. The negative change of free energy (ΔF_2) of the latter reaction would have to be sufficient to overcome the thermodynamic deficit (ΔF_1) due to the condensation reaction ($|\Delta F_2| \geq |\Delta F_1|$).

(a) Peptide

$$NH_2CHR-COOH + NH_2-CHR'COOH \longrightarrow NH_2CHRCO-NHCHR'COOH$$

Amino acid 1   Amino acid 2   Dipeptide $+$ H_2O

(b) Phosphate ester (B = heterocyclic base):[*]

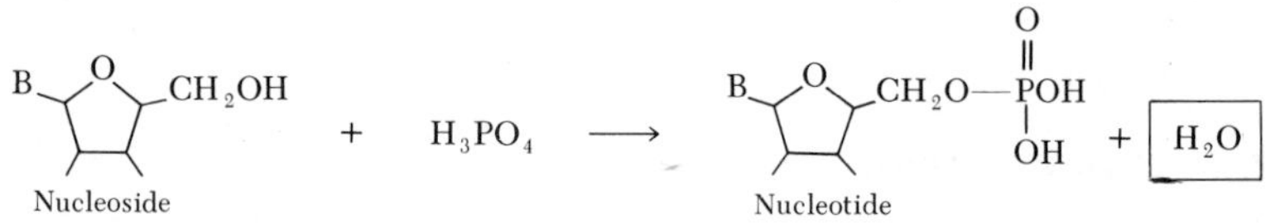

Nucleoside $+$ H_3PO_4 $\longrightarrow$ Nucleotide $+$ H_2O

(c) Carboxylic ester:[†]

$$R-COOH + HOCH_2-R' \longrightarrow RCO-OCH_2R' + H_2O$$

Acid   Alcohol   Ester

(d) Glycoside:[*]

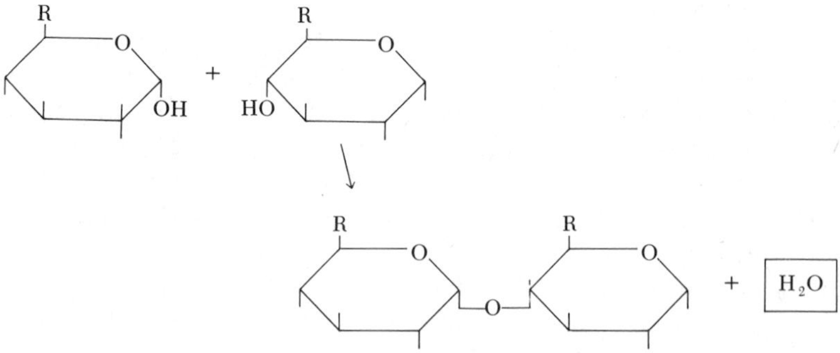

FIG. 5-1   Some examples of the condensation of biologically important monomers, demonstrating that each involves a dehydration process. [*]Branched bonds in pentose and hexose structures represent hydroxyl (OH) groups. [†]If the alcohol is glycerol, the ester product is then a lipid.

(a) $A-OH + H-B \xrightarrow{T>100\,°C} A-B + HOH \uparrow$

(b) $A-OH + H-B \longrightarrow A-B + HOH \qquad \Delta F_1 > 0$

$HOH + C \longrightarrow D \qquad\qquad\qquad \Delta F_2 < 0$

$|\Delta F_2| \geq |\Delta F_1|$ so that $\Delta F_1 + \Delta F_2 \leq 0$

FIG. 5-2 Possible approaches to the promotion of dehydration condensation. (If $\Delta F > 0$, the reaction is unfavored as written, whereas if $\Delta F < 0$, it is favored.) In the first case, an elevated temperature (and preferably anhydrous conditions) leads to the loss of water by boiling (enhanced fugacity). In the second case, the hydrolysis of compound C is coupled to the union of A and B. The thermodynamic barrier for the synthesis of A–B is overcome by the free-energy release in the production of D.

In each case noted in Fig. 5-1 the union of the monomers involved is the result of the removal of a molecule of water. Polymerization is a special case of condensation in which the reactants have two or more functional sites able to enter into the reaction. For example, amino acids have both an amino function and a carboxyl function. When the carboxyl function of one amino acid links with the amino of another, a dipeptide is formed (see Fig. 5-1). When the carboxyl function of the second amino acid reacts with the amino group of a third amino acid, a tripeptide results.

In this chapter we shall discuss various approaches that have been employed in an attempt to elucidate means of condensation of biomonomers which are possibly relevant to chemical evolution. This discussion is structured in terms of the increasing degree of hydration of the environment, ranging from completely anhydrous conditions on the one hand to processes taking place in dilute aqueous solution on the other. Going through such a range of conditions involves the increasing need for high-energy reactants since by the law of mass action, the more water available, the less favored would be the reaction.

5-2 CONDENSATION UNDER ANHYDROUS (NONAQUEOUS) CONDITIONS

Pyrocondensation

The pyrocondensation of anhydrous orthophosphate to give pyrophosphate has been known for some time [2]. Heating of phosphate has been an effective means of making the anhydride dimer. Early attempts to use pyrocondensation of amino acids to form polymers had generally been unsuccessful because of the formation of tarry products. However, when glycine was dissolved in glycerol and heated to 170 to 180°C, diketopiperazine (cyclic diglycine anhydride) and polyglycine (tetramer and higher) were produced [3].

In Chap. 4 we noted that heat, such as emanates from volcanoes, could have served as an effective primordial source of free energy to promote the synthesis of biologically important compounds, in particular, amino acids. With respect to condensation of amino acids, heating is one way of overcoming the problem of removal of water since water readily boils away as it is produced. Amino acids in the solid state will not normally polymerize into linear chains. However, it was found that such a reaction could be promoted if done in the presence of anhydrous glutamic acid [4]. This type of reaction was carried out by either heating glutamic acid and the second amino acid together at 160 to 190°C for up to 2 hr or first liquefying the glutamic acid at 180°C for a half hour and then adding the second amino acid in equimolar proportion. Using this method, several copolymers have been produced and studied (see Table 5-1).

Infrared spectrophotometry showed peaks typical for a linear polypeptide in the product (see Fig. 5-3) [4]. It was found that yields of the copolymerization would go up as the temperature of the reaction and the time of heating were increased. Similarly, the average molecular weight of the product rose as the temperature and time of reaction went up. The average molecular weight was of the order of 10,000 to 20,000 in the dialyzed product. This value was roughly estimated by amino acid analysis of the dinitrophenyl-derivatized polymer.

It was suggested that the role of glutamic acid may be related to the fact that the amino acid forms the lactam pyroglutamic acid

TABLE 5-1 Some amino acid combinations which give a positive biuret reaction upon pyrocondensation [4]*

1. Glutamic acid + glycine
2. Glutamic acid + glycylglycine
3. Glutamic acid + aspartic acid
4. Glutamic acid + asparagine
5. Glycine + aspartic acid
6. Glutamine + aspartic acid
7. Glutamine + asparagine

* The biuret reaction requires the presence of an amino acid polymer containing a linear segment of at least three units.

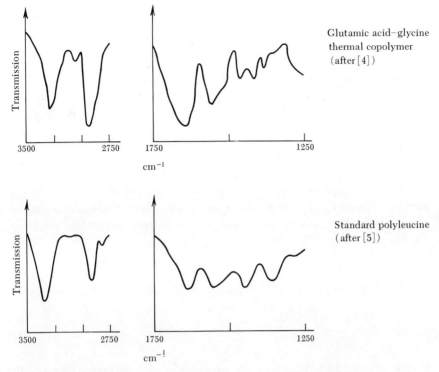

Glutamic acid–glycine
thermal copolymer
(after [4])

Standard polyleucine
(after [5])

FIG. 5-3 Infrared spectrum of a glutamic acid-glycine copolymer produced by pyrocondensation of the monomers. The spectrum of polyleucine produced by standard organic chemical methods is also presented for comparison. The differences in the two may be due to their different amino acid components or the unnatural types of linkages found in the thermal polymer. The latter effect is discussed in detail in the text. (*After* [4,5].)

(2-pyrrolidone-5-carboxylic acid) which melts at 170°C [4]. Under these conditions, the molten lactam could act as a solvent in much the same fashion as the glycerol in the experiments previously mentioned. Furthermore, it is noteworthy that pyroglutamic acid is an anhydride. It seems quite plausible that the fate of the water removed to form the peptide bonds is found in the hydrolysis of the lactam. The reaction is as follows:

$$\text{HOOC(CH}_2)_2\text{CH(NH}_2)\text{COOH} \underset{+\text{H}_2\text{O}}{\overset{-\text{H}_2\text{O}}{\rightleftharpoons}}
\begin{array}{c}
\text{CH}_2\text{———CH}_2 \\
| \qquad\qquad | \\
\text{CO} \qquad \text{CH—COOH} \\
\diagdown \qquad \diagup \\
\text{NH}
\end{array}$$

Glutamic acid   Pyroglutamic acid

It is also possible that the acidic nature of pyroglutamic acid may have catalytically promoted peptide synthesis [4]; thus

$$R-COOH + R'-NH_2 \xrightarrow{+H^+} R-\overset{\overset{\displaystyle OH}{|}}{\underset{\underset{\displaystyle OH}{|}}{C}} \overset{+}{\underset{}{}} \leftarrow \overset{\overset{\displaystyle H}{|}}{\underset{\underset{\displaystyle H}{|}}{N}}-R' \xrightarrow{-H_2O}$$

$$R-\overset{+}{\underset{\underset{\displaystyle OH}{|}}{C}}-NH-R' \xrightarrow{-H^+} R-CO-NH-R'$$

In the copolymerization reaction, the presence of an acidic amino acid is essential [4]. For example, when the copolymerization of phenylalanine and leucine was attempted, diketopiperazine-like products like the following appeared:

$$
\begin{array}{c}
\text{NH} \\
R'-CH \quad \diagdown \quad CO \\
| \qquad\qquad | \\
CO \qquad CH-R \\
\diagdown \quad NH \quad \diagup
\end{array}
$$

It is important to realize that the production of such cyclic compounds would probably represent evolutionary dead ends since no further residues could be readily added to form a multiunit linear polymer, as proteins are. From the standpoint of chemical evolution, it was suggested that the role of glutamic acid here may be related to its high incidence in contemporary proteins [4]. This point will be discussed later in greater detail.

The heating of amino acids under anhydrous conditions was extended to copolymers of up to five different amino acids [6]. Glutamine could be used in place of glutamic acid, and in this case typical products had an average molecular weight of 4,900. It was found that the heating of aspartic acid produced a polyimide polyhydrate (see Fig. 5-7). This structure was deduced from infrared studies. The resultant spectra were unlike those of diketopiperazines, which might also be expected to appear under the reaction conditions used. The biuret test requires the presence of a compound containing two adjacent peptide (amide) bonds, for example, as are found in a linear tripeptide. The product from amino acid pyrocondensation gave a positive biuret reaction, suggesting the presence of a polymer containing at least some linear polyamide (or polyimide) segments. It is also significant that diketopiperazines give a negative response to this test. The polyimide was converted to a polypeptide by mild heating in dilute, aqueous sodium hydroxide. Aspartic acid can be copolymerized with other amino acids, and in this way it replaces the glutamic acid of earlier experiments [6].

The copolymerization of aspartic acid with glutamic acid was studied in greater detail [7]. The yield of the nondialyzable product and its molecular weight increased as the temperature of the reaction was increased. The combination of the two dicarboxylic amino acids together gave higher polymer yields than when the reaction was carried out with either amino acid alone. Temperatures employed in the synthesis were typically in the range of 160 to 180°C. This made the conditions sufficient to give the lactam, but apparently the temperature was not high enough to cause serious decomposition of amino acid residues for the time the experiment was in progress.

It was found that lysine could replace aspartic acid or glutamic acid in the thermal copolymerization reactions [8]. This is apparently due to the fact that this amino acid can also form a liquid lactam at 150 to 170°C. Lysine homopolymerizes at 180 to 230°C. This basic amino acid was shown to copolymerize with glycine, alanine, glutamic acid, or aspartic acid. Infrared spectrophotometry suggested a branched polymer with some linear segments.

These heating experiments were extended to a mixture of 18 natural amino acids. In a typical experiment, an anhydrous mixture was prepared containing 2 parts aspartic acid (by weight), 2 parts glutamic acid, and 1 part an equimolar mixture of 16 other amino acids [8,9]. This was heated to 170°C and maintained at this temperature for 6 hr. A molten mixture resulted because of the formation of pyroglutamic acid. The heating was carried out under a nitrogen atmosphere. During this process, gas evolved, and the color of the liquid changed to amber. The vitreous product yielded a granular precipitate on rubbing with water. The filtrate, after standing overnight, was washed with ethanol and dialyzed for 4 days against water. After lyophilization, a portion of the product was hydrolyzed with 6 N HCl. Typical amino acid compositions are noted in the section on special problems at the end of this chapter. Column chromatography was used to resolve the components of the hydrolyzed polymers. The proportion of serine and threonine was unusually low compared to its initial concentration. The presence of tryptophan was established by the Hopkins-Cole and Salkowski color tests. It was not normally possible to detect this amino acid since it was destroyed by acid hydrolysis during processing of the product. All of the original amino acids were found in the hydrolyzates, indicating that all had been incorporated into the polymer. Here again it was not certain if all the linkages were of the biologically more common alpha type.

In addition to serving as the solvent for the reaction, it would appear that an excess of dicarboxylic or diamino acid is necessary to provide some (as yet undefined) protective effect against the decomposition of the amino acids [9]. Such an effect is lost if the temperature of the reaction is greater than 210°C. The problem of thermal instability of amino acids will be discussed at the end of this chapter.

The polymer produced from the mixture of 18 amino acids was found to have a number of interesting characteristics [9]. The ones in the following list were particularly looked for because a similarity was sought between the polyamino acid and natural proteins:

1. Nutritive value for microbes (*Lactobacillus arabinosus*)
2. Average molecular weight of 3,600 to 8,600
3. Positive biuret, xanthoproteic, Hopkins-Cole, and Salkowski tests
4. Carbonyl and amide bonds observed by IR spectrophotometry
5. Salting out of solution by 0.1 M phosphate buffer (pH of 7.9), saturated ammonium sulfate, or 3.5% sodium chloride
6. Nitrogen content of 13.2 percent (proteins are usually around 16 percent)
7. Electrophoretic mobility
8. Digestion by pepsin and chymotrypsin, but no autodigestion (papain and trypsin are also effective)

Because of its protein-like characteristics, the product was labeled a *proteinoid*, although some observers have criticized the name. No antigenicity was demonstrated by the proteinoid with the guinea pig, rabbit, and uterine strip tests, but this may be related to the low molecular weight or heterogeneity of the product. The degree of branching in the polymer was not determined. In many cases the proteinoid was not 100 percent hydrolyzable in acid or base. Its size prevented it from diffusing through collodion dialysis membranes. The proteinoids produced from mixtures containing an excess of glutamic and aspartic acids exhibited isoelectric points around 2.8, whereas the lysine proteinoids had isoelectric points around 8.4.

A number of means were found to enhance the yield of the reaction. First of all, if one added phosphoric acid (H_3PO_4), the yield of copolymer formed between aspartic acid and another amino acid increased [9,10]. A small amount (≈ 0.4 percent) of phosphate was found to be incorporated into the product itself. For example, when 0.01 mole of aspartic acid and 0.01 mole of glycine were mixed and heated to 160°C, 0.02 gm of nondialyzable product appeared; when the synthesis was carried out in the presence of phosphate (1 ml of 85% H_3PO_4), 0.12 gm of polymer was produced. On the other hand, when the same reaction was carried out at 180°C, the yield of nondialyzable polymer with and without phosphate present was 0.44 and 0.25 gm, respectively. The phosphate may have acted as the solvent or as an acid catalyst for the reaction, or it could have formed phosphorylamino or mixed acid anhydride intermediates (see Fig. 5-4).

Enhanced yields were also obtained if ATP or polyphosphate was

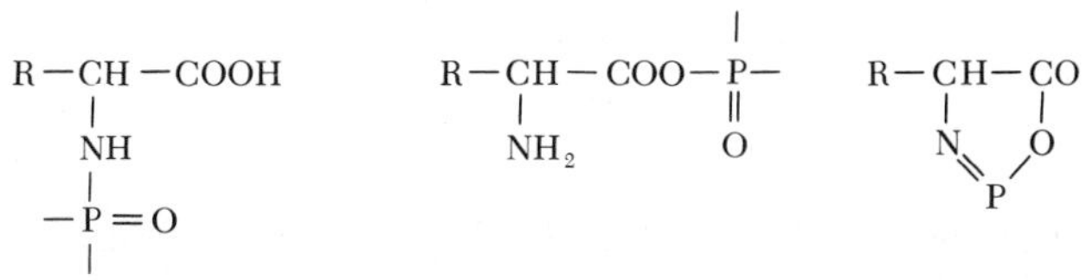

$$R-\underset{\underset{\displaystyle -P=O}{\overset{|}{NH}}}{\overset{|}{CH}}-COOH \qquad R-\underset{\underset{\displaystyle O}{\overset{|}{NH_2}}}{\overset{|}{CH}}-COO-\overset{|}{\underset{\displaystyle \|}{P}}- \qquad R-\underset{N}{\overset{|}{CH}}-CO$$

FIG. 5-4 Suggested intermediates in the pyrocondensation of amino acids carried out in the presence of phosphate [11].

added to the reaction mixture [10,11]. In the latter case, it was possible to get appreciable product yields (see Fig. 5-5) when the reaction was carried out at temperatures as low as 70°C. Because of the lower temperature, presumably less thermal decomposition of the amino acids occurred. The yield-enhancing effects of phosphate may be related somehow to its contemporary biological role since enhanced yields were not observed if H_2SO_4 was added instead of H_3PO_4; sulfuric acid does not have an apparent biological function, although it has been found in one isolated case of tunicates [12]. Thus, the problem of high temperature can be overcome.

The various polyphosphates used in this experiment were prepared by heating phosphoric acid (85%) at various temperatures, such as 200, 250, 300, and 350°C [11].

Using polyphosphoric acid, the copolymerization of aspartic acid and glycine was studied. Polyphosphoric acid produced at 200°C was used. The amount of nondialyzable (i.e., macromolecular) product was measured after 100 hr of heating. When the amino acid polymerization was carried out at 70°C, 0.04 gm of product appeared; at 100°C, 0.13 gm

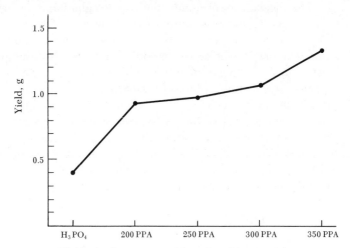

FIG. 5-5 Yield of polyaspartic acid produced by heating 2.7 gm of the amino acid at 100°C for 100 hr in the presence of polyphosphate mixtures (PPA), each of which had been synthesized at various temperatures (200°, 250°, etc.) from 2 ml of H_3PO_4 (85%). (*After* [11].)

$$CH_4 + NH_3 + H_2O \xrightarrow{1000°C} \text{amino acids}$$

$$\text{Amino acids (anhydrous)} \xrightarrow{170°C} \text{proteinoids}$$

FIG. 5-6 Overall scheme of the thermal model of chemical evolution [11].

was obtained, and at 120°C, 0.67 gm. For comparison purposes it is important to note that much longer heating periods (100 hr) were used in this experiment than in the previously discussed thermal procedures (2 to 6 hr). The average molecular weight of the product was between 6,000 and 15,000. Essentially the same product yield of polypeptide was obtained if L-aspartic acid was employed as an initial reactant as compared to DL-aspartic acid. Since heating is needed to synthesize the polyphosphate in the first place, the requirement of elevated temperatures has not been eliminated here, however. The polyphosphoric acid may have acted as the solvent, acid catalyst, or dehydrating agent in this reaction.

As mentioned before, the thermal model of chemical evolution represents events which might have occurred at or near volcanoes or on lava flows. The aqueous hydrolysis step, which (as will be discussed shortly) is an essential part of the synthesis, may have been due to rain. However, the reader will recall that the thermal synthesis of amino acids discussed in the previous chapter took place at temperatures around 1000°C, whereas the thermal polymerizations just mentioned occur at much more moderate temperatures. It is difficult to imagine such a variation of temperatures within a given environment (see Fig. 5-6). It is believed that rain was used to remove the products from the high-temperature region as well. The instability of organic compounds at elevated temperatures will be discussed.

The mechanism of amino acid pyrocondensation, using aspartic acid as an example, and the nature of the bonding in the product have been studied in greater detail. In this synthesis, it was not certain at this point whether the linkage was alpha or beta. Natural proteins are almost exclusively alpha-linked linear polypeptides. The experiment was repeated by heating anhydrous aspartic acid either in vacuo at 200°C for 120 hr or by refluxing the amino acid in tetralin for 100 hr [13]. After standing in 0.1 N NaOH for 1 hr at room temperature, the product was found to be very soluble in water, whereas pure α-polyaspartic acid is known to be insoluble in water. A positive biuret reaction was noted, which α,γ-polyglutamic acid does not give. These results would suggest that both alpha and beta linkages were present in the product; thus

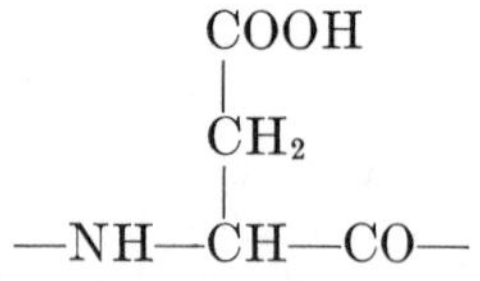

```
        COOH                        CO—
         |                           |
        CH₂                         CH₂
         |                           |
—NH—CH—CO—                  —NH—CH—COOH
  α-Aspartyl residue          β-Aspartyl residue
```

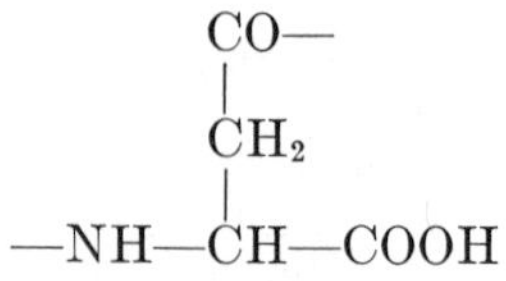

The molecular weight of the product, determined by Van Slyke amino nitrogen, was in the range of 6,000 to 12,000.

The mechanism outlined in Fig. 5-7 was suggested for this reaction [13]. Under the high-temperature conditions of the reaction, polyaspartic acid is unstable, and step 3 occurs, yielding polyanhydroaspartic acid. Hydrolysis under mild conditions gives polyaspartic acid (step 2). Step 1 was suggested by the fact that heating of N-acetylaspartic acid produces the amino acid polymer; this ruled out the possibility of dipeptide intermediates. Thus, the synthesis was apparently the result of an intermolecular transacylation reaction. In step 2, polyaspartic acid is produced from aspartic acid anhydride. Such a process could be expected to lead to both alpha and beta peptide linkages. It was found chemically that at least 33 percent of the linkages were in fact of the biologically uncommon beta type. This was demonstrated with anilide and methyl ester derivatives of the product. Furthermore, ammonolysis produced both isoasparagine and asparagine. These conclusions were similarly corroborated by a Hoffman degradation. If only alpha peptide bonds were present, reaction (a) (Fig. 5-8) would have resulted. However, the products of both reactions (a) and (b) (Fig. 5-8) were found. Polyaspartic acid (thermally produced) has also been reduced with $LiAlH_4$ and hydrolyzed [14]. The presence of α-homoserine, β-homoserine, and aspartic acid gave further evidence for the presence of much branching in the polymer.

As shown in Fig. 5-1, the union of phosphate with a nucleoside also involves a dehydration condensation. When a mixture of these two types of reactants was heated in the absence of water for 2 hr in a sealed Pyrex tube at 160°C, nucleotides resulted [15]. Radioac-

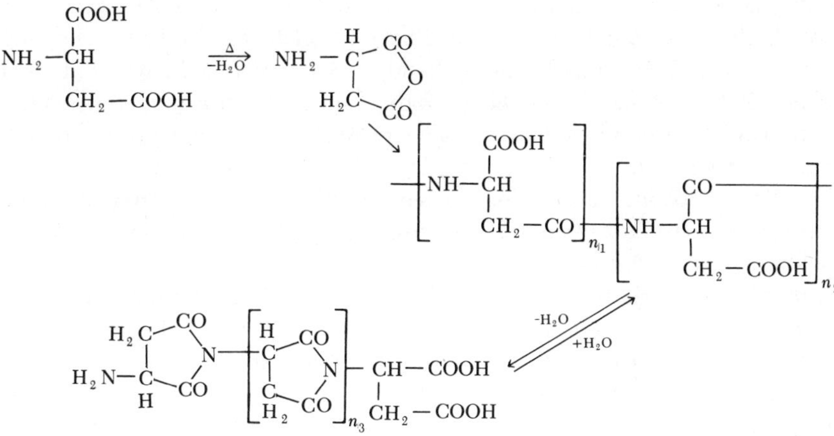

FIG. 5-7 Mechanism suggested for the synthesis of polyaspartic acid by pyrocondensation (see text for details) [13].

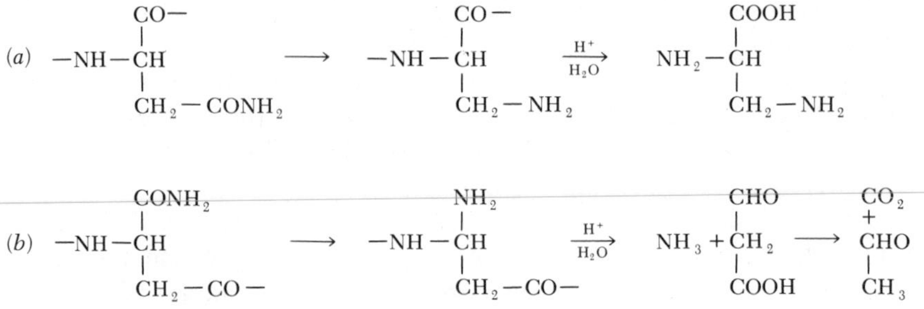

$$(a) \quad -NH-\overset{\displaystyle CO-}{\underset{\displaystyle CH_2-CONH_2}{\overset{|}{\underset{|}{CH}}}} \quad \longrightarrow \quad -NH-\overset{\displaystyle CO-}{\underset{\displaystyle CH_2-NH_2}{\overset{|}{\underset{|}{CH}}}} \quad \xrightarrow[H_2O]{H^+} \quad NH_2-\overset{\displaystyle COOH}{\underset{\displaystyle CH_2-NH_2}{\overset{|}{\underset{|}{CH}}}}$$

$$(b) \quad -NH-\overset{\displaystyle CONH_2}{\underset{\displaystyle CH_2-CO-}{\overset{|}{\underset{|}{CH}}}} \quad \longrightarrow \quad -NH-\overset{\displaystyle NH_2}{\underset{\displaystyle CH_2-CO-}{\overset{|}{\underset{|}{CH}}}} \quad \xrightarrow[H_2O]{H^+} \quad NH_3+\overset{\displaystyle CHO}{\underset{\displaystyle COOH}{\overset{|}{\underset{|}{CH_2}}}} \quad \longrightarrow \quad \overset{\displaystyle CO_2}{\underset{\displaystyle CH_3}{+}{\overset{}{\underset{|}{CHO}}}}$$

FIG. 5-8   Products of Hoffman degradation of thermally condensed polyaspartic acid [13].

tively labeled nucleosides were used in this synthesis to aid in the identification of products. Following the heating, the product mixture was dissolved in water and analyzed by electrophoresis, paper chromatography, and ion-exchange chromatography. The products included cyclic 2',3'-phosphate, 2'-monophosphate, 3'-monophosphate, and 5'-monophosphate. Best results were obtained if the phosphate reactant was $NaH_2PO_4 \cdot H_2O$, in which case the yield of uridine monophosphate was 16 percent. Further study showed that $NaNH_4HPO_4 \cdot 4H_2O$, $(NH_4)_2$-HPO_4, and $Ca(H_2PO_4)_2 \cdot H_2O$ are also good phosphate contributors. If the heating was carried on for an extended period, the peak yield generally occurred at 4 hr. After 2 hr of heating, cyclic phosphate was present in greater amounts than the noncyclic products. Uridine gave the best results of all nucleosides for 4 hr of heating, with a 20.6 percent yield of nucleotide. Others included cytidine (13.7 percent), guanosine (9.8 percent), thymidine (6.3 percent), and adenosine (3.1 percent). Pyrimidines gave better yields than purines. Close examination of the product revealed the presence of 2'-5' and 3'-5' dinucleoside phosphates, among others, even when synthesized at 65°C [16]. As noted, the 20 percent yield of uridine phosphate resulted after heating for 4 hr at 160°C; on the other hand, a 3 percent yield was obtained after 12 days of heating at 80°C, indicating that more moderate conditions could be employed [15]. The possible primordial origins of the nucleosides will be considered later.

The pyrocondensation of nucleoside phosphates to give phosphodiesters was studied further [17]. Anhydrous 2'(3')-cytidine monophosphate (CMP) was heated in the presence of polyphosphate for 2 hr at 65°C. The product was neutralized with aqueous ammonia, dialyzed, and fractionated with Dowex 1. A product yield of 1 percent was obtained. Of those studied, cytidine monophosphate appeared to be the only nucleotide able to self-condense under the conditions employed. The product exhibited alkaline hyperchromicity when incubated at 37°C for 48 hr, as does known poly C. It was also analyzed with enzymes. First, reaction with bacterial alkaline phosphatase gave compound A. This compound was analyzed for terminal phosphate groups. A was then treated with pancreatic ribonuclease and phosphatase to give compound B. Compound B was then analyzed for phosphate groups. The value noted for compound A would be a measure of all terminal phosphates in the product, and the value for compound B would be due to diester phosphate. In typical experiments, the phosphate for compound A amounted to 36 to 40 percent and for compound B, 26 to 29 percent, suggesting that both phosphate ester and phosphodiester linkages were present in the poly C product. It should be noted that the ribonuclease employed works on 3'-phosphates and that the initial reactant used in the synthesis was 2'(3')-CMP. Therefore, one could roughly assume that 40 to 60 percent of the linkages were of the phosphodiester type. These data suggest that the main products were dinucleotides and trinucleotides. It is not sure if they are exclusively branched or are coupled by 2'-5' or 3'-5' bonds; probably both types are involved. The amount of phosphate noted for component A would indicate some branching since much of it in the product appears as end groups, although this may represent a terminal polyphosphate function as well.

It is important to realize that each of the syntheses discussed in this section on pyrocondensation involves the complete initial absence of water. The elevation of ambient temperature promotes the release of water, leading to the production of anhydride bonds (amides and phosphate esters, for example). The presence of water would have most likely prevented the desired reactions from taking place or would have at least reduced yields or required much longer heating periods to remove the extraneous liquid. Therefore, the success of these methods depends on the initial state being anhydrous.

Polymetaphosphate

As mentioned earlier, it is possible to promote the dehydration condensation of one group of compounds by coupling it to the hydrolysis of another. One such condensing compound which has been investigated in the context of possible primitive Earth events is polymetaphosphate ethyl ester [18,19]. Since this compound is susceptible to hydrolysis by water alone, it was necessary to carry out most of the condensation reactions in organic (nonaqueous) solvents. An additional function of this condensing agent, since it is a high-energy compound, is to activate appropriate functional groups of the reactants so that the condensation will take place.

Polymetaphosphate ethyl ester (PMP) was first synthesized in 1910 [20]. Phosphorus pentoxide, one of the compounds from which the ester is produced, is an anhydride which is frequently used as a desiccant. The pentoxide hydrolyzes to H_3PO_4 in the presence of water.

The negative free-energy change of such a reaction could conceivably be coordinated with a dehydration condensation reaction (see Fig. 5-2). The use of PMP in the context of primordial biogenesis was suggested by the biological role of phosphoric acid anhydrides, such as ATP, and by the presence of polyphosphates in microbes [18].

PMP was produced for the syntheses to be discussed here by refluxing 150 gm of phosphorus pentoxide in 150 ml of chloroform and 300 ml of ether for 12 hr [18]. After evaporating off the solvent, the ester was obtained as a viscous, colorless syrup ready for use. (As will be seen later, the mode of preparation of the ester is important in determining the nature of the resultant compound.)

PMP was used in the synthesis of peptides. Through the employment of the ester, polyarginine with an average molecular weight of 4,000 to 5,000 has been synthesized from the amino acid monomer [19]. Similarly, polypeptides of up to 24 units have been produced from alanylglycylglycine. Starting with a mixture of tyrosine, alanine, glutamic acid, and PMP, a polypeptide with an average molecular weight of 7,300 has been fabricated. These syntheses were generally carried out in organic, nonaqueous solvents.

Polynucleotides have also been produced using the metaphosphate. In a typical experiment, 350 mgm of adenylic acid was heated for 18 hr in the presence of 8 gm of the PMP syrup at 55°C under anhydrous conditions [18]. Then the reaction mixture was dialyzed for 4 days. A white, nondialyzable powder representing a 20 percent yield was recovered after lyophilization. Polymers were synthesized from deoxynucleoside-5'-phosphates, 2'-, 3'-, and 5'-nucleoside phosphates (such as the adenylic acid just mentioned), as well as 2',3'-cyclic monophosphates. Complimentarity by interchain base pairing was observed if synthetic poly A was mixed with poly U (see Table 5-2). It was also possible

TABLE 5-2 Characteristics of polymers of nucleotides produced using polymetaphosphate ethyl ester [18]

Polymer*	S_{20}†	$[\eta]_v$†	Molecular weight	Hyperchromicity, %†
Poly A	2.5	25	21,000	37
Poly C	2.0	23	15,000	16
Poly G	2.9	28	28,000	28
Poly U	4.0	35	50,000	20
Poly T	2.3	24	18,000	47

* A = adenylic acid, C = cytidylic acid, G = guanylic acid, U = uridylic acid, T = thymidylic acid.
† For an explanation of the general significance of the values for sedimentation coefficient (S_{20}), intrinsic viscosity ($[\eta]$), and hyperchromicity in describing the nature of biopolymers, see Ref. 21.

to start the reactions with nucleosides since the polymetaphosphate ester could first phosphorylate the appropriate hydroxyl groups and then promote the dehydration condensation reaction. However, in this case the yields were lower than when carried out with nucleotides as starting reagents.

The case of poly U (polyuridylic acid) synthesis using PMP was studied further to elucidate the types of linkages produced. Alkaline hydrolysis and treatment with ribonuclease did not result in the types of products expected from a linear polymer bearing the naturally occurring 3'-5' linkages [22]. Ribonucleic acids found in nature yield mononucleotides upon complete hydrolysis with ribonuclease, for example. However, treatment of the synthetic polymer with the enzyme resulted in the liberation of only very small amounts of mononucleotide. Instead, a complex variety of hydrolysis products appeared. This result suggested a predominance of unnatural linkages and the possibility of branching, crosslinking between chains, and substitution. Similar results were obtained for copolymers of adenylic, uridylic, and cytidylic acids.

These conclusions were further corroborated through studies of PMP-mediated 5'-thymidylic acid polymerization [23]. The structure of the product was studied in detail. Quantitative analysis indicated that the number of incorporated phosphate moieties was 5 to 15 times higher than the number of incorporated mononucleotide units. The nondialyzable (or slowly dialyzing) product was treated with acetic anhydride to cleave nucleotide pyrophosphate linkages. Subsequent enzymatic degradation failed to reveal the presence of long-chain polynucleotides primarily linked by natural phosphodiester bonds. This suggested that there were apparently a number of unnatural pyrophosphate and ether bonds in the high-molecular-weight product first discussed in this section since after cleavage of the pyrophosphate linkages only small molecules remained.

PMP is especially reactive to NH_2- and OH-containing compounds. In the case of amines, for example, it is believed that the mechanism of the reaction involves activation through the formation of a phosphoramide [R—NH—P(O)OH—O—R'], a reactive type of compound [18]. This may be the key to polypeptide synthesis using the metaphosphate. The reaction is

$$R—NH—\overset{\displaystyle OH}{\underset{\displaystyle \underset{\|}{O}}{P}}—O—R' + R''—COOH \rightarrow$$

$$R—NH—CO—R'' + HO—\overset{\displaystyle OH}{\underset{\displaystyle \underset{\|}{O}}{P}}—O—R'$$

The mechanism by which PMP promotes some of the other reactions already discussed (and also found in Table 5-4) has been investigated as well. Using potentiometric titrations, it was found that 1 mole of adenosine in the presence of PMP combines with 2 moles of phosphate during the reaction [18]. This would apparently suggest that the phosphodiesterification reaction is promoted by intermediate activation of the nucleoside by phosphate. Finally, the high-energy phosphate bonds (possibly cyclic phosphates) would be broken to lead to the formation of the desired dimerized product. The actual intermediates have not been isolated and identified.

In the polymerization of ribose (see Table 5-4), the initial ratio of the ester to the carbohydrate was adjusted to 3:1 [18]. One mole of primary phosphate ester appeared after 1 hr of reaction, and ultimately 2 moles resulted. This could suggest that the C_1 and C_5 hydroxyl groups were most likely the ones phosphorylated to form the reaction intermediate. When the reaction between glucose and PMP was carried out, an acidic product, which was found to be absorbable by an ion exchanger, was synthesized. This was taken to indicate that phosphorylation had occurred.

The structure of PMP itself has been studied by infrared spectrophotometry and potentiometric titration in the hope that such investigation might aid in elucidating the mechanism by which it promotes dehydration condensation [24]. The IR spectrum of the compound exhibited bands characteristic of cyclic phosphate compounds. On the addition of water, these bands disappeared, and new ones appeared similar to those characteristic for open-chain polyphosphate esters. These results are summarized in Table 5-3 as a function of time. It would appear that after 3 hr at 100°C the end point of the reaction was reached. These observations back up the earlier suggestion of a cyclic phosphate structure for this compound. This is readily seen in the proposed structures diagramed in Fig. 5-9. A comparison of the results just noted and the figure [primarily structure (a)] sustains this point.

Further information bearing on the structure of PMP was obtained by means of nuclear magnetic resonance studies [25,26]. The chemical shifts followed were the P_t (terminal phosphate), P_m (middle phosphate), and P_b (branched phosphate) absorptions (see Fig. 5-9). The observed data supported both of the structures in Fig. 5-9. In the absence of water, structure (a) constitutes 56 percent and structure (b) 44 percent of the sample according to these results; as small amounts of water are added, P_b disappears, and P_t increases, suggesting a ring opening. P_t continues to increase as P_m diminishes with time. Then, P_t becomes greater than P_m, and a small amount of orthophosphate appears after 5 hr. P_m further diminishes as more orthophosphate appears. Thus, the original polymetaphosphate is definitely unstable and sus-

TABLE 5-3 Results of experiments to document the hydrolysis of polymetaphosphate ethyl ester by infrared spectrophotometry* [24]

Time, hr.	Temperature, °C	Phosphate, groups per each P_4O_{10}	
		Primary	Secondary
0	0	2.3	
1	20	2.7	0.2
1	100	3.6	2.4
3	100	3.8	3.0

* According to Fig. 5-9, if the ester had been entirely in the form of structure (a), four primary and three secondary phosphate groups would have been obtained upon hydrolysis, whereas (b) would have given four primary and four secondary groups. The results of this table suggest that PMP is 85 percent (a) and 15 percent (b).

ceptible to hydrolysis in water. The same pattern of results was observed when ethanol replaced the water. In the case of the use of ethanol as a solvent, the first step of the reaction probably involves the formation of the compound shown in Fig. 5-10. It was also found that the nature of the actual structure of PMP depends markedly on the proportion of reactants and the method of heating used in its synthesis. This may account for the divergence of results noted in the different experiments discussed here.

We can draw a number of important conclusions from the experiments on polymetaphosphates just discussed. First of all, these compounds can be effective agents for promoting the dehydration condensation of nucleotides, as well as amino acids. However, the poly-

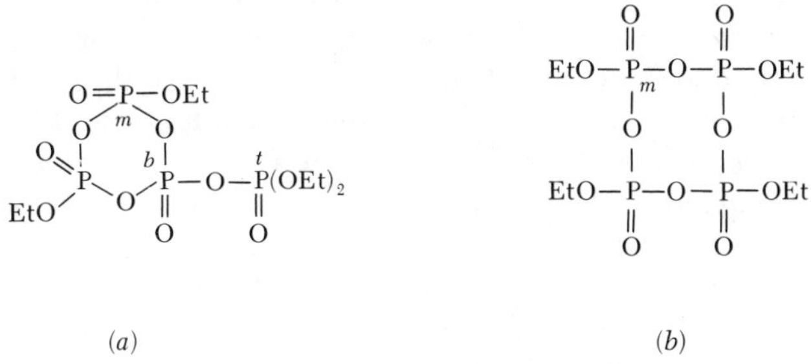

(a)   (b)

FIG. 5-9 Proposed structures of polymetaphosphate ethyl ester based on determinations of changes in the relative magnitudes of pertinent peaks in the nuclear magnetic resonance spectrum of the compound during its hydrolysis [26].

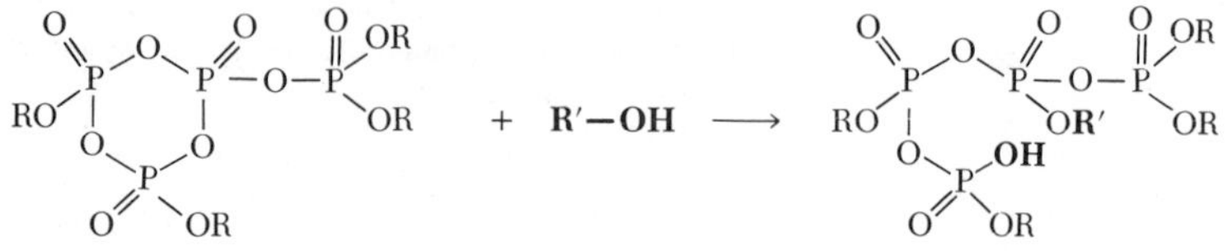

FIG. 5-10 Proposed first step in the reaction of polymetaphosphate ethyl ester with OH-containing compounds, such as alcohols and sugars [24]. The ring opening compares well with the results obtained upon hydrolysis or ethanolysis discussed in the text. In the above diagram, R would correspond to the ethyl group in Fig. 5-9.

nucleotides, in particular, apparently have many unnatural linkages, such as pyrophosphate and interchain bonds. The condensing agent itself is quite susceptible to hydrolysis, so that its primordial origin and maintenance are questionable.

Several other biologically significant polymers have been synthesized with the use of PMP under conditions similar to those used in the nucleotide and amino acid polymerizations already discussed here. These experiments are outlined in Table 5-4.

In summary, two means have been considered in this chapter thus far by which dehydration condensation may have occurred on the primitive Earth under anhydrous (nonaqueous) conditions. The first utilizes evaporation of the water by-product by carrying out the synthesis at elevated temperatures with dry starting materials. It was suggested that these conditions could have prevailed near volcanoes [9]; the instability of organic compounds under such conditions will be discussed. The second method employs high-energy polymetaphosphates to activate the compounds to be united. One of the major drawbacks to this latter model, however, is the questionable stability of this condensing agent under the hydrated conditions that are believed to have existed on the primitive Earth (see Chap. 3). Because of this instability, it was necessary to carry out the reactions in the presence of a minimum amount of water, preferably under anhydrous conditions. Thus, both methods thrive on the initial absence of water in the environment in which the condensations are taking place. On the other hand, significant yields of condensation products did appear. Since large amounts of polymeric compounds were probably needed for biogenesis, these synthetic processes may have been of potentially great utility.

In conclusion, we may note that various explanations are presented in this chapter to elucidate the course of prebiotic polymerizations. The results of these different approaches suggest to us that these reactions could have taken place on the primitive Earth under a variety of conditions, all leading to the same essential products. This was one of the main themes of Chap. 4. In the present chapter as well, it is not really

TABLE 5-4 Synthesis of glycosidic compounds using polymetaphosphate ethyl ester [18]

Linkage	Reactants	Products	Remarks
A. O-Glycoside	1. Glucose + methylglucose	Glucose-1-phosphate; cellulose-like polymer	DMF solvent; suggest that ethyl ester of glucose-1-phosphate or glucose-polyphosphate is intermediate, rather than glucose-1-phosphate itself, in polymerization.
	2. Glucose	Oligosaccharide	Formamide solvent; 30–50% yield; average MW of 50,000; $[\eta] = 100$; $\alpha = +38$ (optically active); IR suggests β-glycoside linkage; periodate suggests 1–4 bonds.
	3. Fructose	Oligosaccharide	Average MW of 40,000.
	4. Ribose	Oligosaccharide	Average MW of 40,000; appears that α 1–5 bond predominates.
B. N-Glycoside	1. Adenine + deoxyribose	Deoxyadenosine	Displays UV spectrum and R_f of standard; 30% yield.
	2. Adenine + ribose	Adenosine	DMF solvent; 20–60% yield.
	3. Apurinic DNA* + purine base	Nucleic acid	Example: 40% incorporation of guanine at 37°C after 24 hr; pyrimidines add more slowly than purines; product susceptible to DNAase and RNAase venom diesterase; purines initially removed by mild acid treatment.

* Apurinic DNA is nucleic acid from which purines have been removed by mild acid treatment.

necessary for us to ascertain which particular approach best resolves the problems under consideration. Rather, it is more important to realize that these necessary polymers most probably *did* appear in any case, as also concluded in Chap. 4 with respect to the biomonomers. The evidence presented in this chapter strongly suggests that the same products arose from very different means, again supporting the concept that chemical evolution was a probable series of events. The extent to which each of the modes of synthesis actually contributed to chemical evolution will probably never be absolutely ascertained.

5-3 CONDENSATION IN AQUEOUS SOLUTION

The biggest problem involved with dehydration condensation taking place in aqueous solution is that one is attempting to remove a molecule of water while the system is dissolved in the presence of water. By thermodynamic considerations such a process seems unfavorable (see Fig. 5-2) unless the reaction is carried out with the use of high-energy reactants or coreactants able to absorb or chemically tie up the water by-product. Such reactants must normally be stable in water, in contradistinction to the polymetaphosphate we already discussed, but must be able to selectively react under the particular conditions in which the compounds to be condensed become available. (Most of the models presented in Chap. 4 suggest that biomonomers ended up in aqueous bodies.) Similarly, it must be shown that such condensing agents could have been synthesized under primitive Earth conditions. Of the models discussed thus far, condensation in aqueous solution best approximates the internal solvent environment of contemporary living cells.

High-energy reactants

It was stated earlier that dehydration condensation in aqueous solutions could be promoted by the employment of high-energy reactants. An example of an active reactant would be one which already contains the type of anhydride bond desired in the final product. The peptide bond is essentially an amide linkage. Thus, we see that the transition from an amide compound ($R-CO-NH_2$) to a peptide ($R-CO-NH-R'$) involves little or no change in energy. The amide is an anhydride linkage like the peptide bond. The synthesis of amino acid amides in simulated primitive atmospheres has previously been demonstrated (see Chap. 4). This is probably the result of partial hydrolysis of nitriles in the aqueous phase:

$$R-C\equiv N \xrightarrow{H_2O} R-\overset{\displaystyle O}{\overset{\|}{C}}-NH_2 \xrightarrow{H_2O} R-\overset{\displaystyle O}{\overset{\|}{C}}-OH + NH_3$$

One example of the use of amino acid amides is in the refluxing of 5 to 10% aqueous solutions of β-L-aspartic acid amide (asparagine) for several days [27]. A yield of peptide of around 60 percent was obtained, whereas when the reaction was carried out at 70 to 75°C, a yield of 18 percent resulted. By the Van Slyke amino-nitrogen and dinitrophenol end-group analyses, the average molecular weight of the product was determined to be between 380 and 530, which is equivalent to 3.3 to 4.4 units per molecule. By paper chromatography, β-aspartyl-aspartic acid, in particular, was identified in the product mixture, suggesting that the association of units was random. Dialysis of the product mixture resulted in the isolation of a polymeric fraction with an average molecular weight of 1,700 to 3,000 (15 to 26 units). This material exhibited a positive biuret reaction for peptides and was highly soluble in water, as one would expect for α,β-polyaspartic acid. Polypeptide bonds were observed by infrared spectrophotometry. These included an NH stretch near 3 μ, the carboxyl CO absorption at 5.85 μ, the amide I bond at 6.06 μ, and the characteristic amide II absorption at 6.55 μ. The mechanism of the reaction was undoubtedly a transamidation like the following:

$$R—CO—NH_2 + NH_2—R'—CONH_2 \rightarrow$$
$$R—CO—NH—R'—CONH_2 + NH_3$$

This is similar to the classical transesterification that has been used in preparative organic chemistry for peptide bond synthesis [28]. In the latter case it is possible to react peptide esters (which are also anhydrides) to obtain polypeptides.

The conditions used in the polyaspartic acid synthesis just discussed may be a little drastic for what is believed to have been the nature of the primitive Earth (see Chap. 3). However, this experiment does show that the amide bond (an anhydride linkage) could have been employed prebiologically for the production of peptide bonds (other examples are listed in Table 5-6). The problem of random bonding in trifunctional amino acids will be brought up again in more detail at the end of the chapter.

Dehydrating coreactants

Other than the use of high-energy reactants, another approach to dehydration condensation has been the use of coreactants able to incorporate the water byproduct into their own chemical structure (see Fig. 5-2). The central role of cyanide in chemical evolution has already been emphasized. For example, nitriles were apparently key intermediates in the synthesis of amino acids by sparking of hypothetically primitive gaseous mixtures [29]. As we shall discover later in this chapter, peptides have also been detected as products of this reaction. In the previous chapter it was noted that polymers of amino acids are produced upon the heating of ammonium cyanide [30]. In a typical reaction, HCN (1.5 M) in aqueous ammonia (1.5 M) was heated at 90°C. The reaction mixture yielded a black amorphous (polymer-like) product when extracted with warm water. Upon hydrolysis, the polymer was found to contain many amino acids, as discussed earlier. There was no optical activity in the amino acid portion of the product, indicating that racemization had taken place. If radioactively labeled glycine, methionine, or alanine was added to the initial reactants, the radioactivity was found incorporated into the polymer product. This would suggest that at least part of the polymer was formed after amino acid synthesis, and this implies a dehydration process. Infrared spectrometry disclosed the presence of peptide bonds. Much urea was also obtained.* From these results it was deduced that cyanide may have served not only as an intermediate in amino acid synthesis but also as a coreactant leading to the dehydration condensation necessary for peptide bond synthesis [31,32] (see Fig. 5-11). The advantage of this procedure in the context of chemical evolution is that it occurs in the presence of an excess of water, as does contemporary metabolism. If HCN were the condensing agent, formamide would be the hydrated by-product of the dehydration reaction, as follows:

$$\text{HCN} \xrightarrow{\text{H}_2\text{O}} \text{H}\overset{\overset{\displaystyle O}{\|}}{-}\text{C}-\text{NH}_2$$

In a related experiment, an aqueous solution of ammonium thiocyanate and formaldehyde yielded amino acids and peptides after several hours at room temperature [33]. That both reactants could have been present on the primitive Earth was discussed in the previous chapter.

The reaction scheme outlined in Fig. 5-11 resembles the mechanism by which the dialkylcarbodiimides (R—N=C=N—R') mediate dehydration condensation [34]. These latter compounds have been used extensively in preparative organic chemistry to synthesize phosphate esters of nucleosides, polynucleotides (phosphodiesters), polypeptides, phosphoramidates, lactones, carboxylic esters, cyclic phosphates, pyrophosphates, and mixed acid anhydrides [34]. Although these syntheses have usually been carried out in nonaqueous solvents, it has also been demonstrated that peptide synthesis using substituted carbodiimides can be achieved in the presence of water [35]. The production of polyglycine with dialkylcarbodiimides gives the best yields at a low pH [35]. Similarly, phosphate esters have been synthesized in the presence of water using disubstituted carbodiimides [34]. In some of these phosphoryla-

---

* Urea is the hydrolysis product of cyanamide. It is interesting to note that urea was also observed in the sparking reactions discussed in Chap. 4.

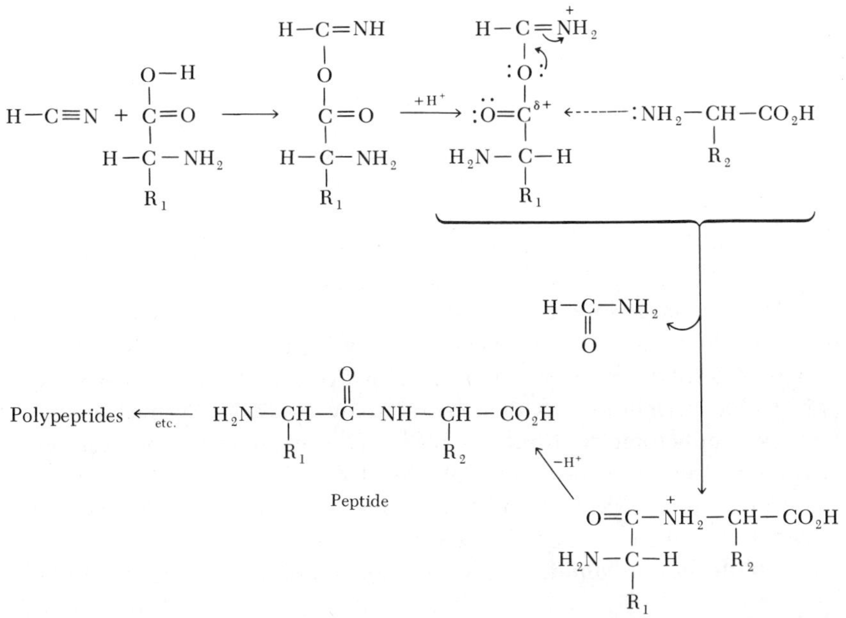

$$H-C\equiv N \;+\; \underset{\underset{R_1}{\overset{|}{H-C-NH_2}}}{\overset{\overset{O-H}{|}}{C=O}} \longrightarrow \underset{\underset{R_1}{\overset{|}{H-C-NH_2}}}{\overset{\overset{\overset{H-C=NH}{|}}{O}}{C=O}} \xrightarrow{+H^+} \underset{\underset{R_1}{\overset{|}{H_2N-C-H}}}{\overset{\overset{\overset{H-C\equiv\overset{+}{N}H_2}{|}}{:O:}}{:O=C^{\delta+}}} \longleftarrow\cdots\cdots \underset{R_2}{\overset{|}{:NH_2-CH-CO_2H}}$$

$$\overset{\overset{H-C-NH_2}{\|}}{O}$$

$$\text{Polypeptides} \xleftarrow[\text{etc.}]{} \underset{\underset{R_1}{\overset{|}{H_2N-CH}}}{} - \overset{\overset{O}{\|}}{C} - NH - \underset{\underset{R_2}{\overset{|}{CH}}}{} - CO_2H$$

$$\text{Peptide}$$

$$\xrightarrow{-H^+} \underset{\underset{R_1}{\overset{|}{H_2N-C-H}}}{O=C-\overset{+}{N}H_2} - \underset{R_2}{\overset{|}{CH}} - CO_2H$$

FIG. 5-11   Suggested mechanism by which cyanide could act as an agent for promoting dehydration condensation [32].

tions, partially aqueous environments were actually advantageous since they enhanced the solubility of the reactants.

However, from the standpoint of chemical evolution there is little reason to suppose that any significant quantity of complex alkyl carbodiimides was present on the primitive Earth.   One possibility, however, is that hydrogen cyanide may have acted as an agent in promoting dehydration condensation.   As indicated in Fig. 5-11, the suggested ability of cyanide to induce peptide formation, on the possibly related basis of the organic chemical use of substituted carbodiimides as condensing agents, would yield formamide ($HCO-NH_2$) as a side product.   In this way, the unwanted water molecule would be removed chemically from the appropriate sites on the reacting molecules.   Such a reaction may have been involved in the production of peptides from the heating of ammonium cyanide solutions as well as in the electron bombardment of hypothetical primitive atmospheres discussed earlier.

Another related candidate for a primordial condensing agent which may operate by a mechanism similar to that presented in Fig. 5-11 is cyanamide, a compound which is hydrolyzed relatively slowly in water and is in fact the tautomer of carbodiimide itself (see Fig. 5-12).

Slightly acid solutions of cyanamide are stable for several months [36].   Urea is produced upon hydrolysis (see Fig. 5-13).   In basic solutions, cyanamide dimerizes to dicyandiamide (DCDA).   Aqueous solu-

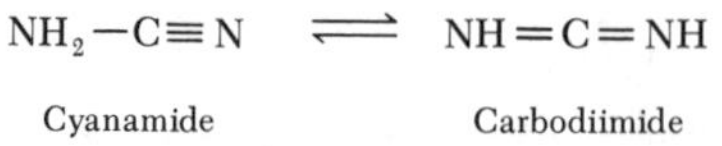

$$NH_2-C\equiv N \rightleftharpoons NH=C=NH$$

Cyanamide   Carbodiimide

FIG. 5-12 Tautomerism of cyanamide to carbodiimide. There is evidence that both forms exist in an aqueous solution [44] although the exact position of the equilibrium apparently depends on the conditions of the medium [45].

tions of DCDA are neutral and decompose very slowly [37]. The hydrolysis of this compound yields guanylurea, a strong base.

Another important relative of cyanamide is dicyanamide (DCA), the dinitrile of iminodicarboxylic acid [38]. Free DCA is difficult to isolate since it tends to polymerize. However, its sodium salt is reasonably stable in solution, as demonstrated by conductivity measurements and spectrophotometric titrations [38]. Dicyanamide exhibits the properties of a strong acid, with a pK of -0.8 [39].

Compounds able to supply an active hydrogen can add across the nitrile function of this group of compounds. For example, hydrazine reacts with dicyandiamide to give aminobiguanide (see Fig. 5-13) [40].

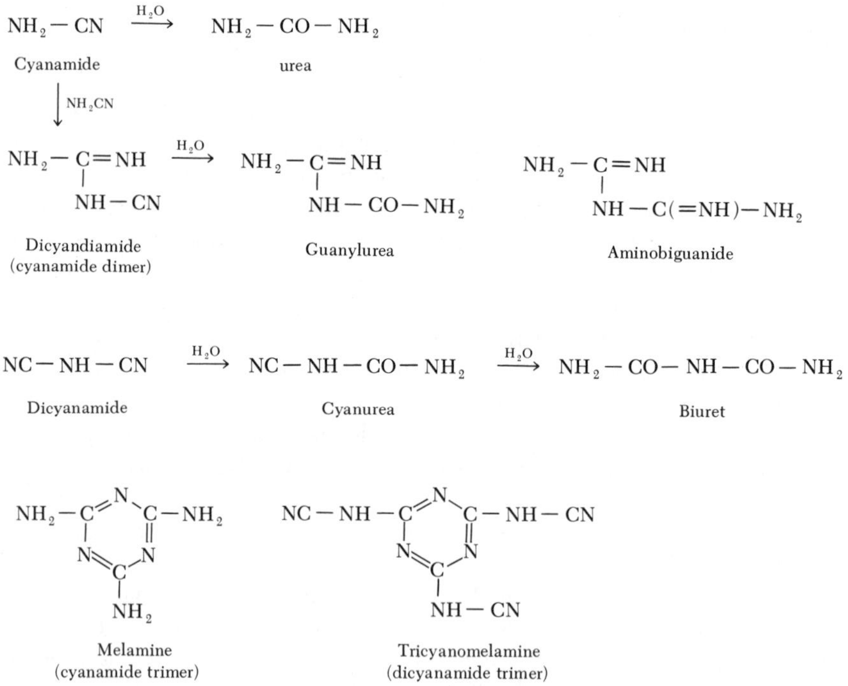

$$NH_2-CN \xrightarrow{H_2O} NH_2-CO-NH_2$$

Cyanamide   urea

$$\downarrow NH_2CN$$

$$NH_2-\underset{NH-CN}{C=NH} \xrightarrow{H_2O} NH_2-\underset{NH-CO-NH_2}{C=NH} \quad\quad NH_2-\underset{NH-C(=NH)-NH_2}{C=NH}$$

Dicyandiamide   Guanylurea   Aminobiguanide
(cyanamide dimer)

$$NC-NH-CN \xrightarrow{H_2O} NC-NH-CO-NH_2 \xrightarrow{H_2O} NH_2-CO-NH-CO-NH_2$$

Dicyanamide   Cyanurea   Biuret

Melamine   Tricyanomelamine
(cyanamide trimer)   (dicyanamide trimer)

FIG. 5-13 Structures and relationships of some cyanamide derivatives discussed in the text. Cyanamide, dicyanamide, dicyandiamide, and tricyanomelamine are able to tautomerize to carbodiimide forms but only the first three have been shown to promote peptide synthesis so far [49].

Dicyanamide has the advantage over dicyandiamide of being able to take up 2 moles of water into its structure as compared to 1 mole with the latter compound (NH_2—CO—NH—CO—NH_2 versus NH_2—C(=NH)—CO—NH_2, respectively) [39].

Several observations have been made which would suggest that cyanamide and related compounds may have been available on the primitive Earth. That these compounds could have been present was demonstrated by their production with electron-beam irradiation of methane-ammonia-water mixtures and by the ultraviolet irradiation of aqueous NH_4CN [41]. The trimer of cyanamide, melamine, has been reported in the Orgueil meteorite [42] (it is known that cyanamide and dicyandiamide are converted to melamine at high temperatures [37,43]). It has been pointed out in many of the cases we have discussed thus far that nitriles appear quite readily in simulated primitive atmosphere experiments.

The experiments to be discussed, in which the cyanamides were employed, have held to certain restrictions set up in an attempt to simulate and duplicate chemical evolution [46]. These included (1) simple, relatively stable reactants, (2) an aqueous environment, (3) a moderate temperature, and (4) dilute concentrations. The simplicity of these reagents makes them a more realistic selection than the more complex dialkylcarbodiimides. Similarly, they are more stable in aqueous solution than the polymetaphosphates discussed earlier. One would expect the organic compounds being joined by the reaction to persist for a longer period of time under the conditions noted above rather than under the circumstances one would find in a hot perivolcanic environment. That chemical evolution could have taken place in nonaqueous organic solvents seems highly unrealistic. The experiments employing the cyanamides were carried out in compliance with the notion that much of prebiological chemical evolution took place in the primitive oceans (see Chap. 3) and with the related fact that contemporary metabolism occurs in the presence of water.

It has been demonstrated that peptide bond synthesis can in fact be promoted by the cyanamides. The first observation in this connection demonstrated that dicyandiamide (DCDA) can mediate the condensation of alanine to form alanylalanine [47]. A yield on the order of 1 percent (in terms of initial alanine) was obtained using dicyandiamide (0.01 M) in an aqueous solution of alanine (0.01 M) and HCl (0.01 N). DCDA was used here because of its relation to cyanamide and its proposed ability to tautomerize to a carbodiimide in a manner similar to that of cyanamide (Figs. 5-12 and 5-13).

Enhanced yields were achieved when dicyanamide (DCA) was employed as the condensing agent instead of DCDA [48]. Under similar conditions, DCA gave about 3 times as much dipeptide as DCDA. The ^{14}C-labeled products were identified by paper chromatography and

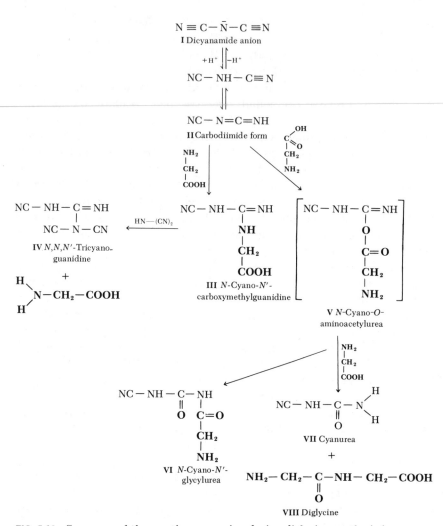

FIG. 5-14 Summary of the reactions occurring during diglycine synthesis in aqueous solutions of glycine, sodium dicyanamide, and HCl [39].

electrophoresis using known standards and were quantified by scintillation spectrometry.

The mechanism by which dicyanamide mediates dipeptide synthesis was studied in detail [39]. The results suggested the mechanism for diglycine synthesis given in Fig. 5-14. This was concluded from the following evidence:

1. The yield of dipeptide increases as the pH of the medium is decreased. Comparative yield studies of DCA-mediated synthesis of

diglycine from glycine and of tetraglycine from diglycine (glycine and diglycine have different carboxyl pK values) at different pH's demonstrated that an undissociated amino acid carboxyl group is required. Also, at pH values significantly below the carboxyl pK of glycine the dipeptide yield continues to increase, suggesting that protonation of the dicyanamide (I) is also necessary.

2. Tautomerism of the DCA would give a carbodiimide form (II) of the compound, assumed to be the reactive species.

3. Diglycine accumulation after addition of the condensing agent was followed as a function of time. The reaction appeared to stop within a few minutes, long before all of the glycine had been used up. Vapor pressure osmometry studies revealed that a large molality drop (larger than could be accounted for by the dipeptide synthesis) paralleled the deceleration of glycylglycine production. The same molality effect was observed if methylamine replaced the amino acid. Through the use of radioactively labeled DCA it was found that this phenomenon is due to an amine-catalyzed dimerization of the condensing agent to a compound (IV) inactive in dipeptide synthesis under the conditions of the experiment. An amine adduct between the glycine and the dicyanamide (III) was found to serve as the intermediate in this reaction. Both compounds III and IV were identified by IR spectrophotometry and by partial degradation to known standards.

4. A rearranged acylurea (VI) was identified by independent synthesis as one of the side products of the reaction. The appearance of this compound supported the proposed acylisourea intermediate (V) of the dipeptide synthesis, formed by addition of the amino acid's carboxyl group across the diimide system of the dicyanamide.

5. Identification of cyanurea (VII), using a known standard, as another side product suggested that this hydrolysis product of dicyanamide represented the compound incorporating the water withdrawn to form the peptide bond of diglycine (VIII).

Therefore, if the amino group of the glycine reacts with the DCA, the condensing agent is catalytically dimerized by the amino acid. On the other hand, if the carboxyl group of the glycine adds to the carbodiimide form of the dicyanamide, an unstable intermediate is produced which can either rearrange to a substituted urea by-product or receive another glycine to yield the dipeptide.

It is apparent that the dimerization of the dicyanamide is second order in the condensing agent, whereas the production of dipeptide is second order in the amino acid. Thus, one would expect to minimize the undesirable dimerization of the condensing agent and maximize dipeptide synthesis by keeping the concentration of the dicyanamide low.

This was in fact achieved by slowly adding the DCA to a solution of the amino acids instead of adding it all at once. This would serve to duplicate the hypothetical primordial phenomenon whereby dicyanamide was continuously produced in the upper atmosphere, gradually washed into the aqueous phase by rain or transported by simple diffusion, and utilized in peptide coupling of the amino acids already in the aqueous body. The results of this experiment are noted in Fig. 5-15 [39]. (Also see Fig. 4-15.)

It is apparent that the cyanamides have overcome the thermodynamic problem encountered in promoting a dehydration condensation reaction in a dilute, aqueous solution. These compounds *preferentially* react with the organic substances to be united rather than directly with the water molecules available in large excess. The use of cyanamides in other dehydration condensations of biological interest, such as lipogenesis, is summarized in Table 5-5.

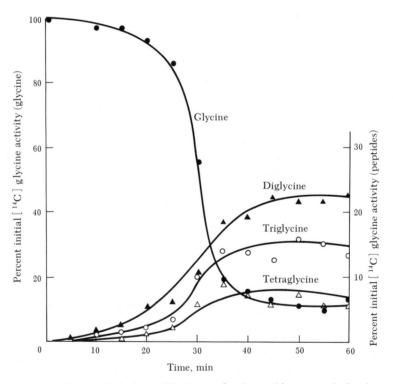

FIG. 5-15   Rates of glycine utilization and polypeptide accumulation in a solution initially containing 2-^{14}C glycine (0.005 M) and HCl (0.1 M). Sodium dicyanamide (in 0.1 M aqueous solution) was added to the reaction mixture by means of a dropping buret at the rate of 0.68 mgm/min for 1 hr. Samples were withdrawn periodically and analyzed by paper electrophoresis [39].

TABLE 5-5 Additional dehydration condensations which have been promoted by simple cyanamide derivatives in aqueous solution* [46,49]

Class	Starting materials	Condensing agents	Condensed product
A. Phosphate ester	1. Adenosine, H_3PO_4	DCDA	Adenosine-5'-phosphate
	2. Ribose, H_3PO_4	DCDA	Ribose-5-phosphate
	3. Glucose, H_3PO_4	DCDA, DCA	Glucose-6-phosphate
	4. Serine, H_3PO_4	DCDA	O-Phosphoserine
	5. Glycerol, H_3PO_4	DCDA	Glycerol-1-phosphate
B. Acid anhydride	1. H_3PO_4	DCDA	Pyrophosphate
	2. Adenosine diphosphate, H_3PO_4	DCDA	Adenosine triphosphate
C. Carboxylic ester	Glycerol, CH_3COOH	DCDA, DCA	Glycerol-1-acetate

* DCA = sodium dicyanamide, DCDA = dicyandiamide. Although most of the syntheses listed have been carried with DCDA as the condensing agent, this should not be taken to mean that DCA was not successful, but rather that the parallel experiment was not performed.

Radiation

Certain amino acids have side-chain groups which absorb light in the range of 2400 to 2800 Å. It was found that such amino acids give higher dipeptide yields in DCA-mediated dimerization upon illumination of the reaction medium while the condensing agent was being added than if the radiation (2537 Å from germicidal UV lamps) was absent [50]. For example, the yield of ditryptophan was almost doubled with (as compared to without) illumination. This did not appear to be due primarily to an effect on the dicyanamide since the yield of glycylglycine decreased 10 percent when radiation was applied to the synthetic process (glycine is essentially transparent at this wavelength). The decrease may have been due to deamination of the amino acid (a known phenomenon under these conditions [51]) or to mild degradation of the DCA (which absorbs weakly at this wavelength). In any case, UV did augment DCA-mediated peptide synthesis involving amino acids which can absorb this energy. UV has also been used in conjunction with the coupling of nonabsorbing amino acids by DCDA [52], but on the basis of the experiments just discussed, this probably led to a decreased dipeptide yield.

Another dehydration condensation in aqueous solution which has also been promoted by the application of ultraviolet radiation and has been especially successful is the synthesis of nucleosides [46,53]. When ultraviolet light was applied to an aqueous solution of a heterocyclic base, such as adenine, plus ribose (or deoxyribose) and a phosphorus source, such as polymetaphosphate or $NH_4H_2PO_4$, nucleosides resulted.

Adenine was selected for detailed study for the following reasons:

1. In previous simulation experiments, more adenine was obtained than any other base.

2. Adenine has the largest absorption cross section between 2400 and 2900 Å of any of the heterocyclic bases of biological importance.
3. Adenine is the most stable of the nucleic acid bases in the presence of ultraviolet radiation.
4. It has relatively long-lived electronic excited states.
5. It has the greatest resonance energy of all the naturally occurring bases.
6. Adenine's excitation energy is readily transferred [53].

By this method, compounds bearing similar properties to adenosine and deoxyadenosine have been synthesized. The ultraviolet source was a low-pressure germicidal mercury lamp emitting a predominant wavelength of 2537 Å. Carbon-14-labeled base was used to aid in the detection of the products. The reaction was carried out in a Vycor or fused silica vessel with high transmittance at 2537 Å. Since adenine has an absorption maximum of 2590 Å, radiation supplied by the mercury lamp acted to excite electrons in the base. In the adenosine synthesis, 10^8 ergs/cm^2 was supplied to the reaction mixture containing adenine $(4.3 \times 10^{-3} M)$, ribose $(8.6 \times 10^{-3} M)$, and H_3PO_4 $(2.9 \times 10^{-2} M)$ during 1 hr [53]. The synthesis was successful whether or not oxygen was present. Typically, a yield of 0.01 percent adenosine (in terms of initial adenine) was identified by paper chromatography and quantified by liquid scintillation spectrometry. In this investigation, the remarkable observation was made that no adenosine was formed when orthophosphate was absent from the reaction mixture, even though the product (adenosine) does not contain phosphate. In the synthesis of a compound resembling deoxyadenosine, it was found that the phosphate could be replaced by a cyanide ion, cyanamide, or magnesium [53]. The reason for this has likewise not been explained as yet, and some question has arisen as to the actual identity of the product. Cyanide may function in this reaction as a condensing agent undergoing hydrolysis to formamide, which in turn is hydrolyzed to ammonium formate, as suggested earlier. The function of the phosphate or the magnesium is unknown. In the deoxyadenosine synthesis, yields on the order of 5 percent were obtained after 2 hr of irradiation; when cyanide was employed, it was possible to obtain yields of 1 percent even without ultraviolet irradiation by allowing the solution to stand at room temperature for 3 days [53]. This observation tends to corroborate the earlier suggestion that cyanide was a functional reagent in simple dehydration condensations taking place on the primitive Earth.

When polymetaphosphate ethyl ester was used in place of the orthophosphate in these experiments, phosphate-containing products also resulted [54]. For example, adenosine monophosphate was obtained upon the UV irradiation of an aqueous solution containing adenine, ribose, and polymetaphosphate. When this experiment was repeated using nucleosides as starting materials, small amounts of AMP, ADP, and ATP (the mono-, di-, and triphosphates of adenosine) were obtained [54]. The instability of polymetaphosphate (PMP) in water, which we discussed earlier, may account for the low yields noted in these experiments.

5-4 FURTHER PEPTIDE SYNTHESES EMPLOYING CYANIDE

In Chap. 4 it was brought out several times that cyanide may well have played a central role in the prebiological production of biomonomers. In the present chapter, several examples have been cited in which cyanide or some of its simple derivatives could have also had a function in the polymerization of these biomonomers. A number of other related reactions where polymers (peptides, in particular) of biological interest are synthesized have also been investigated in the context of possible primitive Earth events. Although these latter experiments may bear much in common with several of those already discussed, they have been reserved for special discussion here. In these syntheses it appears that cyanide could have served as both the building material and the condensing agent for the monomers. One example is the peptide production resulting from the heating or ultraviolet irradiation of ammonium cyanide solutions discussed earlier [30,55]. As another case in point, the sparking of the gaseous mixture of methane, ammonia, hydrogen, and water was repeated [56]. Several ninhydrin-positive products were again observed after several hours of sparking, including aspartic acid, threonine, serine, glutamic acid, glycine, alanine, isoleucine, leucine, and lysine. These results are very similar to those we noted in Chap. 4. However, some of the products isolated in the aqueous phase gave a positive starch-iodine test for peptides. One, in particular, after hydrolysis, yielded glycine and isoleucine in a 2:1 ratio, plus one other unidentified amino acid. Another peptide contained glycine and alanine in a 5:1 ratio with a trace of isoleucine. As before, the concentration of cyanide increased with time of sparking. It may be that this is the key to the polymerization reaction.

Similar results were obtained when only methane and ammonia were sparked initially, followed by mild hydrolysis [57]. This appears to be the result of a polymer representing a polypeptide precursor being synthesized in the sparking portion of the synthesis and then hydrolyzed to a molecule containing a number of peptide bonds. It is likely that hydrogen cyanide and other nitriles played key roles as intermediates. In the actual experiment, the methane and ammonia were initially dried by being passed through anhydrous NaOH. Sparking was carried out for 6 hr. Hydrogen, nitrogen, hydrogen cyanide, acetylene, ethylene,

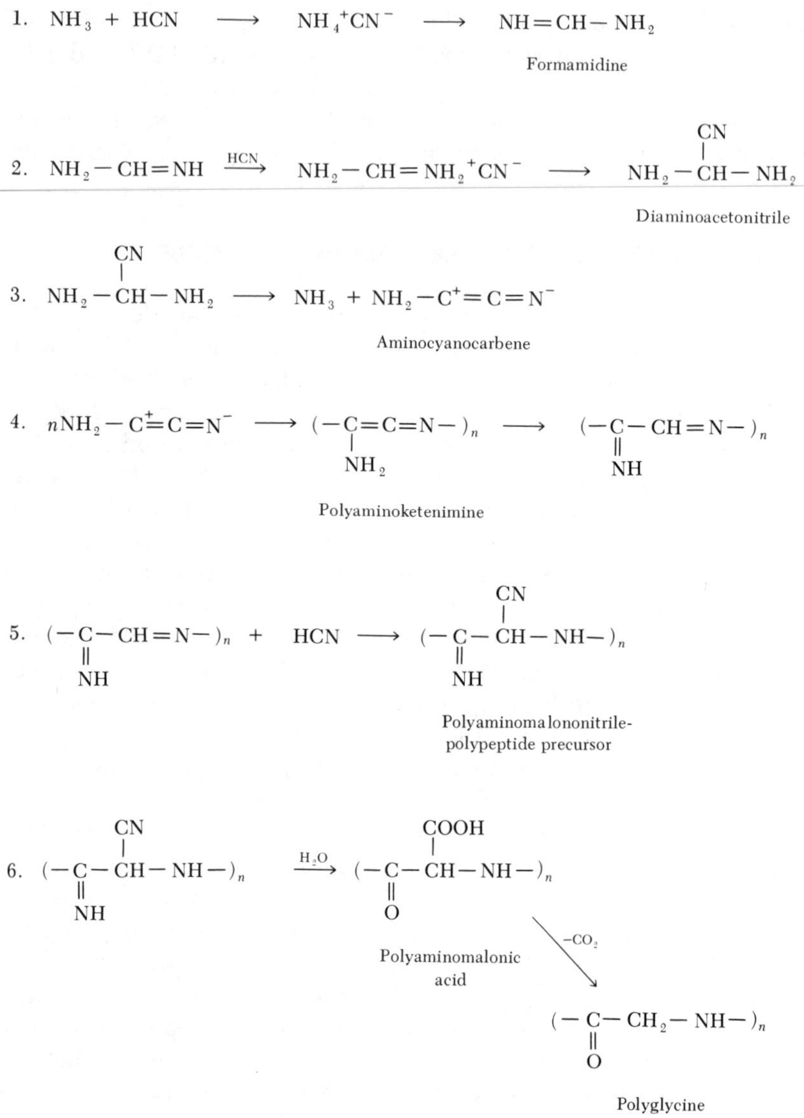

1. $NH_3 + HCN \longrightarrow NH_4^+CN^- \longrightarrow NH=CH-NH_2$

   Formamidine

2. $NH_2-CH=NH \xrightarrow{HCN} NH_2-CH=NH_2^+CN^- \longrightarrow NH_2-\underset{\underset{CN}{|}}{C}H-NH_2$

   Diaminoacetonitrile

3. $NH_2-\underset{\underset{CN}{|}}{C}H-NH_2 \longrightarrow NH_3 + NH_2-C^+=C=N^-$

   Aminocyanocarbene

4. $n NH_2-C^{\pm}=C=N^- \longrightarrow (-\underset{\underset{NH_2}{|}}{C}=C=N-)_n \longrightarrow (-\underset{\underset{NH}{||}}{C}-CH=N-)_n$

   Polyaminoketenimine

5. $(-\underset{\underset{NH}{||}}{C}-CH=N-)_n + HCN \longrightarrow (-\underset{\underset{NH}{||}}{C}-\underset{\overset{CN}{|}}{C}H-NH-)_n$

   Polyaminomalononitrile-
   polypeptide precursor

6. $(-\underset{\underset{NH}{||}}{C}-\underset{\overset{CN}{|}}{C}H-NH-)_n \xrightarrow{H_2O} (-\underset{\underset{O}{||}}{C}-\underset{\overset{COOH}{|}}{C}H-NH-)_n$

   Polyaminomalonic
   acid

   $\xrightarrow{-CO_2} (-\underset{\underset{O}{||}}{C}-CH_2-NH-)_n$

   Polyglycine

FIG. 5-16 Mechanism suggested to explain the observed synthesis of polypeptides from HCN with NH_3 catalysis [57]. Steps 1 to 5 are believed to occur in the anhydrous phase, whereas step 6 requires an aqueous medium. Step 4 employs the cyanide dimer (see text for details).

and ethane were also observed as products. The subsequent hydrolysis was done in 0.1 N HCl for 30 min at 100°C. Following hydrolysis in 6 N HCl, a number of amino acids were identified, including lysine, histidine, aspartic acid, threonine, serine, glycine, alanine, and isoleucine.

In a related experiment, in which anhydrous HCN and liquid ammonia were left at room temperature for 48 hr, products believed to be peptides were again observed [57]. Since the peptide precursors in this case were synthesized in the absence of water, it is suggested that this method provides an alternative to the Strecker mechanism of amino acid synthesis (discussed earlier) since no aldehydes are necessary as intermediates in the present reaction. The mechanism noted in Fig. 5-16 has been proposed for this reason. This model of peptide synthesis is to be contrasted with others that have been discussed involving nitrile compounds. A key point here is that the peptide backbone precursor is synthesized in the absence of water as a result of cyanide polymerization and not of dehydration condensation. The subsequent hydration step produces the peptide bond, and further interaction with cyanide yields the other characteristic amino acid side chains. In other words, the amino acids themselves only appear as amino acids when the peptide bond is formed rather than being united by a dehydration condensation reaction. The problems encountered with this model will be discussed at the end of the chapter.

5-5 MELANIN: A UNIQUE CASE

As discussed above, all of the four major kinds of biopolymers are synthesized in contemporary living things by means of a single, characteristic type of chemical reaction, namely, dehydration condensation. There is, however, a fifth kind of biopolymer of widespread occurrence in contemporary living nature which does not conform to the general pattern of synthesis by dehydration condensation. This class of biopolymer is comprized of a heterogeneous group of brownish or black insoluble materials collectively known as the *melanic pigments,* or *melanins.* The black pigments of certain bacteria and fungi (e.g., *B. niger*) and of the famous moth of industrial melanism, *Biston betularia,* the brown substance which forms on apple slices, the dense black ink by means of which the squid *Loligo opalescens* evades its predators, the black and brown pigments of hair, and the brown pigments of freckles and moles (as well as of suntan) are examples of the variety of biological settings in which the melanic pigments are found [58].

It has been known for many years that the aromatic amino acid tyrosine,

$$HO-\left\langle\underset{}{\bigcirc}\right\rangle-CH_2-\underset{\underset{NH_2}{|}}{CH}-COOH$$

is the starting material for the biosynthesis of the melanic polymers [59]. The results of recent investigations strongly suggest that enzymes are involved only in the first two steps of melanin synthesis in vivo, in particular in the conversion of tyrosine to 3,4-dihydroxyphenylalanine (DOPA) and in the conversion of DOPA

$$HO-\langle\bigcirc\rangle-CH_2-\underset{\underset{NH_2}{|}}{CH}-COOH$$
(with HO on lower left)

to the unstable free-radical species DOPA-semiquinone [60,61]

$$\cdot O-\langle\bigcirc\rangle-CH_2-\underset{\underset{NH_2}{|}}{CH}-COOH$$
(with ${}^-O$ on lower left)

Apparently, once DOPA-semiquinone is formed, free-radical reactions occur spontaneously, leading to the formation of a complex set of intermediates and ultimately, via a number of cross reactions, to the high-molecular-weight melanic polymer. Melanins exhibit stable electron-spin resonance signals indicating the presence of trapped, unpaired electrons within the polymer particles, presumably left over from the free-radical polymerization reactions [60,61].

The molecular architecture of the melanic pigments has been investigated in detail by Nicolaus and his coworkers [60]. The principal biological source of the material for their studies was the cuddlefish (genus, *Sepia*). These investigators degraded the melanic polymer in a variety of ways, including treatment with $KMnO_4$, Br_2–NaOH, and H_2O_2, and identified the low-molecular-weight degradation products by means of paper chromatography. On the basis of these studies, Nicolaus concluded that melanins are cross-linked heteropolymers of a number of different monomers including 5,6-indolequinone, 5,6-indolequinol, the 2′-carboxyl derivatives of these, and various pyrrole carboxylic acids. He concluded further that the monomers are bonded to each other through a variety of covalent linkages such as

—C—C—   —C—O—C—   —C—O—O—C—

and hydrogen bonds of the type

$$\overset{\diagdown}{\underset{\diagup}{}}NH\cdots O=C\overset{\diagup}{\underset{\diagdown}{}}$$

These results allow the construction of an average partial molecular structure statistically representative of the type of order present in natural melanins. Such a structure is shown in Ref. 60.

The widespread natural occurrence of the melanic pigments, together with the fact that they are synthesized in vivo by means of largely nonenzymatic processes involving free radicals, suggests that these polymers are very primitive and, in fact, might have been produced in the primitive oceans during prebiological chemical evolution. Since aromatic amino acids absorb ultraviolet radiation of wavelengths between 2500 and 2800 Å and since such radiation was probably a principal free-energy source at the surface of the primitive Earth (see Chap. 3), a relevant simulation experiment would consist simply of the ultraviolet irradiation of a dilute aqueous solution of an aromatic amino acid.   Such experiments have in fact been performed with the commonly occurring aromatic amino acids phenylalanine, tyrosine, and tryptophan as starting materials [61].   In a typical irradiation experiment, a 0.01 M aqueous solution of DL-phenylalanine

$$\langle\text{\textcircled{}}\rangle-CH_2-\underset{\underset{NH_2}{|}}{CH}-COOH$$

was subjected to UV radiation from a low-pressure mercury arc lamp (maximum output at 2537 Å).   During the irradiation the solution was continuously bubbled with nitrogen containing small amounts of O_2 ($\approx$ 100 to 200 ppm).   This procedure resulted in the appearance of a dark red-brown pigment which eventually settled to the bottom of the reaction vessel under prolonged irradiation.   More recently it has been shown that if the solution is continuously flushed with a special grade of highly purified N_2 (less than 8 ppm O_2) during irradiation, no pigmentation or precipitate is formed.   Therefore, small amounts of molecular oxygen are required for pigment production.   However, if the solution is saturated with molecular oxygen during the run, faint yellow pigmentation develops but then disappears upon prolonged irradiation.   This effect has been shown to be due to formation and subsequent photooxidation of the pigment to colorless substances.

Evidence that the pigmented product is a high-molecular-weight substance was obtained in a series of dialysis experiments [61].   Solutions of ^{14}C-labeled DL-phenylalanine were irradiated at 2537 Å with doses sufficient to produce the maximum amount of pigmentation. When the irradiated solutions were dialyzed, it was found that the radioactivity was lost from the dialysis bag at much lower rates than that observed in a control experiment with unirradiated phenylalanine.

More detailed characterization of the pigment required workable amounts of purified material.   Several hundred milligrams of the red-brown insoluble pigment were produced and collected in a large-scale irradiation experiment [61].   The product was purified by dialysis followed by freeze drying.   Characterization of the resulting material by infrared absorption spectroscopy (in KBr pellets) and electron-spin resonance spectroscopy yielded results virtually identical to those obtained in a similar manner from authentic samples of natural melanin and a synthetic melanin prepared by autoxidation of DOPA.   From these data, it was concluded that the brown pigment produced in UV-irradiated solutions of phenylalanine is very similar to natural melanin. Further evidence corroborating this view was provided by kinetic data which indicated that tyrosine was an intermediate in the synthesis of the pigment [61] from phenylalanine. In addition, detailed investigations utilizing phenylalanine labeled with ^{14}C at specific sites showed that loss of the carboxyl group of the amino acid, presumably via decarboxylation, is a principal photochemical process occurring in the irradiated solutions.

Decarboxylation is also a principal reaction in the proposed scheme for in vivo synthesis of melanins [60,62]. Therefore, it appears likely that the production of melanin-like polymers in UV-irradiated solutions of phenylalanine proceeds by reactions similar to those which occur in the in vivo pathways. However, a major difference between the two sets of reactions is that in the case of the UV-irradiated solutions, several side products are formed, such as aspartic acid, aminomalonic acid, phenyllactic acid, and β-phenylethylamine. Thus, the UV-promoted in vitro system is less efficient than the in vivo system with respect to the extent of conversion of the starting material into melanic polymer.

Many simple aromatic compounds besides phenylalanine can serve as starting materials for the production of nitrogenous or nonnitrogenous high-molecular-weight melanin-like polymers under very simple conditions [61]. A partial list of such compounds includes tyrosine, DOPA, tryptophan, adrenalin, noradrenalin, phenol, catechol, resorcinol, hydroquinone, and benzene. The process appears to be a quite general one requiring only small amounts of molecular oxygen, a suitable free-energy source such as UV radiation of γ rays, and a simple aromatic compound capable of undergoing oxidation to a semiquinone free radical.

Although aromatic amino acids have generally not been detected as products in primitive atmosphere simulation experiments, we indicated one piece of evidence in Chap. 4 suggesting that both phenylalanine and tyrosine are produced in mixtures of methane, ammonia, and water vapor heated to very high temperatures. Also, it is known that acetylene trimerizes to benzene at elevated temperatures. Acetylene has been identified in methane subjected to electric discharge. Benzene and toluene have been detected in similar gaseous mixtures first heated to 1000°C in Vycor tubes and then cooled down to room temperature (see Chap. 4). Therefore, it appears likely that the kinds of simple aromatic substances known to give rise to melanin-like polymers upon ultraviolet irradiation could have arisen on the prebiotic Earth.

On the basis of the lines of evidence discussed above it has been suggested that deposits of melanin-like polymers might have accumulated in the primitive oceans during prebiological chemical evolution. What roles such deposits might have played in chemical evolution is

virtually impossible to determine since so little is known about the biological functions of contemporary melanins (except in those instances
in which the pigment plays an obvious role in protective coloration,
such as in the melanic races of *Biston betularia*). One possibility, however, is that the polymers might have provided a stable organic matrix
active in the concentration of small organic molecules. The variety of
stereospecific adsorption sites provided by the polymers would presumably have been enormously greater than that of sites provided by relatively much more uniform crystalline mineral surfaces [61].

Several other examples of dehydration condensation and polymerization reactions pertinent to our overall discussion are listed in Table 5-6.

5-6   SPECIAL PROBLEMS

It is evident that the nature of many biological functions is dependent
on the character of products which are synthesized in dehydration condensation reactions. Since it is the purpose of the experiments we have
considered in this book to elucidate plausible means by which events
essential to the appearance of living systems occurred, the nature of
these reactions deserves closer consideration. For example, a protein
is a linear polymer of amino acids which are ordered in very definite
sequences rather than in a random fashion. It is the order, as well
as the types of residues, which distinguishes one protein from another.
If the association of amino acids were a random phenomenon, an infinite
variety of sequences could result. However, a supply of similarly sequenced peptides was undoubtedly required for biogenesis to occur
and be subsequently sustained. When someone speaks of a particular
enzyme in a biological milieu (neglecting isozymes for the moment),
he is referring to a large number of polypeptides with the same amino
acid sequence and, therefore, the same biochemical properties. If only
one such polymer molecule existed, its effect on the overall characteristics of the environment would be essentially inconsequential. Therefore,
it is necessary to uncover means that could have operated on the primitive Earth by which a large number of peptides of the same or similar
sequences were produced.

Most of this discussion will be concerned with polyamino acids
since the greatest amount of work has been done in this area. We
shall examine the possibility that the various means for peptide synthesis reviewed in this chapter could have led to the appearance of biologically pertinent polymers. We shall be concerned with such facets as
reactant stability, bond specificity, and nonrandomness involved in the
methods believed to represent primitive Earth phenomena. It is not
sufficient that a particular method promotes dehydration condensation.
Rather, it must also be determined if the products of the synthesis could

TABLE 5-6 Additional polymerization and dehydration condensation reactions

Class	Reactants	Products	Energy source	Reaction medium	Footnote	Reference
A. Polypeptides	1. Diketopiperazine	Polyglycines	Heat, pressure, anhydride bond	Anhydrous		63
	2. Glycine	Polyglycines	Spark discharge	Aqueous	a	64
	3. Amino acids	Polymers	x-rays, UV, or γ rays	Aqueous	b	65, 66
	4. Diketopiperazine or diglycine	Polyglycine	Heat (180°C for 3–7 hr), anhydride bond	50% H_2O, 50% reactant	c	67
	5. Glycine	Polyglycine	140°C, 18 hr	10 N HCl	d	67
	6. Glycine	Polyglycine (up to 18 units)	Heat (140–160°C)	2 N NH_4OH	e	68
	7. Glycinamide	Polyglycine (up to 40 units)	Heat (100°C), anhydride (amide) bond	2N NH_4OH	f	69
B. Polysaccharides	1. Monosaccharides	Disaccharides	UV	Aqueous	g	49, 70
	2. Monosaccharides	Polysaccharides	γ rays	Aqueous		65
	3. Glucose	h	98°C, 10 hr	0.08 N HCl	h	71
	4. Glucose	Polyglucose	Vacuum; 130°C, 20 hr	i	i	71
C. Polynucleotides	Nucleotides	Polynucleotides	γ rays	Aqueous	j	72

a Done at 0°C in evacuated vessel; gave insoluble polymeric product which upon hydrolysis yielded glycine.

b Product called *polymeric* because of increased viscosity, nondialyzability, and precipitation by cetavlon, TCA, or $(NH_4)_2SO_4$; nature of product undetermined; with x-rays, increase viscosity of product further if also heat to 100°C after illumination; also get deamination as side effect; works only with amino acids with cyclic side chains; suggested mechanism for peptide bond synthesis:

$$R\text{—COOH} \rightarrow R\text{—}\underset{\overset{\|}{O}}{C}\text{—OOH} \xrightarrow[R'-NH_2]{} R'\text{—}\underset{\overset{\|}{O}}{C}\text{—NH—}R' + H_2O_2;$$

with γ irradiation it probably is not the peptide bond that is produced since EPR shows $\cdot CH(NH_3{}^+)COO^-$ when crystalline glycine is illuminated.

c No polymer if glycine or triglycine used as reactant; small yield if done at 60°C; 40 percent yield of polymer after 7 hr if reactant mixture is 90 percent diketopiperazine and 10 percent diglycine, whereas yield is 2.5 percent if no diglycine present; yield was a function of time of heating.

d Polymerization did not occur when other amino acids were used.

e Little or no polymer product if heating carried out in neutral water; product gave positive biuret reaction.

f Both α- and β-polyglycine present; 16.5 percent nondialyzable yield; positive biuret; when done in $8 N$ NH_4OH, 74.8 percent yield resulted, with an average degree of polymerization of 29 units.

g Aided by kaolin (role uncertain).

h Products include gentiobiose, isomaltose, maltose, cellobiose, sophorose, and trehalose, among others.

i H_3PO_3:H_2O:glucose (1:2:200, approx., by weight); product highly branched but 1–6 linkage favored.

j Irradiated nucleotides exhibit hypochromicity which is reversed by RNAase or alkaline hydrolysis; fluorescence similar to nucleic acids; susceptible to phosphodiesterase.

have had the characteristics required for subsequent stages of biogenesis.

Reactant stability

One major problem with the thermal model of chemical evolution is that amino acids are especially susceptible to decomposition at elevated temperatures. For example, it has been shown that the half-life of alanine in aqueous solution is 10^{11} years at $25°C$ and only 30 years at $150°C$ [73,74a]. Modifications of amino acids have also been observed in the dry, solid state. Compounds like pyruvic acid are not very stable even at room temperature.

The activation energy in the degradation of amino acids is between 30,000 and 44,000 cal/mole, the latter value being that for alanine [73]. The primary effect is decarboxylation. For example,

$$NH_2CH(CH_3)COOH \rightarrow NH_2CH_2CH_3 + CO_2\uparrow$$
  Alanine   Ethylamine

The rate of decarboxylation was determined in experiments using radioactively labeled amino acids tagged in the carboxyl carbon. With oxygen present, the degradation rate, because of the added factor of oxidation, increased considerably. From these studies, a number of amino acids have been classified according to their stability. The most stable were found to be alanine, glycine, glutamic acid, leucine, isoleucine, proline, and valine. Moderately stable amino acids are aspartic acid, lysine, and phenylalanine. Serine, threonine, arginine, and tyrosine are relatively unstable (see Fig. 5-17). As yet, the thermal stability of amino acid mixtures has not been studied, even though such an investigation might have relevance to the thermal model of polyamino acid synthesis.

A typical example of amino acid heat instability is shown by the fact that 98 percent of an initial threonine sample decomposed when maintained at $113°C$ for 1 year [74a]. Thus one would not expect a persistence of appreciable levels of amino acids in an elevated temperature environment unless some means were operating which was able to replenish them at a rather high rate. In other words, since amino acids decompose at a significant rate at elevated temperatures, amino acids produced under these conditions are not expected to exist for very long. If the rate of synthesis is not greater than the rate of decomposition, one would not expect any significant accumulation of products under these conditions. However, amino acids do become somewhat more resistant to thermal degradation when mixed with clay minerals, such as montmorillonite [74b].

A similar problem is encountered with the aqueous model of peptide synthesis. Since, as we discussed earlier in this chapter, peptide bonds are thermodynamically unfavored, especially in the presence of

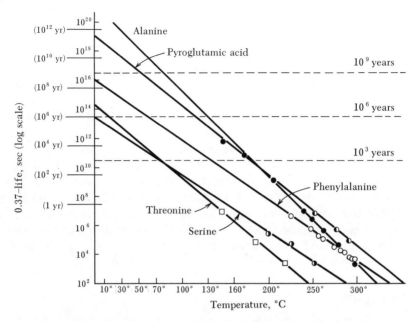

FIG. 5-17 Time-temperature curves for the thermal degradation of selected amino acids in 0.01 M solution contained in oxygen-free sealed tubes [74a]. The rate of decomposition is given as the time needed for 63 percent of a particular amino acid preparation to decompose to something else at the given temperature. In the above graph alanine = ●, pyroglutamic acid = ◐, phenylalanine = ○, threonine = □, and serine = ◑. Similarly, amino acids are unstable when heated in the solid state.

water, it would seem that they would not last very long once produced in a watery milieu. However, one must be careful to distinguish between kinetics and thermodynamics since, as it turns out, peptides are very slow to hydrolyze in an unheated, neutral aqueous solution. This point will be considered again in a later discussion.

It is true that polypeptides of significant length have been produced by the thermal method as well as by the use of the water-unstable polymetaphosphates. On the other hand, the cyanamides have been shown to be quite stable under normal aqueous conditions and are also able to react at moderate temperatures. As yet large polypeptides have not been produced using these latter reagents. However, the assumption is made that given enough time, with the continual production and mixing of the amino acids and condensing agents, polypeptides would eventually result since the bonds linking a polypeptide are of the same chemical nature as that encountered in di- and tripeptides. This is fortified by the observed speed of dicyanamide-mediated peptide synthesis noted earlier in this chapter.

Another factor affecting reactant stability would be the presence of ultraviolet light, as considered in detail in Chap. 3. The absence of a protective ozone layer, as now exists, would have made ultraviolet light a destructive force for many of those compounds originally synthesized with the aid of electromagnetic radiation. However, the collection of these products in water could have served to protect them from the UV. This would give them an advantage over those remaining in a nonaqueous environment. We saw earlier in this chapter that ultraviolet light could have a stimulating effect on those amino acids able to absorb this energy which were participating in peptide bond synthesis. On the other hand, it also leads to some decomposition by deamination of the amino acids dissolved in shallow solutions. It is known that the degree to which UV light, especially $\lambda < 1850$Å, is attenuated rapidly increases as the depth of an aqueous body increases (see Chap. 3). Thus, one would expect less and less decomposition of the reactant amino acids (and also less effect on peptide synthesis) as the location of the compounds in water became deeper and deeper.

Bond specificity

In an earlier discussion we noted that polymerization is a special case of dehydration condensation in which the monomeric units have more than one functional group. For example, nucleotides are characterized by phosphate and hydroxyl groups which join by dehydration to form nucleic acids. Similarly, amino acids possess an amino function and a carboxyl function. Proteins are made up of peptide bonds formed between the carboxyl group and the α-amino function upon the removal of water (see Fig. 5-1). There are a number of amino acids which also contain amino or carboxyl groups in their side chains. The union of a side-chain carboxyl function of one amino acid and the α-amino group of another would represent an unnatural linkage in terms of the majority of present-day naturally occurring proteins. For example, two aspartic acid units [NH$_2$—CH(CH$_2$COOH)—COOH] could unite (if unrestricted) in two ways, as an α-peptide or a β-peptide. Thus we have

$$
\begin{array}{ll}
\text{CH}_2\text{—COOH} & \text{CH}_2\text{—COOH} \\
\quad | & \quad | \\
\text{NH}_2\text{—CH—CO—NH—CH—COOH} &
\end{array}
$$

α-Aspartyl aspartic acid

$$
\begin{array}{l}
\text{CH}_2\text{—COOH} \\
\quad | \\
\text{CH}_2\text{—CO—NH—CH—COOH} \\
\quad | \\
\text{NH}_2\text{—CH—COOH}
\end{array}
$$

β-Aspartyl aspartic acid

The α form is the one most commonly found in biopolymers. In the same sense, if a phosphodiester bond were formed between the number

5 hydroxyl of one nucleoside and the number 2 hydroxyl of another, for example, an unnatural bridge would result (see Fig. 5-1).

It was mentioned in the discussions on pyrocondensation and polynucleotide synthesis using polymetaphosphates that a large percentage of the bonds uniting the monomer units appeared to be unnatural. As yet, a system has not been devised which could have operated under primitive Earth conditions to explain how 3',5'-phosphodiester linkages could have been produced exclusively. According to the results reviewed in Table 5-6, bond randomness is found in polysaccharide synthesis by acid reversion. Similarly, in the pyrocondensation of aspartic acid, for example, close examination yielded evidence of a great deal of side-chain (β) linking in the product, as we saw earlier.

In polypeptide synthesis, in particular, specificity in bonding (for example, α rather than β) would be essential for the development of systems bearing the biochemical properties we know today. This is not to say that the establishment of all the characteristics of contemporary biological entities was essential at the most primitive stages of biogenesis. However, somewhere along the line of evolution the transformation to α linking in peptides had to occur on the basis of what we know of contemporary systems.

In the case of polypeptides, certain experiments have been reported which suggest a means by which α-peptide bonds could have been produced almost exclusively. First of all, a peptide is produced from nonpolar amino acids [75]. Since the side chains of these monomers are unreactive in peptide bond synthesis, only α-peptide bonds would be produced from them. By appropriate reactions, these amino acid units might then undergo conversion to residues with reactive side chains.

It is known that β-hydroxy amino acids are reversibly cleaved in an aqueous solution in the presence of basic catalysts [76]. This reaction could be used to convert glycyl to seryl or threonyl residues. This has been tested by preparing polyglycine in the presence of the clay mineral kaolinite [77]. The combination was mixed with aqueous formaldehyde and basic catalysts, such as K_2CO_3, $NaHCO_3$ or triethylamine, and heated to 60 to 100°C. Hydrolysis of the polymer after several hours of reaction resulted in the liberation of serine, as determined by paper chromatography. Similarly, threonyl residues have been produced using acetaldehyde in place of formaldehyde. In the latter experiment, a threonine-to-allothreonine ratio of 1.8:1 was obtained. When the reaction was carried out at 50°C for 1 hr, a 64 percent yield of threonine residues was produced. With no clay mineral catalyst, no product resulted. It was suggested that the dehydration of serine, followed by reaction with H_2S, could then yield cysteine residues [77]. Similar mechanisms were proposed for the production of other amino acids, involving dehydroalanine [$NH_2—C(=CH_2)—COOH$] as an intermediate.

In the case of dicarboxylic amino acids, it has been demonstrated that electrical discharge promotes the conversion of alanine in aqueous solution into aspartic acid, an amino acid with a reactive side chain [75].* Thus, we could envision first the production of a polypeptide containing some alanine residues. The individual subunits, by interaction with water and carbon dioxide, would then be converted to residues with carboxyl functions in their side chains. Thus,

$$n\,NH_2\!-\!\overset{\overset{\displaystyle CH_3}{|}}{C}H\!-\!COOH \xrightarrow{-H_2O} \left[\!\!-\!\!\overset{\overset{\displaystyle CH_3}{|}}{N}H\!-\!CH\!-\!CO\!-\! \right]_n$$

$$\xrightarrow{CO_2} \left[\!\!-\!\!NH\!-\!\overset{\overset{\displaystyle CH_2\!-\!COOH}{|}}{C}H\!-\!CO\!-\! \right]_n$$

(Corresponding means for the production of amine and sulfhydryl-containing side chains have also been proposed [75].) Since these reactive side-chain functions appear subsequent to the synthesis of the connecting peptide bonds, they would not have interfered with the original polymerization process. The simplicity of such a system suggests that it could have contributed to the course of prebiological chemical evolution.

Nonrandomness

As we discussed earlier in this section, the appearance of biologically essential peptides would have been too improbable and too limited if the union of free amino acids were a completely random process. Given the fact that only a small number of all the possible combinations of the 20 or so different amino acids are found in nature, we must ask ourselves if such sequence specificity could have arisen abiologically, and if so, by what processes and constraints. (This assumes that prebiological amino acid sequencing was not controlled by nucleic acids, as it is today. If it were, means for the ordering of nucleotides would then have to be determined. In either case, a regulating mechanism, either inherent within the uniting monomers or supplied externally, would have had to play a restricting role. Since most of the studies on this problem have been carried out with amino acid polymerization, the emphasis in the present discussion will be centered on it. The question of free amino acid polymerization versus nucleic acid control will be taken up again later.)

If the association of amino acids were a completely random event,

* Such a conversion is plausible in view of the synthesis of alanine ($NH_2CH(CH_3)$-COOH) from CO_2 and ethylamine ($NH_2CH_2CH_3$) upon irradiation by x-rays or 2-Mev electrons [113]. In the synthesis of both alanine and aspartic acid, a carboxylation utilizing gaseous CO_2 as a reactant is involved. This is essentially the reverse of the decarboxylation reaction shown on page 202.

it can readily be seen that there would not be enough mass in the entire Earth, assuming it was composed exclusively of amino acids, to make even one molecule of every possible sequence of the several distinguishable units in a low-molecular-weight protein [78]. However, in the same fashion that the difference in the nature of reactivity of the units of a growing inorganic crystal determines the final constitution of the three-dimensional crystal array, so differences in reactivities of the various amino acids with one another could possibly serve to promote a defined ordering of sequence in a growing peptide chain [79]. In other words, it would appear that the unique nature of each type of amino acid as determined by its side chain could introduce nonrandom constraints into the sequencing process. Therefore, an investigation of the probability of linkage of any one given amino acid to another is in order.

You will recall that polymerization of amino acids into polypeptides has been achieved by heating anhydrous mixtures of these compounds [9]. The amino acid composition of the hydrolyzed polymeric product (called *proteinoid*) prepared from a mixture of 2 parts aspartic acid (by weight), 2 parts glutamic acid, and 1 part of an equimolar mixture of 16 other amino acids (2:2:1) was determined by ion-exchange chromatography. The results noted in Table 5-7 show that aspartic acid is the predominant component of this proteinoid, followed by glutamic acid. Table 5-7 also gives the amino acid composition of a proteinoid produced from a reactant mixture of 2 parts glutamic acid, 2 parts aspartic acid, and 3 parts of the equimolar mixture of the other amino acids (2:2:3). These results together indicate that the composition of the proteinoid products is not necessarily a direct duplication of the composition of the initial reactant mixtures. The relative amounts of the amino acids in the products are quite different from those in the starting materials. This in itself would suggest that the incorporation of units into the polypeptide is not completely random when carried out in the absence of nucleic acids [9].

Further indication of nonrandom association of subunits is provided by analysis of the N-terminus residues of the proteinoids [9]. When the synthesis had been carried out at 160°C, for example, glutamic acid appeared about 8 times as often as aspartic acid in a 2:2:1 proteinoid. Another piece of evidence which tends to indicate some order in the amino acid polymerization based on the nature of the reaction conditions is that the relative amount of incorporated aspartic acid, for example, varies as the time of heating is increased. If the process were random, the relative proportion of aspartic acid in the product at any point in the synthesis would be essentially similar to that found at any other time. On the other hand, the observed variation would suggest that the incorporation of this amino acid is affected by the types of units and the unique physical characteristics (e.g., structure) already a part

TABLE 5-7 Comparison of the composition of selected proteinoids [9a] and a typical natural protein [80]

Amino acid	Proteinoids		Carbonic anhydrase
	2:2:1*	2:2:3*	
Lysine	1.64	5.59	9.12
Histidine	0.95	1.97	5.75
Ammonia	3.60	6.53	1.70
Arginine	0.94	1.87	7.35
Aspartic acid	66.0	50.4	14.71
Glutamic acid	15.8	11.5	11.60
Proline	0.28	...	6.40
Glycine	1.32	2.99	5.40
Alanine	2.30	4.31	4.06
Half-cystine	1.32	2.33	0.34
Valine	0.85	1.81	6.12
Methionine	0.94	2.30	1.60
Isoleucine	0.86	1.77	2.16
Leucine	0.88	1.64	12.40
Tyrosine	0.94	1.99	4.28
Phenylalanine	1.84	3.38	6.95
Total recovery	103	67	100

* For example, a 2:2:1 proteinoid is a polymer produced by
heating at 170°C for 6 hr an anhydrous mixture containing 2
parts (by weight) aspartic acid, 2 parts glutamic acid, and 1
part of an equimolar assortment of 16 other naturally occurring
amino acids. The composition of the dialyzed product was
determined by ion-exchange chromatography following acid
hydrolysis. Values are given in terms of percent by weight of
the residues noted above. Total recovery is the percent of the
total amino acids recovered from the starting polymeric product material.

of the polymer produced. These results would suggest that pyrocondensation of amino acids has some characteristics of nonrandomness which
are influenced by the reaction conditions and the amino acids being
united.

Peptide synthesis as promoted by dicyanamide has also been investigated for evidence of nonrandom associations. Several dipeptide combinations synthesized with the aid of dicyanamide were examined [78].
The results of these experiments indicate that the coupling of selected
amino acids in an aqueous solution, like that in the solid state just discussed, is apparently anything but random (see Table 5-8, first column
of data). Instead, the relative yields in each case are a result of very
definite, unique probabilities. For example, the results in Table 5-8
would indicate that alanine is almost twice as likely to couple with

a glycine as valine with a glycine. Since the primary difference between these two amino acids [NH_2—$CH(R)$—$COOH$] is the size of the nonpolar side chain [R for alanine = CH_3; R for valine = $CH(CH_3)_2$], data in Table 5-8 indicate that these particular amino acids become less reactive with glycine as the size of their side chains increases.

Additional experiments involving the union of amino acids with dipeptides indicated that the unit in the dimer adjacent to the residue forming the peptide bond can also have a small but definite effect on the relative reactivity [78].

Therefore, with a given set of conditions and a given assortment

TABLE 5-8 Comparison of experimentally determined dipeptide yields and frequencies calculated from known protein sequences [50,78]*

Dipeptide	Values (relative to Gly-Gly)		
	Synthetic†	Sequential‡	Random§
Gly-Gly	1.0	1.0	1.0
Gly-Ala	0.8	0.8	0.7
Ala-Gly	0.8	0.7	0.7
Ala-Ala	0.7	0.7	0.5
Gly-Val	0.5	0.2	0.5
Val-Gly	0.5	0.3	0.5
Gly-Leu	0.5	0.3	0.5
Leu-Gly	0.5	0.2	0.5
Gly-Ile	0.3	0.2	0.3
Ile-Gly	0.3	0.1	0.3
Gly-Phe	0.1	0.1	0.3
Phe-Gly	0.1	0.1	0.3

* The dipeptides are listed in terms of increasing volume of the side chains of the constituent residues. Gly = glycine, Ala = alanine, Val = valine, Leu = leucine, Ile = isoleucine, and Phe = phenylalanine. For example, Gly-Ala = glycylalanine.
† The experimentally determined synthetic values were obtained with aqueous solutions containing 0.01 M each amino acid, 0.125 N HCl, and 0.1 M sodium dicyanamide.
‡ The calculated values of dipeptide frequencies in contemporary proteins were based on the known sequences of egg lysozyme [81], ribonuclease [82], sheep insulin [83], whale myoglobin [84], yeast cytochrome c [85], tobacco mosaic virus [86], β-corticotropin [87], glucagon [88], melanocyte-stimulating hormone [89], chymotrypsinogen [90], and clostridium ferredoxin [91].
§ The random probability values are the products of the relative monomer frequencies in the proteins just noted. The differences in the last two sets of figures suggest a degree of selectivity in the sequences retained by contemporary proteins. (See the text for a discussion of the relevance of the three sets of data together.)

of amino acids, certain sequences would be favored over others. The probability of interaction between any two amino acids would depend on the relative abundance of each amino acid available and also their pK values [78]. With all other factors being equal, the chances of union are determined by the size of the side chains of the residues involved, at least in the case of amino acids with nonpolar functions.

With a knowledge of the probability of the linkage of any two monomeric units, one can get an idea of the likelihood of occurrence of certain sequences of these units in polymers. It is important to realize, however, that these dicyanamide studies involved di- and tripeptides. Undoubtedly, as the polymer increases in length, additional constraints would be imposed upon the addition of other members to the chain. For example, it has been suggested that the development of secondary and tertiary structure in a polypeptide would bring certain internal residues into interplay with the site of addition and thus directly affect the subsequent composition of the polymer [92].

In any case, it is apparent that under given conditions, a population of similar, specific polymers would be formed rather than an assortment of every sequence imaginable. However, the relevance this may have to elucidating the phenomena behind biogenesis could be questioned. It may be just an interesting observation that nonrandomness exists in abiotic peptide synthesis and that it means little to the appearance of biodynamic systems. To test this, the relative dipeptide frequencies observed with dicyanamide-mediated synthesis (Table 5-8, column 1) were compared with the frequency of appearance of these dipeptides in contemporary proteins of known sequence (Table 5-8, column 2) [78]. (Certain assumptions were made in these calculations [78], but they will not be reviewed here.) In other words, the experimentally observed reactivities were compared with peptide frequencies of contemporary proteins to determine if such generated sequences may or may not have had biological significance. The parallel decrease in both sets of data with increasing side-chain size would suggest that the observed probabilities of linkage of free amino acids may in fact reflect phenomena which were instrumental in the prebiotic development of sequenced peptides. Such complementarity is not this good in the case of thermal proteinoids (see Table 5-7).

Another residue-specific process has been detected in the relative rates of hydrolysis of particular dipeptides. For example, at 37°C in a 50:50 mixture of 10 N HCl and glacial acetic acid, the trend in the rate of hydrolysis is glycylglycine $>$ glycylalanine $>$ glycylleucine $>$ glycylvaline [93]. In a typical case, the rate of hydrolysis of glycylleucine relative to glycylglycine under these conditions is 0.62:1. As mentioned earlier, the peptide bond is thermodynamically unstable. In an acidic or basic medium the hydrolysis of peptides is greatly accelerated over that found in a neutral solution. Thus, if peptide bond synthesis were a random process, subsequent hydrolysis could selectively preserve certain peptides over others. However, the trends noted here are in contrast to the relative frequencies of these dipeptides found in the contemporary proteins reviewed in Table 5-8. Similarly, on the basis of what was brought out in Chap. 3 on the probable conditions of the primitive Earth and what is known about the low kinetics of hydrolysis of the peptide bond under such conditions, it is unlikely that this process could have been a significant factor in chemical evolution.

In any case, these results taken together prompt the speculation that unique, biologically pertinent peptide sequences may have been produced prebiotically without the involvement of nucleic acids or residue-specific condensing agents. This is due at least in part to preferential interactions of the amino acids as determined by the size of their side chains. Thus, it could well be that sequenced peptides could have arisen prebiologically and that subsequently they served as the template for information storage in polynucleotides, the reverse of the mode of action of current biological systems. As yet, however, no data have been reported to back up this latter suggestion [78].

Autocatalysis

One of the primary reasons that several investigators feel that nucleic acid production had to precede biogenesis, or at least polypeptide synthesis, is that DNA has the ability to reproduce itself by autocatalysis [94]. However, as we saw in the previous section, amino acids apparently have inherent sequence-directing properties which can be translated into ordered peptide chains without mediation by nucleic acids. We can carry this one step further and ask ourselves if peptides also have the ability to promote their own duplication, i.e., if they are autocatalytic.

To examine this possibility, there are several observations we can take into consideration. First, as we shall see in the next section, the clay mineral montmorillonite adsorbs amino acids and can thus catalyze peptide synthesis. It has been shown that this adsorption in the case of glycine peptides increases as the length of the polymer increases [95]. Secondly, you will recall that an undissociated carboxyl group is required in dicyanamide-mediated peptide synthesis. With an increase in the number of units in a glycine peptide, the pK of the terminal carboxyl group goes up [96]. It has been demonstrated that glycine peptides are more reactive in DCA-promoted peptide bond synthesis than the monomer [48].

Thirdly, in the presence of a polypeptide, such as polyglycine, the dimerization of amino acid monomers is enhanced [78]. That the side chains of polypeptides and monomers might interact to transfer or feed back sequence information was suggested by the fact that DL-leucine is less than half as soluble as L-leucine [97]. This observation would imply that a 1:1 association of L-leucine to D-leucine occurs in the crystalline state of the racemate by hydrophobic bonding between the side-chain groups.   When dicyanamide-mediated dimerization of leucine was carried out in the presence of poly-L-leucine, it was found that a smaller dipeptide yield appeared in free solution with D-leucine than with L-leucine [50].   Both values were less than that obtained in the absence of poly-L-leucine.   These observations would tend to confirm the type of constraining interaction between polymer and monomer (i.e., between a polypeptide and a peptide-synthesizing system) suggested above.

Therefore, it is plausible that the polymerization of amino acids was directed by the peptide products themselves.   Although the coupling of amino acids was initially determined by the relative reactivities of the monomers with each other, the resultant peptides could then have had a feedback effect on the rate and course of subsequent bondings.   This is not to say that polynucleotides appearing at about the same geologic time may not also have had an influence on this process, and thus introduce one more degree of constraint.   However, the essential point here is that amino acid sequencing was not necessarily as totally dependent on nucleic acid direction as it now is in biological systems.   It is possible in fact that nucleic acids were not required at all primordially since DNA translation requires enzymes, which are amino acid polymers.   One must first determine the origin of such ordered polypeptides before the functions of nucleic acids can be considered. Also, as you have seen, the non-template-controlled chemical synthesis of polynucleotides does not yield the specificity required in the natural 3'-5' phosphodiester linkage exclusively.

Localized concentration

To enhance the rate of reaction of primitive biocompounds and thus the rate of chemical evolution, it would have been advantageous for the reactants to be locally concentrated by one means or another.   You will recall that the eutectic point of a multicomponent system was used to accelerate the synthesis of adenine from aqueous ammonium cyanide, as reviewed in Chap. 4.   Also, as brought out in detail in Chap. 3, it is quite conceivable that clay minerals could have served as an effective mode for locally concentrating compounds for further development [98].

One example of this would be the condensation of aminoacetonitrile (which can be synthesized from HCHO, NH_3 and HCN) in the presence of kaolin to produce polyglycine [77].   This reactant (NH_2CH_2CN) can be considered an anhydride since its hydrolysis produces glycine (NH_2CH_2COOH), and it is for this reason that the nitrile was used in this reaction rather than the amino acid.   (This reaction should be compared with the anhydrous synthesis of polyamino acid precursors from ammonium cyanide discussed earlier in this chapter since they bear much in common with each other.) In a typical experiment, aminoacetonitrile·H_2SO_4 was mixed with kaolin and heated to 130 to 135°C for 5 hr under anhydrous conditions. The product was extracted with dilute NaOH. Chromatography indicated the presence of diglycine and triglycine. These results would suggest that condensation had taken place on the solid surface, followed by hydrolysis to the peptides upon the addition of the aqueous base.

Other examples of kaolin catalysis in reactions we have already considered would include the UV-promoted synthesis of disaccharides [99] and the dicyandiamide-mediated production of pyrophosphate and adenosine triphosphate [48].

Pyrophosphate has been synthesized from orthophosphate in aqueous solution with cyanate as the condensing agent [100]. However, when the phosphate was concentrated as the mineral calcium apatite, yields of the dimer were greatly enhanced. The apatite was produced from NaH_2PO_4 and $CaCl_2$. In a typical reaction, a 0.001 M potassium cyanate solution was shaken in the presence of calcium apatite for 20 days at 35°C. Chromatography revealed the presence of pyrophosphate in the product, with a small amount of triphosphate also present. Yields were not affected by added calcium or magnesium. A maximum yield of 27 percent was obtained at a pH of 6.5. Less than 2 percent of the anhydride dimer product was obtained if the reactions were carried out in free solution with soluble phosphate under the same conditions. The mechanism suggested for this reaction involves carbamyl phosphate as an intermediate (see Fig. 5-18).

Apatite has also been used to catalyze the phosphorylation of nucleosides [101]. These reactions are aided by the addition of heat. Preliminary evidence for the production of dinucleotides was obtained.

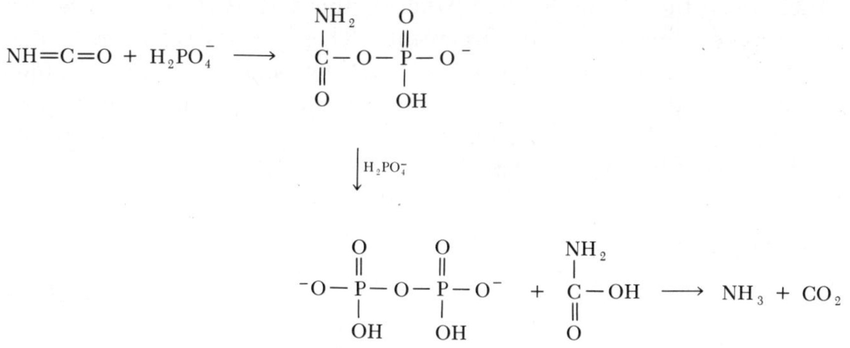

FIG. 5-18 Mechanism proposed for the synthesis of pyrophosphate in aqueous solution with cyanate [100] (see text for experimental details).

This would suggest that such minerals could have served as an effective means for providing phosphate compounds needed in subsequent phases of biogenesis.

The thermal polymerization of amino acids is aided by the presence of lava rock [102]. Generally, montmorillonite is found in lava [103]. Therefore, it is quite possible that the clay mineral was the active component assisting the pyrocondensation.

These experiments involving the clay minerals utilize the property of concentrating reactants in a small volume, and thus they accelerate the reactions employing these compounds. However, as pointed out in Chap. 3, adsorption to clays can also display disadvantageous results. Glycine dimerization promoted by dicyanamide can be catalyzed by bentonite, a montmorillonite-containing sediment [75,104]. In this case, the ability of the montmorillonite component to adsorb amines [95] has been used to advantage. The dipeptide yield was found to be dependent on the amount of the mineral added. When the ratio of glycine to clay was 5:1 (millimoles:milligrams), the diglycine yield was more than 4 times what it was in the absence of the bentonite. In contrast, the dimer yield was less than half of the nonclay value when the initial ratio of glycine to bentonite was 5:6. This would suggest that in the latter set of experiments the required interaction between monomers had been reduced because the average distance between bound glycines was increased as the amount of added clay (and therefore, number of binding sites) was increased.

To ascertain that the above results depended on the ability of clay minerals to exchange ionic species rather than simply on the presence of a solid phase in the reaction medium, a group of experiments was carried out with model compounds [50]. Instead of clays, finely divided cellulose and some of its ion-exchangeable derivatives, such as diethylaminoethyl cellulose and carboxymethyl cellulose, were individually added to solutions containing glycine, HCl, and dicyanamide. Cellulose had no effect on the dipeptide yield, whereas the derivatives each enhanced dimer production by about 10 percent. These results substantiate that a functional concentrating catalyst must not only provide a unique environment distinct from the general medium but must also restrain the reactants at its surface for a sufficient amount of time to permit the reaction of interest to occur.

Optical activity

One of the characteristics of living systems is that the compounds of which they are constructed that have asymmetric carbon atoms are generally stereohomogeneous. For example, amino acids exist in either the L-form or D-form, which are nonsuperimposable mirror images of each other. One form rotates polarized light to the right to the same degree that the other rotates it to the left, displaying their complementary molecular asymmetries:

$$
\begin{array}{cc}
\text{COOH} & \text{COOH} \\
| & | \\
\text{H}_2\text{N}^{\diagup}\overset{\text{C}}{\underset{}{\diagdown}}\text{H} & \text{H}^{\diagup}\overset{\text{C}}{\underset{}{\diagdown}}\text{NH}_2 \\
\text{CH}_3 & \text{CH}_3
\end{array}
$$

L-alanine   D-alanine

For some reason and by some means which we shall attempt to uncover, natural polymers of amino acids (proteins) came to be made up of L-amino acids almost exclusively. Similar stereohomogeneity (and therefore optical activity) is now found in polysaccharides and polynucleotides. This homogeneity is preserved through stereospecific, asymmetric catalysts (enzymes) which select the isomers to be incorporated into the polymers.

Because of the probable absence of stereoselective catalysts and surfaces it would seem quite likely that the amino acids produced under abiotic conditions would be an equal (racemic) mixture of L- and D-isomers, even though, as we have seen, there is considerable evidence for other kinds of nonrandom constraints operating in abiotic syntheses. This is supported by the observation noted in the previous chapter in which the alanine produced by electron bombardment of a gaseous reactant mixture was found to be racemic. Similarly, the polymerization of amino acids by heating shows a marked degree of racemization of the optically active starting reagents [9]. The advantage for biopolymers of being stereohomogeneous is not immediately clear. It has been suggested that racemic polyamino acids are unable (or less able) to form α helices, a major stabilizing and structure-promoting factor found in optically pure (stereohomogeneous) polypeptides (e.g., natural proteins) [105,106].

In any case, the presence of optical activity in contemporary biopolymers is a fact, and it is up to us to determine how it could have evolved, how L-amino acids, for example, could have been selected over the D-isomers. Several suggestions have been made as to which phenomena would have contributed to stereoselectivity in polypeptide synthesis, for example. Some investigators have proposed that this resulted from prebiological stereoregulated polymerizations taking place on optically active quartz surfaces [105]. However, when quartz is used to orient the formation of amino acid crystals, D-amino acids are affected to about the same degree with left-handed quartz as with right [107]. In the case of polymerization of aminoacetonitrile on kaolinite, discussed earlier, it has been suggested that proper alignment of the resultant polymer units could serve to direct the addition of side-chain functions and thus produce residues of the same stereochemical sense throughout the peptide chain [77]. However, this has not been demonstrated experimentally as yet.

Another suggestion is that stereoselectivity took place under the influence of polarized solar radiation [105]. However, this possibility has been tested experimentally, and very little rotation has resulted from syntheses involving irradiation of selected compounds with circularly polarized light [108]. In addition, natural light is not nearly as polarized as the light used in these experiments. Also, spontaneous crystallization of one optical isomer from a racemic mixture in solution probably would not lead to a universally similar selection since in one case L-leucine might be isolated and in another D-serine might be isolated. Even if this process were instrumental in prebiological evolution, it still would not explain why one form was selected over the other.

One other means that has been considered is stereoselectivity based on preferential interactions [109]. Polymerization of amino acids with carbodiimides involves a rather small degree of racemization [110]. Dehydration condensation of amino acids promoted by dicyanamide apparently proceeds by a mechanism similar to that found with the carbodiimides [39], as we discussed earlier. Using dicyanamide, therefore, the possibility of stereoselectivity based on the nature of interaction of the amino acids being coupled (rather than on the characteristics of the means employed to bring about this union) could be studied. Experiments with the dimerization in aqueous solutions of amino acids with nonpolar side chains have suggested [109] that stereoselectivity does not exist at this level of polymerization, however. In other words, an L-amino acid appears to react just as readily with a D-amino acid as with another L-residue.

Studies on the polymerization of N-carboxyanhydrides of certain amino acids in nonaqueous solvents indicate that a small degree of stereoselectivity is found, possibly promoted by enhanced α helix formation, as discussed earlier [105,106,111]. However, the differences are small and still do not explain why one isomer was retained by biological systems over the other.

The ideas just expressed suggest an experiment which has not been tried as yet. As noted earlier, amino acids which absorb ultraviolet light are more reactive during abiotic peptide synthesis in the presence of UV radiation than in its absence. If an acidic racemic mixture of tryptophan ($a_M = 5550$; $\lambda_{max} = 278$ mμ), for example, were irradiated with circularly polarized ultraviolet light, it is conceivable that the resultant peptides would be richer in one optical isomer than the other. Although the added degree of constraint would admittedly be small, the effect would be magnified by its long-term repetition and by stereoselective interactions between existing polypeptides and peptide synthesizing systems of the types already discussed here. Even though this effect would involve mainly those few amino acids with UV-absorbing side chains, the selectivity also would carry over to some extent to the aliphatic residues because of the enhanced stability of stereohomogeneous polypeptides. The combination of repetition and feedback selectivity would greatly multiply an initially small constraint acting on the system, which by itself would be essentially insignificant in an independent, one-cycle process such as amino acid synthesis. In any case, such an idea remains to be evaluated and tested in the laboratory.

5-7 CONCLUSIONS

It should be evident by now that several approaches have been employed to explain how dehydration condensation took place on the primitive Earth. The methods discussed have ranged from completely anhydrous environments to reactions with dilute reactants dissolved in aqueous solution; experimental conditions have varied from high temperature and ultraviolet excitation to moderate and low temperatures without irradiation.

Investigations employing each method have sought to overcome the thermodynamic barrier involved in the removal of the molecule of water which is essential for the condensation reactions to take place. The variety of the experimental conditions and the successes achieved through their employment might suggest that only some of these circumstances actually represent primordial events. On the other hand, this could be taken to mean that dehydration condensation occurred during a number of different stages of the Earth's development, or simultaneously in several different environments, each of which yielded very similar products. This is related to the point made in the previous chapter where it was noted that α-amino acid synthesis, for example, could result from very different reactants and applied energy sources.

One general requirement we need to make in evaluating the plausibility of the explanations of primordial condensation that we have considered in this chapter is that the experimental conditions and the reactants must be simple enough to have occurred prebiotically. It is for this reason, for example, that the disubstituted carbodiimides have not been utilized in peptide synthesis in the context of chemical evolution. We pointed out that several of the approaches discussed here require rather special conditions. One such case is the direct synthesis of peptide precursors from HCN with ammonia as a catalyst under anhydrous conditions. This procedure could be questioned from the standpoint of the geochemical plausibility of a subsequent step in the reaction allowing hydrolysis to take place. Such a sharp divergence of conditions within a reasonably close proximity in nature is not commonly observed. Similarly, in the thermal model of chemical evolution, amino acids have been synthesized at temperatures around 1000°C, followed by condensation at 160. Although certain isolated examples have been cited for such conditions in nature [11,112], as yet this does not appear to be a general phenomenon. However, according to the discussion in Chap. 3, it is not really necessary for us to restrict our experiments to presumed general conditions since life may have in fact evolved in a local milieu. However, such an environment must not be totally out of the realm of what we now know of natural science. One example of this is the use of polymetaphosphates; this is tenuous because not a single pyrophosphate- or polyphosphate-containing mineral has been identified so far [100]. The same criticism could be raised for the use of polyphosphates in the pyrocondensation experiments. Similarly, phosphorus pentoxide, which you recall is a starting material in the synthesis of ethyl metaphosphate, does not occur naturally on the Earth either. (The instability of these phosphate compounds in the presence of water has already been discussed.)

Another problem is the acidic or basic conditions employed in some of the syntheses we have reviewed. For example, with cyanamide-mediated reactions it was pointed out that the best yields were obtained at a low pH. That the pH of primitive bodies of water is still an unsettled point was brought out in Chap. 3. Whatever the case, it has been demonstrated that detectable yields of dipeptides can also be obtained using dicyandiamide at a neutral pH, although these yields are definitely smaller than those found at lower pH values [47]. Therefore, it is reasonable to conclude that substantial amounts of peptides can be obtained by this method, even under neutral conditions.

The debate about the oxidation state of compounds found on the primitive Earth was the subject of a detailed discussion in Chap. 3. You may recall that in the synthesis of polysaccharides by acid reversion reviewed in the present chapter, H_3PO_3 was successfully employed. On the other hand, in the pyrocondensation of amino acids, H_3PO_4 was effective in permitting lower temperatures to be used. Thus, the divergence is seen in these two examples as well, even though these experiments were not necessarily carried out to pursue this particular question.

Although the concentration of reactants available to participate in chemical evolution would not be expected to be very great (see Chap. 3), those reactions which have been carried out with fairly high concentrations of compounds can still be important to consider in that similar products but lower yields would be expected in more dilute reactant mixtures. Also, in many of the cases we discussed, radioactively labeled reactants have been used to detect products which appeared in very low yields. As mentioned in Chap. 2, chemical evolution is now believed to have occurred over a period of about 2 billion years. With this in mind, those reactions which permit a slow but gradual accumulation of desired products may also bear significance to this discussion.

It is interesting to note from the experiments we reviewed in this chapter that the evolution of biologically important macromolecules may well have been markedly influenced by the same types of weak interactions which now play key roles in living systems.   For example, hydrophobic and hydrogen bonds, both relatively weak, noncovalent linkages, are fundamental to the maintenance of the three-dimensional structures of contemporary proteins.   A number of the experiments we considered in this chapter point to the likely involvement of such interactions in initially constraining a seemingly random distribution of events, thus leading to unique macromolecular phenomena.

From the overall results reviewed in this chapter, it appears to be quite evident that dehydration condensations essential for biogenesis could very likely have taken place under the conditions believed to have existed on the primitive Earth.   The probable role of nitriles in chemical evolution, first proposed in the previous chapter, has been further emphasized in the present discussions.   These experiments have also demonstrated some of the areas of chemical evolution that need further investigation.

It can be concluded further that the primordial production of essential condensation compounds was a probable occurrence which could have taken place in a variety of environments.   It is very difficult to establish which of the models considered represents the most significant contributions to this phase of chemical evolution.   To answer this question is really of little importance since what has been demonstrated is that the appearance of these classes of compounds was very likely, in terms of what is considered to have been the nature of the primitive Earth.   In other words, the production of compounds essential to biogenesis cannot be looked upon as being improbable.   With this in mind, the origin of life itself would therefore have to be considered as a probable consequence of the inherent tendencies of the available reactants within the primordial environment.   The steps subsequent to the appearance of biocompounds would be expected to follow the course established by the more primitive phases of chemical evolution.   There is little reason to doubt that the chemical and physical phenomena which were in effect in the early stages continued to operate right up to the appearance of biological systems themselves.   It is these latter steps which remain to be elucidated, as we shall see in Chaps. 6 and 7.

REFERENCES

1. Borsook, H.: *Advan. Protein Chem.*, **8**:128 (1953).
2. Latimer, W. M., and H. J. Hildebrand: "Reference Book of Inorganic Chemistry," p. 179, The Macmillan Company, New York, 1929.
3. Maillard, C.: *Ann. Chim.*, **1**:519 (1914); **2**:210 (1914).
4. Harada, K., and S. W. Fox: *J. Am. Chem. Soc.*, **80**:2694 (1958).
5. Blout, E. R., and S. G. Linsley: *J. Am. Chem. Soc.*, **74**:1947 (1952).
6. Fox, S. W., and K. Harada: *Science*, **128**:1214 (1958); Vegotsky, A., K. Harada, and S. W. Fox: *J. Am. Chem. Soc.*, **80**:3361 (1958).

7. Harada, K., and S. W. Fox: *Arch. Biochem. Biophys.*, **86**:274 (1960).
8. Harada, K.: *Bull. Chem. Soc. (Japan)*, **32**:1007 (1959); Fox, S. W., K. Harada, and Rohlfing: in M. A. Stahmann (ed.), "Polyamino Acids, Polypeptides, and Proteins," p. 47, The University of Wisconsin Press, Madison, Wis., 1962.
9. (a) Fox, S. W., K. Harada, K. R. Woods, and C. R. Windsor: *Arch. Biochem. Biophys.*, **102**:439 (1963); (b) Krampitz, G.: in M. A. Stahmann, (ed.), "Polyamino Acids, Polypeptides, and Proteins," The University of Wisconsin Press, Madison, Wis., 1962; Fox, S. W., and K. Harada: *J. Am. Chem. Soc.*, **82**:3745 (1960); Krampitz, G.: *Naturwiss.*, **46**:558 (1959).
10. Fox, S. W., and K. Harada: *Arch. Biochem. Biophys.*, **86**:281 (1960); Vegotsky, A., and S. W. Fox: *Federation Proc.*, **18**:343 (1959).
11. Fox, S. W.: in S. W. Fox (ed.), "The Origins of Prebiological Systems," pp. 289, 381, Academic Press Inc., New York, 1965.
12. Pirie, N. W.: in A. I. Oparin (ed.), "The Origin of Life on the Earth," p. 80, Pergamon Press, New York, 1959.
13. Kovacs, J., H. Nagy Kovacs, I. Konyves, J. Czaszar, T. Vajda, and H. Mix: *J. Org. Chem.*, **26**:1084 (1961).
14. Antrim, R.: M.S. thesis, Penn. State Univ., 1967.
15. Ponnamperuma, C., and R. Mack: *Science*, **148**:1221 (1965).
16. Moravek, J., and J. Skoda: *Collection Czech. Chem. Commun.*, **32**:206 (1967); Skoda, J., and J. Moravek: *Tetrahedron Letters*, **35**:4167 (1966); Moravek, J.: *Tetrahedron Letters*, **37**:1707 (1967); Beck, A., R. Lohrmann, and L. E. Orgel: *Science*, **157**:952 (1967).
17. Schwartz, A. W., E. Bradley, and S. W. Fox: in S. W. Fox (ed.), "The Origins of Prebiological Systems," p. 317, Academic Press Inc., New York, 1965; Schwartz, A., and S. W. Fox: *Biochim. Biophys. Acta*, **87**:696 (1964); **134**:9 (1967).
18. Schramm, G., H. Grotsch, and W. Pollmann: *Angew. Chem. Intern. Ed.*, **1**:1(1962).
19. Schramm, G., H. Grotsch, and W. Pollmann: *Angew. Chem.* **73**:610 (1961); Schramm, G., and H. Wissman: *Chem. Ber.*, **91**:1073 (1958); Schramm, G.: in S. W. Fox (ed.), "The Origins of Prebiological Systems," p. 299, Academic Press Inc., New York, 1965.
20. Langheld, K.: *Chem. Ber.*, **43**:1857 (1910).
21. Bull, H. B.: "Introduction to Physical Biochemistry," F. A. Davis Company, Philadelphia, 1964.
22. Kochetkov, N. K., E. I., Budowsky, V. D. Domkin, and N. N. Khromov-Vorissov: *Biochim. Biophys. Acta*, **80**:148 (1964); Gottich, B. P., and O. I. Slutsky: *Biochim. Biophys. Acta*, **87**:163 (1964).
23. Hayes, F. N., and E. Hansbury: *J. Am. Chem. Soc.*, **86**:4172 (1964).
24. Pollmann, W., and G. Schramm: *Biochim. Biophys. Acta*, **80**:1 (1964).
25. Van Wazer, J., C. Callis, J. N. Shooley, and R. C. Jones: *J. Am. Chem. Soc.*, **78**:5715 (1956); Burkhardt, G., M. P. Klein, and M. Calvin: *J. Am. Chem. Soc.*, **87**:591 (1965).
26. Weill, G., M. Klein, and M. Calvin: *Nature*, **200**:1005 (1963).
27. Kovacs, J., and H. Nagy: *Nature*, **190**:531 (1961).
28. Fischer, E.: *Chem. Ber.*, **39**:471 (1906).
29. Miller, S. L.: *J. Am. Chem. Soc.*, **77**:2351 (1965); Miller, S. L.: *Biochim. Biophys. Acta*, **3**:480 (1957).
30. Lowe, C. V., M. W. Rees, and R. Markham: *Nature*, **199**:219 (1963).
31. Calvin, M.: *A.I.B.S. Bull.*, **12**:29 (1962).
32. Calvin, M., and G. J. Calvin: *Atom to Adam*, Am. Scientist, **52**:163 (1964).

33. Herrera, A. L.: *Science,* **96**:14 (1924).
34. Khorana, H. G.: "Chemistry of Phosphate Esters of Biological Interest," John Wiley & Sons, Inc., New York, 1961; DeTar, D. F., R. Silverstein, and F. F. Rogers: "The Mechanism of the Reactions of Carbodiimides," Florida State University, Tallahassee, Fla., 1965.
35. Bradbury, J. H., and D. C. Shaw: *Australian J. Chem.,* **12**:300 (1959); Sheehan, J. C., and G. P. Hess: *J. Am. Chem. Soc.,* **77**:1067 (1955).
36. Pink, L. A., and A. Hetherington: *Ind. Eng. Chem.,* **27**:834 (1935).
37. Grube, K., and G. Kruger: *Z. Physik. Chem.,* **86**:65 (1913).
38. Madelung, W., and E. Kern: *Ann.,* **427**:1 (1922).
39. Steinman, G., D. H. Kenyon, and M. Calvin: *Biochim. Biophys. Acta,* **124**:339 (1966).
40. Stolle, S., and K. Krauch: *J. Prakt. Chem.,* **88**:306 (1913).
41. Schimpl, A., R. M. Lemmon, and M. Calvin: *Science,* **147**:149 (1965).
42. Hayatsu, R.: *Science,* **146**:1291 (1964).
43. Dreschsel, D.: *J. Prakt. Chem.,* **13**:331 (1876).
44. Migrdichian, V.: "Chemistry of Organic Cyanogen Compounds," Reinhold Publishing Corporation, New York, 1947.
45. Werner, E. A.: *J. Chem. Soc.,* **107**:715 (1915).
46. Steinman, G., R. M. Lemmon, and M. Calvin: *Proc. Natl. Acad. Sci.,* **52**:27 (1964).
47. Steinman, G., R. M. Lemmon, and M. Calvin: *Science,* **147**:1574 (1965).
48. Steinman, G., D. H. Kenyon, and M. Calvin: *Nature,* **206**:707 (1965).
49. Steinman, G.: "Protobiochemistry," doctoral dissertation, University of California, Berkeley, Calif., 1965.
50. Steinman, G., and M. N. Cole: unpublished results.
51. Lieben, F., and F. Molnar: *Biochem. Z.,* **230**:347 (1931); Lieben, F., and F. Urban: *Biochem. Z.,* **239**:250 (1931).
52. Ponnamperuma, C., and E. Peterson: *Science,* **147**:1573 (1965).
53. Ponnamperuma, C., R. Mariner, and C. Sagan: *Nature,* **198**:1199 (1963); Ponnamperuma, C., and P. Kirk: *Nature,* **203**:400 (1964); Reid, C., L. E. Orgel, and C. Ponnamperuma: *Nature,* **216**:936 (1967).
54. Ponnamperuma, C., C. Sagan, and R. Mariner: *Nature,* **199**:222 (1963).
55. Abelson, P. H.: *Proc. Natl. Acad. Sci.,* **55**:365 (1966).
56. Grossenbacher, K. A., and C. A. Knight: in S. W. Fox (ed.), "The Origins of Prebiological Systems," p. 173, Academic Press Inc., New York, 1965; Oró, J.: *Nature,* **197**:862 (1963).
57. Matthews, C. N., and R. E. Moser: *Proc. Natl. Acad. Sci.,* **56**:1087 (1966); Kliss, R. M., and C. N. Matthews: *Proc. Natl. Acad. Sci.,* **48**:1300 (1962); Moser, R. E., J. M. Fritsch, T. L. Westman, R. M. Kliss, and C. N. Matthews: *J. Am. Chem. Soc.,* **89**:5673 (1967); Matthews, C. N., and R. E. Moser: *Nature,* **215**:1230 (1967) and personal communication.
58. West, E. S., W. R. Todd, H. S. Mason, and J. T. VanBruggen: "Textbook of Biochemistry," p. 1221, The Macmillan Company, New York, 1966.
59. Raper, H. S.: *Physiol. Rev.,* **8**:245 (1928).
60. Nicolaus, R. A.: *Rass. Med. Sper. Anno IX,* **Suppl. 1**:1 (1962).
61. Kenyon, D. H.: "Photochemistry of D, L-Phenylalanine," doctoral dissertation, Stanford Univ., Stanford, Calif., 1964; Kenyon, D. H., and M. S. Blois: *Photochem. Photobiol.,* **4**:335 (1965); Blois, M. S.: in S. W. Fox (ed.), "The Origins of Prebiological Systems," p. 19, Academic Press Inc., New York, 1965.
62. Nakamura, T.: *Biochem. Biophys. Res. Comm.,* **2**:111 (1960); Lerner, A. B.: *Advan. Enzym.,* **14**:73 (1953); Mason, H. S.: *J. Biol. Chem.,* **172**:83 (1948); Cromartie, R. J. T., and J. Harley-Mason: *Biochem. J.,* **66**:713 (1957).
63. Polyakovo, R., and A. Vereschagin: *Doklady Akad. Nauk.,* **64**:607 (1949).

64. Otozai, K., S. Keime, S. Nagai, T. Jamamoto, and S. Fukushima: *Bull. Chem. Soc.* (*Japan*), **27**:476 (1954).
65. Barker, S. A., S. A. Grant, M. Stacey, and R. B. Ward: *J. Chem. Soc.,* 2648 (1959); *Nature,* **183**:376 (1959).
66. Loiseleur, J.: in P. B. Rottier, et al. (eds.), "Proceedings First International Photobiology Congress," p. 167, H. Veenan and Zonen, Armsterdam, 1954.
67. Meggy, A. B.: *J. Chem. Soc.,* 851 (1953); 1444 (1956).
68. Oró, J., and J. Guidry: *Arch. Biochem. Biophys.,* **93**:166 (1961).
69. Oró, J., and J. Guidry: *Nature,* **186**:156 (1960).
70. Goda, T.: U.S. Patent 3,066,086, November, 1962.
71. Mora, P. T., *et al.: J. Am. Chem. Soc.,* **80**:685,693,3700 (1958); **81**:5449 (1959); **82**:3418 (1960); Mora, P. T.: in S. W. Fox (ed.), "Origins of Prebiological Systems," p. 281, Academic Press Inc., New York, 1965; Dutton, G. S., and A. M. Unrau: *Can. J. Chem.,* **40**:1196, 1479 (1962); Thompson, A., K. Anno, M. L. Wolfrom, and M. Inatome: *J. Am. Chem. Soc.,* **76**:1309 (1954).
72. Contreras, G., R. Espejo, E. Mery, A. Ohlbaum, and J. Toha: *Biochim. Biophys. Acta,* **61**:718 (1962).
73. Abelson, P. H.: *Geol. Soc. Amer. Mem. vol. II,* **67**:87 (1957); Abelson, P. H. (ed.): "Researches in Geochemistry," p. 80, John Wiley & Sons, Inc., New York, 1959; in I. Berger (ed.), "Organic Geochemistry," p. 431, Pergamon Press, New York, 1963; Vallentyne, J. R.: *Geochim. Cosmochim. Acta,* **28**:157 (1964).
74. (*a*) Vallentyne, J. R.: in S. W. Fox (ed.), "The Origins of Prebiological Systems," p. 105, Academic Press Inc., New York, 1965; (*b*) Kroepelin, H.: *Fortschr. Mineral.,* **43**:22 (1966).
75. Steinman, G.: *Science,* **154**:1344 (1966).
76. Snell, E., D. Metzler, and J. Logenecker: **75**:2786 (1953); Wieland, T., and K. Dose: *Angew. Chem.,* **66**:781 (1954).
77. (*a*) Akabori, S.: *Science* (*Japan*), **25**:54 (1955); in A. I. Oparin (ed.), "The Origin of Life on the Earth," p. 189, Pergamon Press, New York, 1959; (*b*) Akabori, S., K. Okawa, and M. Sato: *Bull. Chem. Soc.* (*Japan*), **29**:608 (1956); **30**:937 (1957).
78. Steinman, G.: *Arch. Biochem. Biophys.,* **119**:76 (1967); **121**:533 (1967); Steinman, G., and M. U. Cole: *Proc. Natl. Acad. Sci.,* **58**:735 (1967).
79. Pattee, H. H.: in F. F. Nord and C. H. Werkman (eds.), "Advances in Enzymology," vol. 27, John Wiley & Sons, Inc., New York, 1965.
80. Tristram, G. R., and R. H. Smith: in H. Neurath (ed.), "The Proteins," vol. I., p. 45, Academic Press Inc., New York, 1963.
81. Phillips, D. C.: *Sci. Am.,* **215**:78 (1966).
82. Anfinsen, C. B.: in P. D. Boyer *et al.* (eds.), "The Enzymes," Academic Press Inc., New York, 1961.
83. Brown, H., F. Sanger, and R. Kitai: *Biochem. J.,* **60**:556 (1955).
84. Kendrew, J. C.: *Science,* **139**:1259 (1963).
85. Margoliash, E., and A. Schejter: *Advan. Protein Chem.,* **21**:113 (1966).
86. Tsugita, A., and H. Fraenkel-Conrat: *Proc. Natl. Acad. Sci.,* **46**:626 (1960); Anderer, F. A., and D. Handschuh: *Z. Naturforsch.,* **17b**:526 (1962.)
87. Howard, K. S., R. G. Shepherd, E. A. Eigner, D. S. Davis, and P. H. Bell: *J. Am. Chem. Soc.,* **77**:3419 (1955).
88. Bromer, W. W., L. G. Sinn, and O. K. Behrens: *J. Am. Chem. Soc.,* **79**:2807 (1957).
89. Geschwind, I. I., C. H. Li, and L Barnafi: *J. Am. Chem. Soc.,* **79**:620 (1957).
90. Walsh, K. A., and H. Neurath: *Proc. Natl. Acad. Sci.,* **52**:884 (1964).

91. Tanaka, M., T. Nakashima, A. M. Benson, H. F. Mower, and K. T. Yasunobu: *Biochem.*, **5**:1666 (1966).
92. Pattee, H. H.: in S. W. Fox (ed.), "The Origins of Prebiological Systems," Academic Press Inc., New York, 1965.
93. Synge, R. L. M.: *Biochem. J.*, **39**:351 (1945).
94. Lederberg, J.: *Science*, **131**:269 (1960); **132**:393 (1960); Horowitz, N. H., and S. L. Miller: *Fortschr. Chem. Org. Naturstoffe*, **20**:423 (1962).
95. Greenland, D. J., R. H. Laby, and J. P. Quirk: *Trans. Faraday Soc.*, **58**:829 (1962); **61**:2013,2024 (1965).
96. Dawson, R. M. C.: "Data for Biochemical Research," Oxford University Press, Fair Lawn, N.J., 1959.
97. Greenstein, J. P., and M. Winitz: "Chemistry of the Amino Acids," p. 564, John Wiley & Sons, Inc., New York, 1961.
98. Bernal, J. D.: "The Physical Basis of Life," p. 34, Routledge & Kegan Paul, Ltd., London, 1951.
99. Goda, T.: U.S. Patent 3,066,086, November, 1962.
100. Miller, S. L., and M. Parris: *Nature*, **204**:1248 (1964).
101. Ponnamperuma, C., and R. Mack: *Science*, **148**:1221 (1965).
102. Fox, S. W.: *Nature*, **201**:336 (1964).
103. Ries, H.: "Clays, Their Occurrence, Properties, and Uses," John Wiley & Sons, Inc., New York, 1906.
104. Steinman, G.: unpublished results.
105. Wald, G.: *Ann. N.Y. Acad. Sci.*, **69**:352 (1957).
106. Blout, E. R., P. Doty, and J. T. Yang: *J. Am. Chem. Soc.*, **79**:749 (1957).
107. Seifert, H.: in B. Becher (ed.), "Vom Unbelebten zum Lebendigen," p. 68, Ferdinand Enke Verlagsbuchhandlung, Stuttgart, 1956.
108. Kuhn, W., and E. Braun: *Naturwiss.*, **17**:227 (1929); Kuhn, W., and E. Knopf: *Naturwiss.*, **18**:183 (1930); Mitchel, S.: *J. Chem. Soc.*, 1829 (1930).
109. Steinman, G.: *Experientia*, **23**:177 (1967).
110. Kovacs, J., L. Kisfaludy, and M. Q. Ceprini: *J. Am. Chem. Soc.*, **89**:183 (1967).
111. Blout, E. R., and M. Idelson: *J. Am. Chem. Soc.*, **78**:497,3857 (1956); Tsuruta, T., S. Inove, and K. Matsuura: *Biopolymers*, **5**:313 (1967).
112. Fox, S. W.: *Nature*, **201**:335,336 (1964).
113. Dose, K., and K. Ettre: *Z. Naturforsch.*, **13B**:784 (1958); McKusick, B. C., W. E. Mochel, and F. W. Stacey: *J. Am. Chem. Soc.*, **82**:723 (1960).

development of morphological complexity and dynamic organization

6-1 INTRODUCTION

On the basis of the principle of biochemical similarity discussed in Chap. 1, we must now examine the means by which primitive chemical systems became organized into autonomous units. The primary structural and functional unit of organisms today is the cell, and it is the primordial origin of this entity which we must now consider. Within the living cell the essential functions of metabolism, assimilation, reproduction, excretion, and the like take place.

The internal characteristics of a living cell are quite different from the nature of the environment in which it is found. This is possible partly through the action of a dynamic limiting barrier, or membrane. The concentrations of certain internal components may vary greatly from that found in the environment because of selective passage of these materials inward or outward. For example, the protein concentration within an amoeba is usually much higher than that found in the aqueous medium in which the organism is located.

Thus far we have discussed evidence showing that essentially all the classes of compounds presumably required for biogenesis could very likely have been produced during prebiological chemical evolution. Since contemporary metabolism is largely localized within well-defined, bounded regions (cells), we must search for plausible collecting mechanisms by which biologically significant monomers and polymers might have become organized primordially into small units. Such concentration would undoubtedly have aided further sophistication.

The elucidation of this stage of biogenesis must be considered in the context of the phenomena exhibited by relatively simple constituents and driving forces. Although unsophisticated protoenzymes or other organic catalysts may have been available at this stage, well-integrated reaction systems analogous to contemporary glycolysis or the tricarboxylic acid cycle, for example, would most likely not have been on hand. Therefore, an examination of the characteristics of relatively uncomplicated molecular systems may well provide clues to the nature of protocell development.

On the basis of the experiments we are about to discuss, a general picture of how primitive cells may have evolved can be derived. As with the other phases of chemical evolution that we have discussed, here again we cannot be certain that the observations we make do in fact reflect actual primordial events. However, taken together, these observations indicate that the information and essential driving forces that could have brought about the evolution of protometabolism and primitive cells can be identified in simple compounds and reaction conditions. The scheme of events that we conclude to have taken place is essentially hypothetical and is the result of experimental observations made under proposed primordial conditions. It is not immediately clear why cellular organization appeared in the first place or for what reason metabolism evolved. However, since we do observe these phenomena in contemporary biological systems, it can be concluded that these events constituted an essential aspect of primordial biogenesis. On the other hand, the experiments we are about to discuss indicate that the types of compounds that could have been produced during chemical evolution exhibit inherent tendencies toward self-organization and morphogenicity. Thus it becomes less important to question why or for what purpose or to satisfy what demand the metabolizing cell evolved. Rather, we should look for phenomena and underlying mechanisms which could have participated in this event.

6-2 PRIMITIVE METABOLISM

Organization as a biodynamic characteristic

Contemporary living cells possess a complex, ordered arrangement of enzyme-mediated reactions. Specialized components of these systems trap solar energy and convert it into chemical bond energy in the form of ATP, glucose, and the like. Other cells are then able to break down these sources of energy for their advantage to maintain their internal integrity and growth. It is quite likely that the most primitive protocells lacked the integrated system of biochemical reactions of the types now found in nature. Rather, these early developing units had to take advantage of simple catalysts and reactions to provide them, at a more inefficient level, with materials required for their continued maintenance.

The problem that remains to be elucidated is how dispersed, seemingly unrelated processes became organized into metabolizing units. This is perhaps the most difficult enigma to overcome in the ultimate elucidation of the origin of life. The appearance of entities that could be termed "living" was undoubtedly a very gradual chain of events leading to increased complexity rather than an abrupt occurrence. In other words, evolving systems went through increasing degrees of becoming "alive" as we know it today. It is evident that to determine at which stage an evolving molecular system can be considered to be alive, in contradistinction to inanimate, requires an evaluation of the essential attributes of systems now designated as living and thus the establishment of a definition to serve as a criterion for the test. Such a definition is very difficult to formulate unequivocally. Living cells, whether they be bacteria or human liver cells, carry on metabolism which involves ingestion, digestion, energy conversion, assimilation, secretion, and excretion. Cells respond to stimuli and are able to reproduce. However, response to stimuli is not unique to living cells since, for example, a cube of sugar in the presence of sufficient heat and oxygen responds by going to an oxidized product. Similarly, elemental sulfur vacillates between various allotropes with changes in temperature [1].

The fact that living bodies are able to grow is not unique to these systems since crystals also exhibit this function [2]. Similarly, reproduction is not an essential attribute for an organism to be classified as living since a denucleated amoeba or a mule is reproductively dead [3]. However, they certainly go on with their normal metabolic functions for an extended period and bear the usual properties of a living system (except reproduction). Growth in protocells could have resulted from continuous accumulation of material through selective membranes and catalytically enhanced alteration of these materials into various constituents. Multiplication would occur once the unit passed a critical size of expansion which exceeded the capacity of surface tension to hold the unit intact. This would result in separation into small units, each carrying portions of the acquired characteristics (e.g., catalysts and membranes).

The capacity to change and also reproduce such a change would seem to be unique to living systems. Just as the essence of biological evolution is the survival of those organisms which have by chance developed traits which enhance their survival potential, so the evolution of protobiological systems could have depended on the chance acquisition of valuable traits from the environment, such as a useful catalyst. These acquired advantageous traits could then be passed on to successive progeny by the types of processes already mentioned. The current excitement over nucleic acids has led many investigators to suggest that no system of biological significance can bear biodynamic characteristics unless it possesses these polymers to direct its course of existence [4]. From what we discussed in Chap. 5 and will also consider in the present chapter, it is apparent that this was not an absolute requirement. For example, sequenced, biologically pertinent peptides have been produced under presumed primordial conditions in the absence of nucleic acids [5]. Although the developmental processes proposed here resemble Darwinian evolution of living organisms, which depends on chance mutations of genotypes, the essential difference in the present case involves primary alterations of physicochemical properties. In the manner once thought to explain phenotypic changes of gene-regulated phenomena, environmental changes would be met in this proposed prenucleic acid stage by chance acquisition of survival-enhancing mechanisms and reactions. Thus primitive evolution was not necessarily restricted by the possible initial absence of nucleic acids.

In our search for a basic set of criteria to define a living system, we can note that each biological function can be reenacted individually in the test tube with the appropriate selection of reagents and catalysts. However, under such conditions, the reaction is often less efficient and slower than it had been in vivo. For example, it has been calculated that the measured rates of cellular respiration could not occur if the individual enzyme participants were dissolved in free solution rather than arranged in their semi-solid-state array on the mitochondrial membrane [6]. Also, the colloidal properties of living protoplasm, as will be discussed more fully, are known to enhance catalytic action by the resultant heterogeneous character of the system which can promote adsorption and orientation of the reacting molecules [7]. Changes in the colloidal properties of cells can directly affect enzyme activity [8,9]. A mixture of all the cellular substances in a test tube obviously lacks many of the characteristics displayed by the intact cell itself.

There is nothing supernatural about the way a cell is able to organize isolated reactions into a coordinated, coupled whole. This association is undoubtedly governed by the known laws of chemistry and physics. Therefore, a major, essential (but not necessarily exclusive) consideration in deciding if a system is living or not is the observation of whether it bears the inherent properties giving it the potential for organizing the necessary, useful component reactions into an integrated assemblage of dynamic events. In this sense, a complex machine is still not alive since it does not utilize the materials it is processing for its own existence and survival (e.g., the sheet metal being formed by a punch press). Even a machine programmed for self-repair and self-duplication would fail this test since it could not improve itself by selectively acquiring factors from the environment to augment its performance capability and efficiency. Also, it could not build itself from a pile of component parts in the first place without direction supplied by another programmed machine or a human.

The raison d'etre and purposiveness of a machine must be built into it. From what we have seen already and shall review in this chapter, the development of probiogenetic characteristics would appear to be inherent in the compounds produced and in fact would be difficult to prevent under appropriate conditions. The main problem now seems to be the determination of which phenomena induced isolated events to become coordinated prebiotically into an evolving, progressive organism. The validity of several suggestions put forth must be subjected to experimental verification.

Activity in protobiochemicals

The first step involves the identification of biological activity in compounds believed to have been produced under primitive Earth conditions. Heating glucose together with asparagine has been reported to give nicotinic acid [10]. The product exhibited activity in bioassay. The tripeptide glutathione has limited redox function by itself [11]. This trimer has been synthesized from the free amino acids through the action of dicyanamide [12].

The active site of the hydrolytic enzyme chymotrypsin contains a histidine residue [13]. Its reaction is apparently a base-catalyzed process. When the histidine residue is photooxidized, the activity of the enzyme is lost. In model systems, it has been shown that imidazole, the functional side-chain group of histidine, can itself promote the type of hydrolysis mediated by the enzyme, but it does so at a much slower rate [14]. Model peptides were synthesized containing histidine and some of the other portions of the known sequence of chymotrypsin [15]. These peptides catalytically hydrolyzed the model ester, p-nitrophenyl acetate, and showed stereoselectivity in the hydrolysis of the antipodes of esterified phenylalanine derivatives. However, the degradation of serum albumin, which would normally be attacked by chymotrypsin, was not promoted by histidine- and serine-containing peptides [16]. These experiments show that limited, nonspecific, enzyme-like catalytic activity can be found in small peptides. The specificity and immense rate acceleration typical of high-molecular-weight, three-dimensionally arrayed proteins most likely would not have occurred at this primitive level. As one might expect, biological systems probably improved as they became more complex with time.

It was noted earlier that various activities are often aided in the cell through involvement of its colloidal properties. For example, lipid droplets in protoplasm are usually stabilized by the formation of a protective colloid coat around them [3]. Proteins are macromolecules whose functions often depend on the colloidal characteristics of these compounds. It is probable that these events involve interface and surface phenomena. Along these lines, colloidal micelles were prepared from

N-α-myristoyl-L-histidine and cetyltrimethylammonium bromide [17]. This biphasic system promoted the hydrolysis of p-nitrophenyl acetate and p-nitrophenyl caprylate at a much higher rate than imidazole or histidine did in free solution. The nature of the kinetics of this phenomenon suggested that a surface-catalyzed reaction was involved. Although the actual constituents of this reaction were a little more complex than probably would have occurred under primitive Earth conditions, these experiments demonstrate that employment of biphasic colloidal environments may well have catalyzed the reactions of interest.

In a related experiment, the heterogeneous nature of a water-oil interface was found to cause linoleic acid to be rapidly oxidized by O_2, whereas no oxidation took place when added ethanol made the mixture homogeneous [18]. Catalysis in colloidal systems will be discussed in more detail later in the chapter.

A simple form of catalytic activity based on structural orientation has been demonstrated with styrene [19]. First, an iron porphyrin, like that found in hemoglobin, was set in a polystyrene matrix in the presence of carbon monoxide. Then the CO was removed. It was found that the formed polymer could bind O_2 and CO reversibly like hemoglobin.

It has been shown in a number of cases that the catalytic activity of enzymes results from the interaction of particular residues of the polypeptide with the substrate. For example, chymotrypsin has an active site sequence of glycine-α-aspartic acid-serine-glycine [20]. From what we discussed at the end of Chap. 5, it can be concluded that the coupling of amino acids under prebiological conditions was anything but random. Rather, there appear to be certain preferences in sequence generation. The biological significance of such sequences may be questioned. In Chap. 5 it was noted that there appears to be a direct relationship between such preferences found in abiological syntheses of polyamino acids and the frequency of certain peptide sequences in contemporary proteins. This sequencing occurs without the presence of nucleic acids. To consider another possible application of such ordering to a biological problem, the generation of the active site sequence of chymotrypsin was examined [5]. In a solution containing aspartic acid, serine, and dicyanamide, a larger yield of α-aspartyl-serine, the dipeptide constituting the center of the active site of chymotrypsin, was obtained when N,N-dimethylformamide was added to the reactant mixture than when the amide was absent. You will recall that chymotrypsin is a peptidase, an enzyme capable of hydrolyzing peptide linkages. The peptide bond is essentially an amide linkage. Thus, in the presence of an amide, say dimethylformamide, an association of amino acids with the potential substrate apparently led to an enhancement of the generation of a portion of the active site sequence of the enzyme. In other words, it would seem that potential substrates served as templates around which the protoenzyme could have evolved. The classical lock-and-key model of enzyme activity visualizes a lock (the enzyme) specifically associating with particular keys (substrates) [21]. The experiments just discussed would suggest that during prebiological development, the lock itself formed around the key. Thus, the specificity and nature of the resultant enzyme were determined by the types of potential substrates available during its fabrication. Again, nucleic acids were not required for this phenomenon to take place.

The proteinoid discussed in Chap. 5 and synthesized by anhydrous heating of a mixture of amino acids appears to possess some enzymatic activity [22]. First, when glucose was added to the polymer, evolved CO_2 was detected. Also, the proteinoid seems to catalyze the hydrolysis of p-nitrophenyl acetate, although this can be promoted by a number of simpler substances [13,14]. However, these experiments have been criticized because of the detection of bacterial contamination in the polymer preparations [23].

Another property of living systems is autocatalysis (observed in certain biosynthetic pathways such as heme formation) and, at higher levels of complexity, self-replication. It was noted in Chap. 5 that peptide bond synthesis promoted by dicyanamide is autocatalytic; i.e., the rate of peptide bond production increases with the appearance of more polymeric material [24–26]. Additional evidence suggested information transfer between a polypeptide and a peptide-synthesizing system [27]. Information inherent in the already-synthesized polymer selectively constrained the dimerization reaction and had a controlling influence over it. Thus, it can be concluded that many of the organizing characteristics thought to be unique to nucleic acids are also shared by polypeptides.

The course of metabolic development

The nature of the coordination of protometabolic development presents another problem to be considered here. It seems likely that the most primitive form of metabolism involved heterotrophic nourishment [8]. As noted earlier, chemical evolution undoubtedly provided great stores of ready-made "food" for the earliest evolving systems. One good piece of supporting evidence that heterotrophic metabolism was the most primitive is that many autotrophic organisms now are also able to function as heterotrophs if the situation so demands, but the opposite arrangement is not observed. Once the most readily utilized nutrients (A) were completely consumed, those eobionts (primitive prototypes of living cells) able to recycle and make A from other accessible compounds (B) probably had the greatest survival potential [28]. When the supply of secondary nutrient B diminished in turn, it was necessary to make A and B from C, and so forth. The acquisition of appropriate catalysts to promote these reactions would govern the rate of sophistication of this process. Although this model, in the form it was originally proposed [28], employs sophisticated enzymes and thus may not necessarily reflect actual primordial events, it serves as a good means of visualizing how coordination of required reactions could also have occurred with simpler available catalysts.

The course of evolution of a metabolic system for replenishing one or more depleted compounds has been considered in greater detail. One possibility for nutrient B in the scheme just discussed is glycerate-2-phosphate (A would be something like ATP) [29]. It is argued that simple reactions involving this acid phosphate could have provided the starting point for the evolution of major phases of metabolism such as high-energy phosphorylation, oxidation-reduction (triose phosphate would act as the H carrier), amino acid and sugar synthesis, and the production of metabolic intermediates (see Fig. 6-1). That such an occurrence is possible nonenzymatically has not been demonstrated experimentally as yet. However, if this type of scheme did indeed occur, it would represent the evolution of metabolic pathways whereby one catalyst-promoted step was added at a time. Such a suggestion is quite plausible.

The direct (autotrophic) utilization of sulfate, nitrogen, carbon dioxide, hydrogen, and oxygen most likely required the appearance of appropriate porphyrins, probably at a later date. The possible means for the primordial appearance of such compounds have been discussed in Chap. 4. It has been suggested that in the most primitive stages in the evolution of metabolism, aqueous cations were employed to catalyze essential reactions [30]. One such reaction might be the reduction of hydrogen peroxide to water ($2H_2O_2 \rightarrow 2H_2O + O_2$). The hydrated ferric ion is itself able to enhance the rate of spontaneous decomposition of peroxide. It has been suggested that this catalytic activity would be enhanced nearly 1,000 times with the addition of a porphyrin ring to the cation. Other reactions employing an iron moiety could be similarly augmented. It was also proposed that iron porphyrin could catalyze its own duplication since an oxidation step is apparently involved in its synthesis. We saw in Chap. 4 that in fact such a phenomenon has been observed in the laboratory. This apparently utilized the ability of iron porphyrins to catalyze oxidation reactions.

Those primitive units which then made use of pigment sensitizers had a supplementary means for more efficient utilization of organic substances [8]. An example of this would be direct photosynthetic phosphorylation. Contemporary organisms use various phosphorylated compounds, such as adenosine triphosphate (ATP), as the means for storing and transporting required energy in the form of chemical bonds. Invoking the principle of biochemical similarity, we see that the appearance

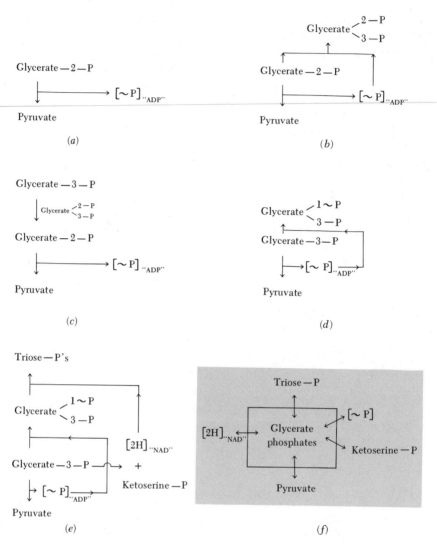

FIG. 6-1 Hypothetical steps in the proposed prebiotic evolution of a metabolic system starting from glycerate-2-phosphate [29]. This is known as the *reaction-core* hypothesis. It takes into account several aspects of contemporary metabolism.

of a phosphorylating mechanism, possibly employing photosynthetic activation, was a necessary development. The readily available solar radiation would provide the energy needed to promote such a process.

A group of experiments has been carried out which could suggest the key to the most primitive form of photosynthetic phosphorylation [31]. This process could have provided a continuous source of ATP based on utilization of solar radiation. A mixture of an iron porphyrin, phosphate, imidazole, and ADP, when irradiated by incandescent lamps or a quartz iodine vapor lamp, yielded ATP. The intermediate of this reaction was found to be 1-phosphoimidazole; one could also phosphory-late AMP to ATP by this method. The reaction was carried out in N,N-dimethylacetamide. Similarly, when a solution of porphyrin, imidazole, AMP, and orthophosphate was photoreduced under nitrogen and then reoxidized by exposure to air, phosphorylation resulted. (Various means for the possible primordial appearance of each of these classes of reactants have been reviewed in previous chapters.) The phos-phorylation was found to occur during the oxidation steps. It was apparently the result of the formation of the 1-phosphoimidazole interme-diate which subsequently phosphorylated AMP or ADP. (Phosphohisti-dine has been implicated as a possible active intermediate in coupling electron transport to phosphorylation in the mitochondrion [32].) Thus, any simple oxidation-reduction system promoted by solar radiation which can lead to the phosphorylation of imidazole conceivably could have served as a primitive means for photosynthetic phosphorylation. Such a process would be an example of a reaction that could have been utilized by primitive metabolic systems to overcome the depleted supply of re-quired energy-rich compounds. However, it still remains to be demon-strated that this reaction can also take place under aqueous conditions.

Whereas the mode of sophistication of metabolism to its present-day level resulted from the complex interplay of several environmental and physicochemical factors, the following hypothetical scheme represents one general developmental pathway by which this could have taken place. It is likely, because of the suspected initial lack of atmospheric oxygen and excess of hydrogen, that the first multistep metabolizing systems were anaerobic [33]. The energy sources available to these primitive systems included ultraviolet and visible light, ionizing radia-tion, heat, and chemical energy. The reactions of the systems probably involved simple compounds. Next, as greater amounts of oxygen ap-peared and hydrogen decreased, metabolism remained anaerobic; since compounds being used by the evolving systems (which by this time reflected the characteristics of living entities) were now more complex, visible light could be utilized effectively. According to this hypothetical scheme, organic reservoirs from prebiotic chemical evolution became depleted, and living cells had to resort to photoreduction to satisfy en-ergy requirements. Ozone now helped to protect these units from the hazards of ultraviolet radiation. Finally, chlorophyll-utilizing photosyn-thesis emerged to greatly increase the availability of oxygen, making aerobic respiratory systems possible. In terms of the types of metabolic processes involved, this hypothetical (since, to say the least, it has not been repeated experimentally) course of evolution can be outlined [34] as shown in Table 6-1. The active phosphate produced in step 1 could then have served as an energy source for further reactions. Step 3

TABLE 6-1 Suggested pathway for the evolution of energy metabolism [34]

Anaerobic phase

1. *Fermentation:* a chemical source of energy; by-product CO_2
   for example, $C_6H_{12}O_6 \rightarrow 2C_2H_5OH + 2CO_2 + 2 \sim P$

2. *Hexosemonophosphate cycle:* metabolic hydrogen for reductions
   $6C_6H_{12}O_6 + 6H_2O + 12 \sim P \rightarrow 12H_2 + 5C_6H_{12}O_6 + 6CO_2$

3. *Photophosphorylation:* light into high-energy phosphates
   $$\xrightarrow[\text{chlorophylls, cytochromes}]{\text{light}} \sim P$$

4. *Photosynthesis:* light into new organic molecules; by-product O_2

   Bacteria: $6CO_2 + 12H_2A \xrightarrow[\text{chlorophyll}]{\text{light}} C_6H_{12}O_6 + 6H_2A + 12A$

   Algae, higher plants: $6CO_2 + 12H_2O \xrightarrow[\text{chlorophyll}]{\text{light}} C_6H_{12}O_6 + 6H_2O + 6O_2$

Aerobic phase

5. *Respiration:* metabolic energy from combustions
   $C_6H_{12}O_6 + 6H_2O + 6O_2 \rightarrow 6CO_2 + 12H_2O + 30\text{-}40 \sim P$

involved the direct use of sunlight and required the appearance of metalloporphyrins. The ultimate evolution of aerobic respiration (step 5) led to the most efficient use of chemical energy. How the catalysts needed to bring about these complex systems appeared and were coordinated into an effective entity remains to be determined.

Since the oceans are too immense for us to assume that chemical evolution provided a sufficient concentration of compounds to make these bodies of water one big unit going through the steps of metabolic evolution just outlined, a major problem that remains is how local agglomerations of compounds occurred. In other words, it is necessary to elucidate the means by which boundaries appeared to provide local concentrations of chemicals which were partially partitioned from the external environment and were able to develop semi-independently.

6-3 MORPHOGENICITY DISPLAYED BY SIMPLE SYSTEMS

Primitive gases

With the possibility that the products of spark discharge experiments might also have the inherent characteristics able to lead to the ultimate formation of protocells, close examination of the products of electron bombardment of simple mixtures of methane, ammonia, hydrogen, and water was also made for microsphere formation. Such an experiment was carried out using electric discharge as the energy source [35]. Microscopic spherules were observed after 48 hr of sparking. When the bombardment was carried on for 624 hr, spherical objects of about 0.26 μ in diameter were observed. These are pictured in Fig. 6-2. Standard microbiological procedures ruled out the possibility that these might

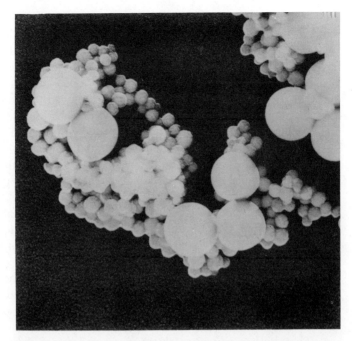

FIG. 6-2   Spherical solid material produced by sparking a mixture of CH_4, NH_3, and H_2O for 624 hr [35].   The largest spheres are polystyrene latex beads added for visual (electron microscope) size comparison.

be forms of bacterial contamination.   Prior to electron-microscope examination, the spheres were collected by mild centrifugation and washed.   This demonstrated their structural stability.   Analysis of the solid material showed that it consisted of 10.3 percent carbon, 1.9 percent hydrogen, and 1.0 percent nitrogen, with a density of more than 1.8.   These results suggest that these spheres are composed of a large amount of inorganic material, possibly silicates extracted from the borosilicate glass of the sparking apparatus itself when exposed to ammonia. This is not entirely out of the realm of possible primitive Earth events since common sand is a silicate and thus provides a readily available source of building material.   Acid hydrolysis of the spherules revealed compounds which had chromatographic and colorimetric properties of amino acids.

Aldehydes and nitriles

The ability of aldehydes and nitriles, known intermediates in spark discharge syntheses, to self-condense under appropriate conditions was brought out by several examples cited in the preceding chapters.   Their interaction with each other has also been shown to bear possible significance to the primordial appearance of protocells. One such system specifically utilizes ammonium thiocyanate and formaldehyde [36]. It was found that when NH₄SCN was dissolved in HCHO, spread in thin layers, and incubated for several hours, active microscopic structures resembling living cells appeared. In previous chapters it was pointed out that these conditions have also been employed to produce such compounds as amino acids, peptides, and polysaccharides. The morphogenetic experiment was repeated many times, resulting in a large variety of forms bearing a strong resemblance to living cells. This included such things as internal movement, vacuole exclusion, and translocation. Due to this similarity, this particular phenomenon was given the name *plasmogeny*.

These experiments were extended, and the formation of microspheres was found to be enhanced by ultraviolet radiation [37]. The presence of this energy source permitted the use of more dilute (0.025 to 0.75 M) aqueous reactant mixtures. As with the polyamino acid microspheres to be discussed later in this chapter, the incorporation of zinc into the formaldehyde-thiocyanate structures led to a localized ATPase-like activity. The exact chemical nature of the macromolecules produced by this method was not definitively established.

That both ammonium thiocyanate and formaldehyde could have been found on the primitive Earth was demonstrated by experiments discussed in Chap. 4. Typical spheres produced from this reactant mixture had a diameter of 1 to 5 μ [37]. When water was placed at the periphery of a drop containing the formaldehyde-thiocyanate spheres, much larger structures (10 to 100 μ in diameter) developed. Much internal movement was observed. These spheres were found to be able to concentrate dyes from the external medium. Also, vacuoles which developed within the spheres gradually moved to the surface and were excluded, as seen in Fig. 6-3. In many cases the chemical and physical properties of these spherules are reminiscent of some of the microfossils we discussed in Chap. 2.

The apparent central role of cyanide in chemical evolution has been emphasized several times in previous chapters. Its reactions were pursued further, and it was found that when aqueous 1 M NH₄CN was heated at 90°C for 4 hr, microsphere production resulted [38]. Electron micrographs of the spheres closely resembled those displayed by other models to be discussed in this chapter. Hydrolysis of the microspheres yielded guanidine, glycocyamine, urea, glycine, alanine, aspartic acid, lysine, serine, threonine, histidine, α-aminobutyric acid, ornithine, and glutamic acid. (These results should be compared to those of the corresponding experiments considered in Chaps. 4 and 5.) The presence of histidine is especially significant in view of its possible roles in the protometabolism just discussed. The amino acids of the microspheres apparently were not linked by peptide bonds because of a negative

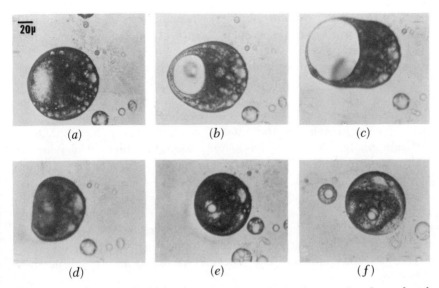

FIG. 6-3   Time-lapse sequence showing vacuole exclusion by a spherule produced from formaldehyde and ammonium thiocyanate [37].

biuret reaction, the ineffectiveness of trypsin incubation, and the lack of characteristic infrared spectral bands.

The simplicity of the reactants used in this model of protocell development suggests that the ability to organize into complex supermolecular structures is found in the types of compounds that may well have been produced during chemical evolution.   These formations then could have served as a matrix within which subsequent stages of biogenetic evolution could have occurred.   We must bear in mind that this or any of the model systems to be discussed in this chapter cannot be considered as being alive.   Rather, these experiments exhibit means by which a delimited, localized environment could have arisen, bearing many of the characteristics likely to be required for a biodynamic system to evolve.   Because of their ability to interact dynamically with the environment and locally to concentrate essential factors, the cyanide microspheres can be regarded as a specific example of a possible precursor to subsequent higher levels of organization.

Simple organic and inorganic reactants

In Table 4-10 it was pointed out that amino acids could be synthesized by exposing aqueous solutions of paraformaldehyde and nitrate to sunlight.   These experiments were extended, and it was found that solar irradiation of an aqueous solution containing amino acids, sucrose, and ferric chloride leads to the production of peptides [39].   Cosmic radiation, as well as solar radiation, contributed to this effect since an opaque cloth decreased the yield of peptides, whereas lead shielding eliminated it entirely. In a typical experiment, a 0.1% glycine solution was irradiated in a quartz vessel. After 300 hr, glycylglycine appeared in detectable yields. Using similar methods, mixed peptides were also produced. These were identified by hydrolysis followed by paper chromatography. When the peptides were prepared in the presence of divalent cations, they exhibited a small amount of pyrophosphatase-like activity, i.e., the capacity to enhance the rate of hydrolysis of pyrophosphate to orthophosphate. Although this activity was also observed in nonirradiated samples, more of it was found in the exposed solutions. Boiling of the product resulted in loss of the activity. In addition to the peptides, it was found that these conditions also yielded microscopically visible particles. These spherical structures exhibited simple cell-like morphology and were named *Jeewanu*, a Sanskrit word meaning "particles of life." With their appearance, the phosphatase activity decreased in the aqueous medium and became locally concentrated in these spherules.

The experiment was repeated from its most elementary stage by exposing an aqueous solution of molybdic acid, paraformaldehyde, and ferric chloride to bright sunlight [39]. The use of molybdate was suggested by the role that this function plays in plant biochemistry. After 600 hr, the solution became turbid. Microscopic examination revealed the presence of spheres of 0.28 to 0.5 μ in diameter. They were mobile, exhibited an external membrane-like structure, and had a dark interior. No spheres appeared in reactant mixtures left in the dark. In solutions irradiated for 1,000 hr, the resulting spheres increased to 1 to 1.5 μ in diameter and developed structures resembling buds (see Fig. 6-4). Hydrolysis of the product indicated the presence of amino acids. These microspheres provide another means for establishing a delimiting bound-

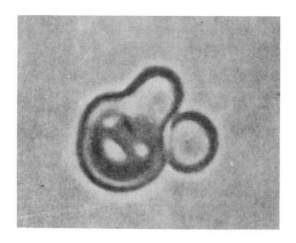

FIG. 6-4 Jeewanu particle showing tendency of budding. Such structures typically appeared upon sunlight irradiation of an aqueous mixture of molybdate, paraformaldehyde, and ferric chloride [39].

ary from the external environment since it was found that the constitution of the interior of the spheres differed from that of the external medium. The various phenomena associated with these structures were apparently not due to microbial contamination since bacteria were not observed by microscopic examination, the products would not grow on bacterial nutrients, and the experiment was carried out under aseptic conditions.

Another type of microsphere synthesis utilized the autocatalytic production of copper oxide from Fehling's solution in the presence of sugar [39]. Such a process yielded spheres without the need for irradiation. When the product was heated and used as a source of seeding nuclei, the spheres formed in a cold reactant mixture utilizing such seeds were found to increase in size and number with time, suggesting growth. The appearance of buds also suggested multiplication. Addition of ammonium molybdate to the reaction mixture resulted in enhanced budding. The increase in the number of spheres was accelerated upon the addition of a gum arabic-sucrose mixture into the reaction vessel. The addition of salts enhanced the inherent movements of the spheres and their growth. The copper oxide spheres were found to consist of 48.8 percent copper, 4.2 percent carbon, and 0.3 percent nitrogen. It was possible to favor budding over an increase in the appearance of new spheres with time by using dilute reactant mixtures. The CuO spherules demonstrated a localized catalase-like activity by their ability to accelerate the breakdown of hydrogen peroxide. A product of moderate dimensions was indicated by the fact that such activity dialyzed very slowly.

Several other amino acid combinations were found to yield protocells in the same manner [39]. These spheres exhibited vacuoles, inclusions, and exterior walls, thus supporting the suggestion that they could have served as an effective primitive cell form. That they could interact with the environment was indicated by the fact that these spheres took up dyes. These protocells demonstrated primitive lifelike characteristics by their ability to grow, multiply, and carry on simple localized catalytic processes. A strong argument in support of this model is that such spheres result from the interactions of very simple molecules and that a similar phenomenon is observed with a variety of starting reactants.

It is essential to realize that in this model, as well as in the others to be discussed, the microspheres produced exhibit certain properties also common to living cells. However, other aspects of cellular function are missing. Therefore, each type of microsphere preparation, although possessing distinct merits, can only be considered a partial model system. We shall try to examine the characteristics each type has in common with the other proposed models and then draw overall conclusions concerning the possible nature of primordial protocell development in general.

Amino acid thermal polymers

The production of polymers of amino acids by pyrocondensation has been discussed in Chap. 5. It was pointed out there that the polyamino acids (known as proteinoids) synthesized by this method bear many of the properties of naturally occurring proteins. However, much of the bonding in these synthetic polymers is unnatural in terms of the types of linkages commonly found in contemporary proteins. In addition, decomposition of amino acids at elevated temperatures might have been a serious limiting factor in the synthetic process. However, these criticisms do not necessarily detract from the possible relevance of this phenomenon to primordial biogenesis. It is not clear if most primitive proteins did in fact bear α-peptide linkages exclusively. Similarly, it now appears that large quantities of amino acids, as well as other biochemicals, could have been produced during chemical evolution, thus compensating somewhat for subsequent thermal decomposition.

It has been found that these amino acid polymers bear an interesting property that may have been related to the production of protocells. When acidic proteinoids are boiled in water and allowed to cool, small spherical structures, called *microspheres*, appear [40–42]. A typical

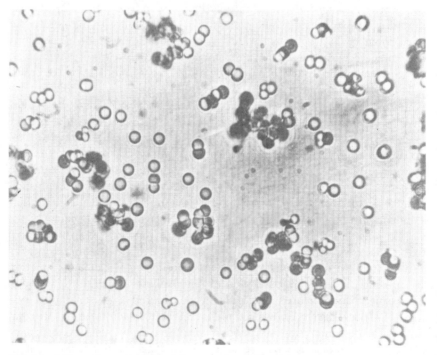

FIG. 6-5 Microspheres formed when an amino acid polymer (proteinoid) was boiled in water. The proteinoid was produced by pyrocondensation of the anhydrous monomers [40b].

TABLE 6-2 Effect of concentration of aqueous sodium chloride on diameter of proteinoid microspheres [40a]

Concentration* of sodium chloride solution, %	Diameter of spherules, μ
0.15	1.4
0.31	1.6–1.8
0.63	1.6–1.8
1.25	2.3–2.7
2.5	2.0–2.1
5.0	0.7–0.9
10	0.4–0.6
20	Almost no spherules

* The approximate salt concentration in sea water today is 3.4% [43].

preparation is shown in Fig. 6-5. The microspheres are usually about 2 μ in diameter. When 15 mgm of proteinoid was boiled in 3 ml of seawater for 1 min, 10^6 to 10^8 microspheres appeared upon cooling. It was possible for these microspheres to be stored for several weeks and to retain their structural integrity during that time. The microspheres were collected by centrifuging them at 3,000 rpm for 5 min. Again, their shape and integrity were maintained. The size of the microspheres was altered by the addition of salt. This is shown in Table 6-2. The effect is apparently an osmotic one and suggests an interplay between the internal and external environments. In general, the most distinctive microspheres were produced from proteinoids that resulted from the pyrocondensation of the 18 common amino acids. Polyglycine or polyaspartic acid alone formed no spherules.

Microspheres prepared from acidic proteinoids were found to take up Gram stain but were negative whereas the ones from basic proteinoids were gram-positive [42]. It was proposed that this observation indicated similarities of surface composition in proteinoid microspheres and bacteria. Observations with the optical microscope suggested the presence of a double boundary [41]. This observation was extended by fixing the microspheres with osmic acid, sectioning them, and then viewing the resultant specimens with the electron microscope. As shown in Fig. 6-6, the double-layer fabrication is clearly observed. This experiment also emphasized the stability of the microspheres. It is important to realize, however, that generally the external barrier of these proteinoid microspheres is considerably thicker than the unit membrane found in living cells.

Close examination of Fig. 6-5 also suggests that some of the microspheres may be dividing in half [41]. Time-lapse photography further

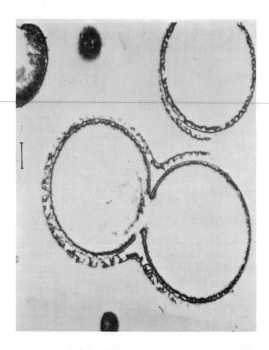

FIG. 6-6 Electron micrograph of stained proteinoid microspheres (see Fig. 6-5) suggesting division and a bilaminar boundary [41]. The standard dimensional unit shown is 1 μ long.

supports this suggestion. Micrographs of the microspheres reveal the presence of bud-like appendages, usually less than 1 μ in diameter. The buds generally appeared after the microspheres were allowed to stand in solution for 1 to 2 weeks. The buds were removed through the use of mechanical, thermal, or electrical shock, and collected by centrifugation [44]. They were stained with crystal violet and transferred to a solution saturated with thermal proteinoid at 37°C. The buds were observed to increase in size in 30 to 90 min when incubated at 25°C, suggesting growth by incorporation of external materials.

When suspensions of microspheres were subjected to slight external pressure, chain formations resulted [41]. When the pressure was increased, a splitting within the structures was observed. Upon the addition of a basic protein, such as histone, to a suspension of microspheres, the periphery of the spheres became rougher in appearance.

Under certain conditions, proteinoid microspheres exhibited localized enzyme-like activity. Such structures were prepared from proteinoid and fresh zinc hydroxide [41]. The microspheres were synthesized as before. The washed spheres were tested for their ability to hydrolyze adenosine triphosphate by making use of the known ATP-hydrolyzing capacity of divalent cations. These results are noted in Fig. 6-7. Such an effect was not observed with proteinoids lacking zinc. The hydrolytic effect was directly proportional to the amount of zinc present, but no enhancement of activity was observed over that found with an equivalent amount of zinc alone.   However, this experiment did demonstrate a means of localizing this hydrolytic function.   Other aspects of catalysis by proteinoids have been considered in Chap. 5.

The thermal model for chemical evolution, already discussed in detail in Chaps. 4 and 5, is believed to represent events that could have occurred, for example, near the dry or hypohydrous regions surrounding volcanoes.   To ascertain if the phenomena observed thus far actually could have taken place under such conditions, a mixture of anhydrous amino acids was prepared and heated to 170°C for 3 to 4 hr while placed on a piece of lava rock [45].   The product was washed with 1% aqueous sodium chloride solution, and the resultant aqueous phase was examined.   A large number of microspheres were identified in the mixture.

The experiments we have considered thus far in this chapter have demonstrated the morphogenicity inherent in simple compounds.   In the next section we shall examine the self-organizing capacity of macromolecular colloidal systems and determine how well this behavior compares to actual cellular manifestations.

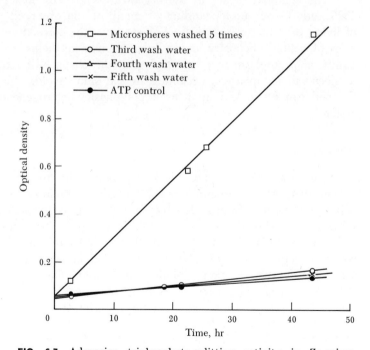

FIG. 6-7 Adenosine triphosphate-splitting activity in Zn-microspheres.   Optical density is molybdate color intensity measuring release of phosphate.   The spheres were produced by cooling a heated aqueous mixture of proteinoid and zinc hydroxide [41].

6-4 MORPHOGENICITY IN COLLOIDAL SYSTEMS

The key to much of cellular activity appears to lie in the colloidal properties of protoplasm. Colloidal systems are characterized by the presence
of particles in the 1-to-1,000-mμ size range [46,47]. Such structures can
be clearly seen with the aid of the electron microscope, and they give
characteristic light scattering patterns. In general, such particles do
not pass through the pores of celluloid membranes. In this sense, the
membrane can act as a sieve to hold back the colloidal particles and
permit smaller structures to pass through. Typically, colloidal particles
diffuse more slowly than smaller molecules. Sodium ions diffuse 20,000
times faster in water than does the colloidal protein albumin. Charged
functions on the surface of colloidal particles lead to the development
of an interface between the particle and the environment, and thus permit
an interplay between the two. This activity can also cause an interaction between two colloidal particles within the medium. Colloidal systems may be homogeneous, such as a protein dissolved in an aqueous
solution, or heterogeneous, such as biphasic suspension of oil droplets
in water.

The colloidal theory of the organization of cells, first proposed in
1925, aids in our understanding of many of the observed phenomena
of living protoplasm [3,46,47]. For example, the correlation of the theories of colloid chemistry and cellular phenomena helps to explain the
ability of protoplasm to go through periodic changes of viscosity, such
as occur in cytoplasmic streaming in the slime mold. In this sense,
the cell can be looked upon as a polyphasic, heterogeneous colloidal
system.

Cell extracts

An indication that the substances of which cells are composed have
within them the information needed to direct their organization into
cell-type structures is provided by the following experiment [48]. The
ether-soluble (lipoid) and water-soluble (protein) fractions of animal
brain were isolated from one another. Upon recombination, small,
round structures were observed under the light microscope. Some of
the spherules had smaller globules inside and cilia-like structures on
their periphery. These spherules were observed to grow in size with
time. By keeping the reaction mixtures sterile, it was possible to preserve the structures for long periods of time. The gross characteristics
of the spherules varied with the pH of the surrounding medium. It
was possible to stain them with rhodamin, sudan, and Nile blue.

Living cells are characterized by a number of features including
unique morphology and chemical constitution [48]. As we mentioned
before, a living cell also exhibits coordinated synthetic and decomposing

reactions (metabolism), the ability to reproduce itself through growth and division, and various responses to changes in the external environment. A more thorough discussion of the characteristics of living cells can be found in any good book on cell physiology. For our purposes at the moment it is sufficient for us to note that the structures formed by the reconstitution of brain extracts exhibited certain peculiarities which are also common to living cells. Morphologically the spherules grossly resembled cells and were of course made up of the types of compounds commonly found in cells. Because of the presence of enzymes in the protein fraction, oxygen uptake and the release of CO_2 were observed. When the structures, called *autosynthetic cells*, were incubated for several hours, a phenomenon resembling cell division was observed. With the addition of salts to the surrounding medium, the electrophoretic characteristics of these spherules changed, apparently as a result of an insulation of charged groups on their surfaces. It was found that heat and x-rays, which are usually deleterious to living cells, had a destructive effect on the autosynthetic cells. These observations support the contention that the properties needed to organize cellular formations are apparently inherent in the compounds of which cells are composed. Therefore, protocells would be expected to have appeared under primitive conditions once the necessary materials had been produced by any of the means discussed in earlier chapters. Although the mixtures used to form autosynthetic cells are rather complex and are most likely out of the realm of primitive stages of biogenesis, the self-organizing phenomena which they exhibit are pertinent to our inquiry.

Coacervates

From the above discussion it may be seen that an appreciation of the fundamentals of colloid chemistry could provide illuminating insight into the origin of protocells. Therefore, one possible approach to recreating primitive cell formation in the laboratory would be to search for simple colloidal phenomena which may have operated prebiologically.

One such phenomenon is coacervation. [This system will be considered in detail here because it exhibits many of the properties possessed by other models and provides a basis for closely examining the general principles of the study of protocellular development. However, it is important to realize that the coacervate model, by itself (like the other models we have discussed), can be considered only a partial answer to the problem of the origin of the cell. This is because it exhibits some but not all of the features of present-day cells. The model is very useful for experimental purposes in deriving an overall hypothetical scheme for protocell development and especially in stimulating perspective and thought for further experimentation.]

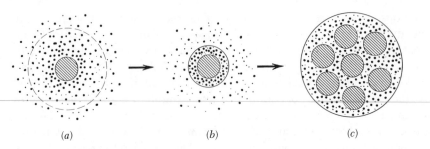

(a)   (b)   (c)

FIG. 6-8 Suggested model for coacervation. Colloidal particles associate and mutually exclude the solvating water, leading to a tightly bound sphere. The dots represent water molecules, and the shaded circles represent the macromolecules being united. (*After* [47].)

Simple coacervates are believed to result from a reduction of the hydration layer around colloidal particles [47] (see Fig. 6-8). A number of such particles unite, with the mutual exclusion of water. Thus, anything promoting partial dehydration can generally enhance coacervate formation. In complex coacervates, the additional feature of mutual attraction of opposite charges on the interacting particles enhances the association phenomenon. In the modern theory of this effect it is suggested that the affinity of the various surface groups of the colloidal particle for the solvent, such as water, decreases while the affinity for groups on other particles increases. For example, when the concentration of KCl is slowly increased in an aqueous solution of potassium oleate, a biphasic system ultimately forms. In the upper phase, small droplets appear, and these are known as coacervates. The added salt has competed for the solvent (water) molecules, and the decreased interaction between the solute molecules and the solvent has resulted in an association of the long-chain fatty acids. Spherical micelles result. Coacervation can also be achieved with proteins. For example, a complex coacervate can be formed between positively charged gelatin and negatively charged gum arabic. This type of coacervate can also be formed between a basic protein, such as a histone, and a nucleic acid (see Fig. 6-9). Other such associations are possible. It is of interest to note that coacervation can take place in very dilute solutions [47]. Coacervates show many of the morphological characteristics of cellular inclusions such as vacuoles and lipid droplets [49].

It has been proposed that the phenomenon of coacervation could have served as a primitive protocell-forming mechanism [8,50–52]. With the realization that salts were undoubtedly present in the primitive bodies of water and the suggestion that appropriate coacervate-forming large molecules could have been synthesized by this stage of evolution, the possible role of primordial coacervates in the appearance of protocells has been investigated in detail. This phenomenon would provide a means for the establishment of bounded internal environments for the localized development of protometabolic reaction sequences.

Coacervate formation not only serves to provide a locally segregated environment distinguished by a boundary from the exterior, but also permits the internal components to interact with the environment as an open system. In general, most coacervates are stable within relatively narrow limits of pH. Coacervate droplets can be separated from their original solution by mild centrifugation. In high centrifugal fields coalescence results, however. The formation of the boundary permits each unit to acquire a certain degree of individuality. Coacervation may be looked upon as a spontaneous process occurring when the conditions are right and the appropriate reactants are present. Coacervate droplets may be produced from the types of organic materials already discussed in Chaps. 4 and 5, as well as from inorganic compounds such as sodium silicate, alcoholic ammonia, and the complex salts of cobalt. Inorganic colloids have the ability to form microspheres under appropriate conditions which resemble certain types of cellular inclusions [53]. The ubiquitous occurrence of silica on the surface of the Earth and in several types of primitive organisms suggests that such a model may have some relevance to our inquiry.

The ability of coacervates to take up and concentrate materials

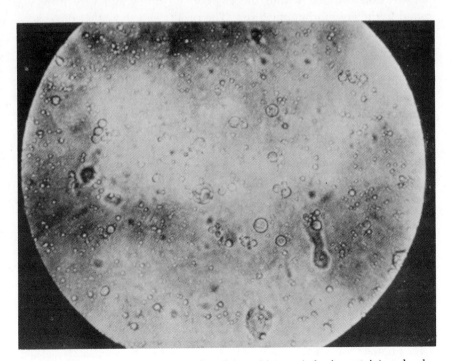

FIG. 6-9 Complex coacervates produced from histone (a basic protein) and polyadenylic acid [52].

from their environments is illustrated by an experiment in which coacervates were suspended in a solution of nucleic acids [51]. Through the use of the ultraviolet microscope and a luminescent screen it was demonstrated that the concentration of nucleic acid in the coacervates became much higher than that found in the equilibrium liquid surrounding them. From spectrograms it was determined that a typical spherical coacervate droplet had a diameter of 29 μ at an internal nucleic acid concentration of 760 mg percent, which was about 15 times greater than that of the overall system for this particular experiment.

Coacervate droplets have been shown to be able to draw enzymes into themselves from the surrounding aqueous medium [51]. In a typical experiment, coacervates were prepared from gum arabic and protamine sulfate within a solution containing bacterial lysate in phosphate buffer. The lysate was especially rich in catalase activity. Hydrogen peroxide was added, and the enzyme activity was followed with potassium permanganate titrations. It was possible to inactivate the enzyme by adding dilute sulfuric acid. Appropriate mixtures were prepared of coacervates containing active and inactive enzymes. The coacervates in each case were separated by centrifugation and remixed with the equilibrium (external) liquid. These experiments are summarized in Table 6-3. The results in this table indicate that catalase activity was concentrated within the coacervate drops and very little was found in the equilibrium mixture. The results also show that the coacervates could be isolated and resuspended in another medium while retaining particular internal characteristics.

In a related experiment, coacervation was achieved in a solution containing gum arabic and histone (or gelatin) as well as glucose-1-phosphate and potato phosphorylase [51,52]. The accumulation of starch within the droplet was revealed by the iodine test. On the other hand, when starch and β-amylase initially replaced the sugar phosphate

TABLE 6-3 Determination of the activity of catalase in coacervates [51]

System	0.01 N KMnO$_4$, ml*		
	Time of incubation with H$_2$O$_2$		
	2 min	3 min	5 min
Coacervate A (coacervate drops + equil. fluid)	2.23–2.55	1.50	0.73
Coacervate B (enzyme inactivated)	7.23–7.30	7.0	7.25
Coacervate drops A + equil. liquid B	2.10–2.20	1.70	0.70
Equil. liquid A + coacervate drops B	7.05–7.05	7.23	7.00

* The titrations indicate the amount of H$_2$O$_2$ left after the indicated time of incubation with each system. The greater the titrant volume, the less was the peroxide decomposition. Catalase promotes the reaction $2H_2O_2 \rightarrow 2H_2O + O_2$.

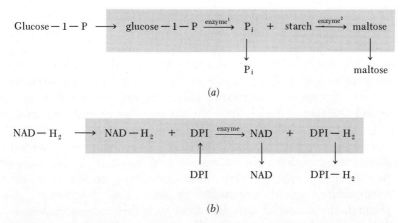

(a)

(b)

FIG. 6-10 Schematic drawings suggesting means by which coacervates (shaded areas) interact with the external environment. Encapsulated enzymes provide a localized metabolic system [52].

and phosphorylase, the starch was concentrated within the coacervates (4.5 times higher than in the equilibrium fluid). Because of the presence of the enzyme, the starch (glucose polymer) was hydrolyzed, with some of the maltose (glucose dimer) remaining inside the coacervate and some of it ending up in the equilibrium fluid, as noted by permanganate titration. Appropriate control experiments employing coacervates containing inactivated enzyme were carried out. They showed that the maltose found within the coacervates in the original experiment was not a carbohydrate recovered from hydrolysis product in the external equilibrium fluid. Rather, it was the result of an internal reaction. This phenomenon is summarized in Fig. 6-10(a). Under conditions in which reaction 1 was favored over reaction 2, the size of the coacervate increased, and this may be interpreted as a primitive form of growth as a result of the synthesis and accumulation of starch. Thus it can be concluded that coacervates are open systems.

A simple anaerobic oxidation-reduction system was achieved by adding bacterial oxido-reductase to a coacervate system containing NADH [52]. This is summarized in Fig. 6-10(b). DPI is a dye used to follow the redox reaction. It is also possible to accumulate chlorophyll within coacervates [52]. When ascorbic acid was added to the medium of such a preparation, a primitive photosynthetic system was obtained upon irradiation with visible light.

It is important to emphasize at this point that coacervation is not necessarily taken here to be the one and only phenomenon behind protocellular development. In fact we cannot be certain if this phenomenon had anything at all to do with the primordial origin of cells. However, observations made with coacervation provide a means for examining how protocell sophistication may well have occurred in general. In this case, we realize that the scheme we are about to review for proto-cellular evolution is almost entirely hypothetical and could, in certain aspects, be just as readily applied to the other models we have dis-cussed. However, it does take into account known characteristics of coacervates and will be discussed within this frame of reference.

The argument is as follows [54]: As previously noted, by taking in and utilizing materials from an environment already rich in organic material from previous stages of chemical evolution, the mass of the coacervate population would increase. The ability of coacervates to absorb material from the exterior would result in a size increase or growth of the sphere. Those units exhibiting greater rates of mass accumulation would eventually displace less progressive systems. Through the action of external forces such as wind and waves, separa-tion (or division) would result. An increase of internal activity with the assemblage of beneficial chemical reactions would rapidly alter the properties of the coacervate, causing disturbances and further pro-moting fragmentation of the units, or division. The coordination of growth with this division would amount to reproduction. The available supply of organic materials for direct use was, of course, limited, and only those coacervates whose development had led to the acquisition of traits superior to those of other units would continue to exist. The ability to repeat successful processes would enhance the survival. Once repeated action became coordinated into the reaction systems of the unit, self-duplication would become possible and life in its most basic sense would have appeared.

The purposiveness of these systems would be the development of traits with which to stabilize themselves and to cope with and utilize the environment so as to survive less successful competitors. By its physicochemical nature, a coacervate droplet is only moderately stable and is prone to dissolution with changes in the environment. For ex-ample, a complex coacervate formed between a basic and an acidic macromolecule is stable only when the pH of the environment is between the isoelectric points of the two constituents [47]. Similarly, coacerva-tion in an oleic acid-water mixture occurs only within well-defined limits of added potassium chloride concentration. That coacervates are espe-cially sensitive to changes in the external environment would further suggest that there is a direct interplay between the coacervate and the exterior. Such an effect would not necessarily be disadvantageous in evolving protocells in that it would provide a means for their further advancement. Spontaneous development of increased stability by ac-cumulation of valuable factors found in the environment would serve as such a driving force.

Catalytic functions would be improved by sophistication and modi-fication of the original incorporated materials. Further specialization would have led to regions of the biological unit taking on individualized functions and structures, and association of units would lead to inter-dependent colonies.

Thus it may be seen that coacervation can serve as a good model for determining a general picture of how protocell development may have taken place.

Although coacervates in particular display many interesting proper-ties shared with living cells, the exact means for internal differentiation to specific cellular inclusions is unclear.   The spontaneity of formation of coacervates would suggest that under appropriate conditions the ap-pearance of these structures would be favored.   No coacervate has yet been reported which shows in its boundaries the structural regularity found in living cells.   The coacervates which have just been discussed were each prepared under different, specific conditions.   Thus, it would be difficult to imagine a variety of types of coacervates existing in the same general environment.   For a given pH, one type would be favored over others.   More generally it can be concluded, however, that if an assortment of compounds able to exhibit associative colloidal properties became available, the formation of this kind of protocell would appear to have been a likely event.

Biphasic mixtures

Large molecules with both polar and nonpolar regions have the ability to form micelles in aqueous solutions [46]. This phenomenon results from the nonpolar regions of several such molecules coming close enough together to mutually exclude much of the water in their immediate vicinity.   At the same time the polar ends face outward to the aqueous environment.   An example of this is formation of micelles in a mixture of phosphatides (phosphorylated lipids) in water.   A bilamellar lipid-protein micelle is envisioned in the classical concept of the cellular "unit membrane" [55] (see Fig. 6-11).   The nonpolar ends of parallel long-chain fats form hydrophobic bonds with each other by mutually creating a nonpolar environment.   According to this scheme, the polar ends are contiguous with a protein coat on each side.

Although it would appear that nearly all living cells have both proteins and lipids in their membranes, one apparent drawback to the majority of models discussed in this chapter thus far is that in general they consist of only one class of compounds.   However, one model that has been proposed includes the two-substance aspect of biological mem-branes [56]. Its principles are based on the observations noted upon the collapse of surface films.   This phenomenon occurs when a thin film is spread on the surface of a body of liquid.   When the film is made to collapse by wind, solution flow, or (as is done in the laboratory) by the movement of wax barriers toward one another, spheroid structures result.   A simple example would be the formation of air pockets in

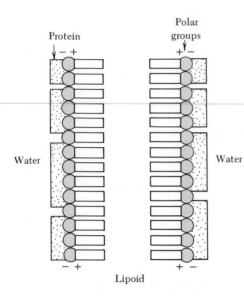

FIG. 6-11 Classical picture of the association of lipid and protein in the cell membrane [55].

choppy waves. These studies were extended to dilute protein solutions on which lipid films were formed. An example of this would be an oleic acid monolayer spread on a solution of egg albumin. The two systems are immiscible with one another. With mechanical collapse, round structures form. A number of observations suggested that these structures were internally hollow. A means by which these structures are believed to have been formed is indicated in Fig. 6-12. Moving outward from the center of the formed structures, it is concluded that one would encounter first protein, then two layers of lipid, and then protein again. The marked resemblance of this to the classical picture of the unit membrane discussed earlier is significant. The formed structures were found to have a diameter of about 1 to 10 μ. However, these structures are not spherical in shape, but rather they are elongated tubules. Under the experimental conditions used, a double lipo-protein "membrane" is readily produced. Similar structures were also found in nature where oily surface films had been collapsed by air or water movement.

These structures would provide another means for keeping an isolated medium with a relatively constant composition distinct from that of the external environment. Again it must be pointed out that they can in no way be considered to be living, but rather they could have provided the means by which localized environments became isolated and subsequently developed into unique, specialized, metabolizing systems.

In addition to the systems already mentioned, a large number of organic and inorganic mixtures have resulted in the production of cell-like figures [53,57]. Although some of these combinations appear unrealistic in terms of what is believed to have been the nature of the primitive Earth, they further demonstrate the predisposition of a large variety of molecular combinations to organize into structures.

Several interesting points of comparison can be made between the systems discussed in this chapter. For instance, with regard to the coacervates and proteinoid microspheres, it has been observed that in fact the two may be closely related [58]. Proteinoid microspheres were prepared by the means already discussed. The aqueous suspension was dried and then rehydrated with a citrate-phosphate buffer at a pH of 8.0. The dehydration-rehydration process (as may be found at seashores due to waves and tides) was repeated three or four times. Microscopic examination of the resultant mixture revealed the presence of coacervate-like spheres. The spheres were able to concentrate methylene blue stain. The final spheres were 10 to 30 μ in diameter, whereas the initial microspheres were of the typical 2-μ size. The final large spheres were able to coalesce with one another, whereas proteinoid microspheres do not normally carry on such a process. These experiments may provide evidence of a link between coacervates and proteinoid microspheres. Such similarities may also exist between the other

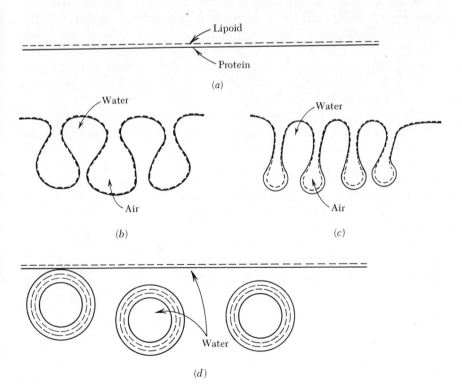

FIG. 6-12 Proposed model for the appearance of biphasic vesicles produced when wave motion upsets a protein solution bounded by a lipid surface [56].

models discussed here, although this has not been closely examined as yet. The aspects which coacervates and cellular colloidal phenomena have in common have already been pointed out.

6-5 CONCLUSIONS

Perhaps the most important point to be drawn out of all the experiments discussed in this chapter, whether they be concerned with Jeewanu, proteinoid microspheres, coacervates, or even air bubbles in seawater [59], is that there appears to be an inherent morphogenicity and ability to locally concentrate materials in the types of compounds that may very well have existed on the primitive Earth. It has been shown in this chapter that cell-like structures could have resulted from the interactions of a wide variety of compounds including substances as simple as thiocyanate and formaldehyde. The more complex reactants, such as polypeptides, could have appeared by the types of processes discussed in Chap. 5. Given the set or variety of sets of conditions that are believed to have existed on the young Earth, the appearance of protocells would appear to have been a likely event. This is not to say that any of the processes discussed in this chapter in fact represents a direct synthesis of complete living cells themselves. It is important to realize that the evolution of living cells most probably did not occur as an abrupt event. Rather, it was probably the result of a large number of very small, gradual steps, ultimately leading up to the development of a structure bearing the specialized characteristics of the biological cell. More will be said about this in Chap. 7.

Membranes such as those known to exist in contemporary cells consist of a complex association of proteins and lipids, as we have discussed earlier in this chapter. The proteinoid microspheres, on the other hand, are made up of polyamino acids alone. Whether primitive cells required both protein and lipid in their limiting membranes is not certain. If, for example, the proteinoid microsphere was in fact the most prevalent form of the primordial cell prototype on the primitive Earth, a means would then have to be devised to explain how it evolved to the more complex type of assemblage found today. Also, living cells carry on a number of interrelated, integrated functions which are lacking in the protocell models considered here. The mode of origin of these associations remains to be examined. In any case, the results thus far suggest that the spontaneous development of a self-sufficient pattern of chemical reactions and structures is well within the realm of comprehensible natural phenomena.

From all that has been discussed in this and preceding chapters it would appear that the conditions and compounds found on the primitive Earth had a built-in predisposition which ultimately led to the development of biological systems as we know them today. As we noted in preceding chapters, one conclusion that could be drawn from

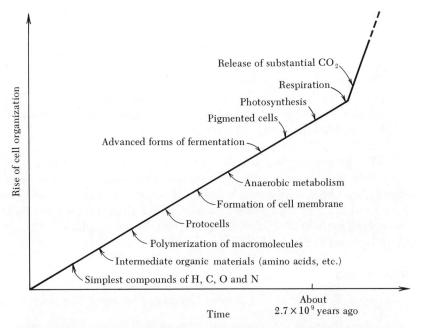

Release of substantial CO_2

Respiration

Photosynthesis

Pigmented cells

Advanced forms of fermentation

Anaerobic metabolism

Formation of cell membrane

Protocells

Polymerization of macromolecules

Intermediate organic materials (amino acids, etc.)

Simplest compounds of H, C, O and N

Time   About 2.7 × 10⁹ years ago

Rise of cell organization

FIG. 6-13 Diagrammatic representation of a possible scheme of primordial bio-genesis. This figure is highly over-simplified and is intended only as a convenient means of visualizing the probable sequence of phases in the overall process. (*Based on* [61].)

all of the experimental work that has been done so far is that biogenesis may be looked upon as a probable complex of events in the context of what are assumed to have been the conditions prevailing on the primitive Earth. The observations we have reviewed in the present chapter support the contention that the appearance of localized environments should not be looked upon as a highly improbable occurrence, but rather as one which may in fact have been difficult to prevent. These experiments would suggest that given any of a large variety of possible primitive Earth conditions, the production of protocells seems to have been a likely event. In other words, the suggestion now seems well founded through laboratory demonstration that the steps leading to the origin of living organisms were the results of reproducible physi-cal and chemical phenomena. The actual factors behind further sophis-tication beyond the protocell stage need merely to be elaborated through further experimentation.

Thus, inherent self-organization is observed on several levels of pre-logical order as follows:

1.   The same essential kinds of biomonomers can be synthesized from a large variety of plausible starting reactants through the application of different free-energy sources.

2. Nonrandom sequences of amino acids, some of which bear limited catalytic activity, result from seemingly nondirected associations of free amino acids (protein tertiary structure is apparently determined by the primary sequence of residues [60]).
3. The types of compounds thought to have been produced during prebiological chemical evolution exhibit the capacity to form proto-cellular structures in which subsequent stages of metabolic and biological development could have taken place.

This general outline leaves a number of gaps in the continuum of natural systems from the simple to the complex. Many of the particular details have been discussed already in this book or remain to be investigated and filled in with more evidence, as we shall consider in Chap. 7. An overall hypothetical scheme for the probable major phases of biogenesis is depicted in Fig. 6-13.

REFERENCES

1. Heslop, R. B., and P. L. Robinson: "Inorganic Chemistry," Elsevier Publishing Company, Amsterdam, 1960.
2. Roberts, R. B.: in J. L. Oncley (ed.), "Biophysical Science—A Study Program," John Wiley & Sons, Inc., New York, 1959.
3. Giese, A. C.: "Cell Physiology," W. B. Saunders Company, Philadelphia, 1962.
4. Horowitz, N. H.: in A. I. Oparin (ed.), "The Origin of Life on the Earth," Pergamon Press, New York, 1959; Lederberg, J.: Science, 131:269 (1960); 132:393 (1960).
5. Steinman, G.: Arch. Biochem. Biophys., 119:76 (1967); 121:533 (1967); Steinman, G., and M. N. Cole: Proc. Natl. Acad. Sci., 58:735 (1967).
6. Ogston, A. G., and O. Smithies: Physiol. Rev., 28:283 (1948).
7. Lumry, R.: in P. D. Boyer, et al. (eds.), "The Enzymes," vol. 1, Academic Press Inc., New York, 1959.
8. Oparin, A. I.: "Origin of Life," Dover Publications, Inc., New York, 1953.
9. Davidson, J. N.: "The Biochemistry of the Nucleic Acids," Methuen & Co., Ltd., London, 1960.
10. Fox, S. W., A. Vegotsky, K. Harada, and P. D. Hoagland: Ann. N.Y. Acad. Sci., 69:328 (1957).
11. Isherwood, F. W.: in E. M. Crook (ed.), "Glutathione," Cambridge University Press, New York, 1959.
12. Steinman, G.: Science, 54:1344 (1966).
13. Bruice, T. C., and S. J. Benkovic: "Bioorganic Mechanisms," vol. 1, W. A. Benjamin, Inc., New York, 1966.
14. Koltun, W. L., R. N. Dexter, R. E. Clark, and F. R. N. Gurd: J. Am. Chem. Soc., 80:4188 (1958); Bender, M. L., and B. W. Turnquest: J. Am. Chem. Soc., 79:1652 (1957); 79:1656 (1957); Bruice, T. C., and G. L. Schmir: J. Am. Chem. Soc., 79:1663 (1957); 80:148 (1958).
15. Katchalski, E., G. D. Fasman, E. Simons, E. R. Blout, F. R. N. Gurd, and W. L. Koltun: Arch. Biochem. Biophys., 88:361 (1960); Merrifield, R. B., and D. W. Wooley: Federation Proc., 17:275 (1958); Cruickshank, P., and J. C. Sheehan: J. Am. Chem. Soc., 86:2070 (1964); Kopple, K. D., and D. E. Nitecki: J. Am. Chem. Soc., 84:3000 (1962); Sheehan, J. C., G. B. Bennett, and J. A. Schneider: J. Am. Chem. Soc., 88:3455 (1966).

16. Wooley, D. W.: *J. Am. Chem. Soc.*, **88**:2309 (1966).
17. Ochoa-Solano, A., G. Romero, and C. Gitler: *Science*, **156**:1243 (1967).
18. Haurowitz, F., and P. Schwerin: *Enzymologia*, **9**:193 (1940).
19. Wang, J. H.: *J. Am. Chem. Soc.*, **80**:3168 (1958).
20. Shaffer, N. K., et al.: *J. Biol. Chem.*, **225**:197 (1957).
21. Fisher, E.: *Chem. Ber.*, **27**:2985 (1894).
22. Fox, S. W., and G. Krampitz: *Nature*, **203**:1362 (1964); Fox, S. W., K. Harada, and D. L. Rohlfing: in M. A. Stohman (ed.), "Polyamino Acids, Polypeptides, and Proteins," University of Wisconsin Press, Madison, Wisc., 1964.
23. Bahadur, K.: *Agra Univ. J. Res. (Science)*, **14**:41 (1965).
24. Steinman, G., D. H. Kenyon, and M. Calvin: *Biochim. Biophys. Acta*, **124**:339 (1966).
25. Steinman, G., D. H. Kenyon, and M. Calvin: *Nature*, **206**:707 (1965).
26. Steinman, G.: *Arch. Biochem. Biophys.*, **119**:76 (1967).
27. Steinman, G., and M. N. Cole: unpublished results.
28. Horowitz, N. H.: *Proc. Natl. Acad. Sci.*, **31**:153 (1945).
29. Eakin, R. E.: *Proc. Natl. Acad Sci.*, **49**:360 (1963).
30. Calvin, M.: *Science*, **130**:1170 (1960).
31. Brinigar, W. S., and J. H. Wang: *Proc. Natl. Acad. Sci.*, **52**:699 (1964); *Proc. 6th Intern. Congr. Biochem., New York*, **132**:263 (1964); Brinigar, W. S., and D. B. Knaff: *Biochemistry*, **4**:406 (1965); Brinigar, W. S., D. B. Knaff, and J. H. Wang: *Biochemistry*, **6**:36 (1967).
32. Boyer, P. D., et al.: *Proc. 5th Intern. Congr. Biochem., Moscow*, **5**:274 (1961);
33. Gaffron, H.: *Grad. J.*, **4**:82 (1961); Berkner, L. V., and L. C. Marshall: *Proc. Natl. Acad. Sci.*, **53**:1215 (1965); *J. Atmos. Sci.*, **23**:133 (1966); **22**:225 (1965).
34. Wald, G.: *Proc. Natl. Acad. Sci.*, **52**:595 (1964).
35. Grossenbacher, K. A., and C. A. Knight: in S. W. Fox (ed.), "The Origins of Prebiological Systems," p. 73, Academic Press Inc., 1965.
36. Herrara, A. L.: *Science*, **96**:14 (1942); *Bull. Lab. Plasmogenie*, **2**:1 (1940–1942).
37. Smith, A. E., J. J. Silver, and G. Steinman: *Experientia*, **24**:36 (1968); unpublished results.
38. Labadie, M., R. Jensen, and E. Neuzil: *Bull. Soc. Chim. Biol.*, **49**:673 (1967).
39. Bahadur, K.: "Synthesis of Jeewanu the Protocell," Ram Narain Lal Beni Prasad, Allahabad, India, 1966.
40. (a) Fox, S. W., K. Harada, and J. Kendrick: *Science*, **129**(3357):1221 (1959); (b) Young, R. S.: in S. W. Fox (ed.), "The Origins of Prebiological Systems," p. 347, Academic Press Inc., New York, 1965.
41. Fox, S. W.: in S. W. Fox (ed.), "The Origins of Prebiological Systems," p. 361, Academic Press Inc., New York, 1965.
42. Fox, S. W., and S. Yuyama: *J. Bacteriol.*, **85**:279 (1963); *Ann. N.Y. Acad. Sci.*, **108**:487 (1963); *Comp. Biochem. Physiol.*, **11**:317 (1964); Fox, S. W.: *Biosci.*, **14**:13 (1964); *Nature*, **201**:336 (1964).
43. Emmons, W. H., G. A. Thiel, C. R. Stauffer, and I. S. Allison: "Geology," p. 308, McGraw-Hill Book Company, New York, 1955.
44. Fox, S. W., R. J. McCauley, and A. Wood: *Comp. Biochem. Physiol.*, **20**:773 (1967).
45. Fox, S. W.: *Nature*, **201**:336 (1964).
46. Wilson, E. B.: in J. Alexander (ed.), "Colloid Chemistry," p. 512, Reinhold Publishing Corporation, New York, 1928; McBain, J. W.: "Colloid Science," D. C. Heath and Company, Boston, 1950; Heilbrunn, L. V.: "Dynamics of Living Protoplasm," Academic Press Inc., New York, 1959; Heilbrunn, L. V.:

"Colloid Chemistry of Protoplasm," Verlag von Gebriiden Borntraeger, Berlin, 1928.
47. Booij, H. L., and H. G. Bungenburg de Jong: "Biocolloids and Their Interactions," Springer-Verlag OHG, Vienna, 1956.
48. Crile, G., M. Telkes, and A. F. Rowland: *Protoplasma,* **15:**337 (1932).
49. DeRobertis, E. D. P., W. W. Nowinski, and F. A. Saez: "General Cytology," W. B. Saunders Company, Philadelphia, 1954.
50. Mitchell, P.: in A. I. Oparin (ed.), "The Origin of Life on the Earth," p. 437, Pergamon Press, New York, 1959; Evreinova, T. N.: in A. I. Oparin (ed.), "The Origin of Life on the Earth," p. 493, Pergamon Press, New York, 1959; Macovschi, E.: in A. I. Oparin (ed.), "Origin of Life on the Earth," p. 466, Pergamon Press, New York, 1959.
51. Oparin, A. I.: in A. I. Oparin (ed.), "The Origin of Life on the Earth," p. 428, Pergamon Press, New York, 1959.
52. Oparin, A. I.: in S. W. Fox (ed.), "The Origins of Prebiological Systems," p. 331, Academic Press Inc., New York, 1965.
53. Herrera, A. L.: *Arch. Plasmologie Gen.,* **1:**55 (1912).
54. Oparin, A. I.: "Life, Its Nature, Origin and Development," Oliver & Boyd Ltd., Edinburgh, 1961.
55. Danielli, J. F.: in H. Dawson and J. F. Danielli (eds.), "Permeability of Natural Membranes," Cambridge University Press, New York, 1943.
56. Goldacre, R. J.: in J. F. Danielli, K. G. A. Pankhurst, and A. C. Riddiford (eds.), "Surface Phenomena in Chemistry and Biology," p. 276, Pergamon Press, New York, 1958.
57. Herrara, A. L.: in J. Alexander (ed.), "Colloid Chemistry," p. 75, Reinhold Publishing Corporation, New York, 1928; Smith, A. E., F. T. Bellware, and J. J. Silver: *Nature,* **214:**1038 (1967).
58. Smith, A. E., and F. T. Bellware: *Science,* **152:**362 (1966).
59. Sutcliffe, W. H., E. R. Baylor, and D. W. Menzel: *Deep-Sea Res.,* **10:**233 (1963); Baylor, E. R., W. H. Sutcliffe, and D. W. Hirschfeld: *Limnol. Oceanog.,* **8:**369 (1963).
60. Anfinsen, C. B., E. Haber, M. Sela, and F. H. White: *Proc. Natl. Acad. Sci.,* **47:**1309 (1961); Epstein, C. J., R. F. Goldberger, and C. B. Anfinsen: *Cold Spring Harbor Symp. Quant. Biol.,* **28:**439 (1963); Schachman, H. K.: *Cold Spring Harbor Symp. Quant. Biol.,* **28:**409 (1963).
61. Berkner, L. V., and L. C. Marshall: *J. Atmos. Sci.,* **22:**225 (1965).

conclusions
and prospectus

(This chapter is a compilation of a series of discussions between the authors of this book, here designated as **A** and **B**. Key words are printed in **boldface** to facilitate the location of topics of specific interest.)

7-1 EMERGENCE OF ORDER IN PROBIOGENESIS

A: On the basis of the discussions of the previous six chapters, what do you feel are the major conclusions we can draw at this point?

B: First of all, it is apparent that a great variety of **biomonomers** and **biopolymers** have been produced in primitive Earth simulation experiments.

A: Although it is an interesting laboratory observation that one can produce these biomonomers and biopolymers under relatively simple conditions, do these observations really have any bearing on the possible mode of origin of living systems?

B: Let's back up just a little bit. We saw that various mixtures of primitive gases give rise to a variety of organic compounds, among which are the α-amino acids occurring in contemporary proteins. We also saw that in the polymer-synthesizing reactions, these amino acids enter into specific associations with one another so that certain dimers are favored over others. We should also point out that the biopolymers that have been synthesized themselves have the ability to organize into primitive cell-like structures.

A: In spite of the validity of these observations, do you really think they have any bearing on our ultimate understanding of the primordial appearance of living systems?

B: The very fact that primarily the biomonomers (i.e., biologically significant compounds), rather than nearly all conceivable kinds of other organic compounds, are formed in the simulation procedures shows that these experiments, at least in that sense, may have pertinence to the origin of life. Also, since these monomers, under certain conditions, can spontaneously form polymers such as those occurring in contemporary living systems, it seems to me that the experiments have relevance, at least insofar as we are seeing the formation of the *right kinds* of compounds.

A: However, I can think of several reactions of interest to the organic chemist that can also lead to the production of the types of compounds we find in living systems. Will these latter reactions also be of any significance at all to the elucidation of the origin of life?

B: What you are referring to here is **synthetic organic chemistry** and, true enough, many biologically important compounds can be synthesized by the organic chemist in vitro. But the point about the simulation experiments is that sophisticated biologically important substances are formed from simple reactants under **possible primitive Earth conditions** without the intervention of the experimenter once the experiment gets started. The yields may be very much lower than the organic chemist gets in his syntheses, but, nevertheless, the important point is that the biologically important compounds are being formed without outside manipulation at several stages once the starting conditions are set up.

A: You have referred to primitive Earth conditions. How can you really be sure that you are working under primitive Earth conditions?

B: In Chap. 3 we made an attempt to assemble lines of evidence bearing on the nature of the surface of the primitive Earth in which we think the chemical evolutionary reactions must have taken place. We saw there that we could set broad limits on the physical and chemical conditions, such as the probable temperature ranges and the fact that there was liquid water on the surface of the primitive Earth, and we could say something about the gases in the primitive atmosphere. In the simulation experiments we don't try to duplicate in detail the surface of the primitive Earth, since we will probably never know what it may have been like. We try to duplicate what we think were the most general conditions, and then we use very simple reactants, start the experiment going, and watch to see what compounds come out. Because we do find biologically important compounds being produced, we think that we at least have a **geochemically plausible picture** emerging of what might have happened.

A: However, do you think we can extend this to say that many model systems might be useful even though the geochemical plausibility is doubtful (e.g., the nonaqueous organic solvent systems that have been employed to synthesize polynucleotides)?

B: In the design of simulation experiments, one must not employ reaction conditions which are so improbable in the context of possible primitive Earth events that they would not be expected to have been found in the early days of the Earth, since the results you would get may not have any relevance at all to probiogenetic events. We can't forget geochemical realities in a simulation experiment.

A: It does not appear that it is really necessary for us to determine in detail the actual conditions on the primitive Earth. Rather, what we must attempt to do is to determine what the likelihood was that these biologically significant compounds could have been produced under any one of a variety of possible conditions. If many variations of the conditions turned out to be suitable, then we could say that the primordial production of biocompounds was probable. This has, in fact, been shown to be the case. For example, in Table 4-4 we noted that amino acids can be produced from a wide **variety of starting reactant gaseous mixtures.** Thus, it becomes less important for us to determine which one of these particular circumstances actually simulates primitive Earth conditions since the conclusion becomes apparent that the **appearance of amino acids was a very likely occurrence** under any one of these possible sets of conditions.

B: That's right. I would also add the point that it doesn't seem to matter what particular **free-energy source** is applied to the initial gaseous mixture, whether it be x-rays, gamma rays, ultraviolet radiation, or thermal energy. Essentially the same array of compounds emerges in the reaction vessels under all these conditions. Not only can we relax the requirements on the initial gaseous mixtures to some extent (for example, use carbon dioxide in place of methane), but we can also almost completely relax any specific requirements on the free-energy input. Therefore, the directions that the reactions take appear to be *determined more by the nature of the reacting elements themselves than by the general environmental parameters* of the simulation experiments.

A: Are you saying that if one merely has a source of carbon, oxygen, hydrogen, and nitrogen, he can expect to get the required biomonomers in any case?

B: I'm not going that far because the experimental data that we have accumulated until now don't allow us to do that. We haven't tested many possible carbon sources, such as normal paraffins of long chain length or graphite, for example. What I am saying is that many simple gaseous compounds of the element carbon apparently can serve as suitable carbon sources.

A: Then let us accept for the moment the conclusion that the essential biomonomers could well have been produced under primitive conditions. We know that living systems at the present time depend upon such complex compounds as proteins, nucleic acids, polysaccharides, and the like. How can we say that we have some insight into the origin of these types of compounds as well?

B: Extension of the simulation experiments into the aqueous and solid phases using already-formed monomers as starting materials has shown that we can synthesize under plausible geochemical conditions all of those classes of **macromolecules** that you spoke of. For instance, amino acid polymers of molecular weights running into tens of thousands have been synthesized. Even polynucleotides have been formed under conceivable geochemical conditions. So, I think we do have abundant evidence that not only can the biomonomers be synthesized in the simulation experiments, but that most of the essential kinds of biopolymers can also be formed.

A: However, contemporary proteins, for example, consist of very **definite linear sequences** of amino acid residues. There is a large amount of information present in the architecture of these amino acid polymers, and the characteristics of the polymers are largely determined by the sequence of the monomeric units. How is it possible to visualize the origin of such specific sequences rather than some random array of monomeric units?

B: In Chap. 5 we reviewed abundant evidence showing that amino acids do not link up at random, but rather are apparently highly **constrained** to link up in certain preferred ways. Although the particular synthetic methods described in previous chapters may or may not represent the most prominent reactions operating on the primitive Earth, these studies do point out the tendencies for organization inherent in simple biocompounds. For example, glycine is coupled to another glycine molecule to form diglycine much more readily than to a phenylalanine molecule to form glycylphenylalanine.

A: In other words, you're saying that there are **inherent characteristics within these reactant molecules** which will determine the ultimate nature of the polymers produced. In that sense, one might define "information" as that which sets or reflects a particular pattern of organization.

B: That's what I'm suggesting.

A: But even if this is true, what does it tell us about the origin of biological order? Even though we may see in the laboratory certain sequences being preferred over others when amino acid polymerization is carried out in the absence of nucleic acids, does this give us any inkling that the processes are really relevant to biogenesis? Are the polymers produced by such a process at all significant in the context of living systems as they exist today?

B: You recall we discussed evidence showing that if you arrange the probabilities of formation of the different dimers of a number of particular amino acids from the most probable dimer down to the least probable and then construct a similar scale based on analysis of **contemporary protein sequences** (particularly nearest-neighbor frequencies), you find that the two sets of probability data show surprisingly similar trends.

A: That's right; so, in summary we can state first that we can account for the appearance of biomonomers under possible primitive conditions.

B: Yes.

A: In addition, we see that the polymerization of these units also could have occurred quite readily under primitive conditions.

B: Yes, I would agree with that.

A: And not only do we observe the production of biopolymers, but these biopolymers apparently contain certain specific sequences which have been determined by characteristics inherent in the coming together of the units.

B: That's right; but isn't it true that so far we've only studied the formation of dimers, so we don't know really how far this sequence specificity extends?

A: Yes, but the chemical nature of the **peptide bond** at the dimer level is essentially the same as that found at the polymer level. Therefore, I suspect that those phenomena which we observe at the dimer level play a major role at the polymer level as well.

B: You're saying, then, that a major force which determines sequence generation is the **nearest-neighbor interaction.** Extending this line of reasoning, it seems reasonable that interactions due to secondary and tertiary structure would also be significant at higher levels of polymerization, as we've indicated in Chap. 5. However, once life did emerge and Darwinian evolution began to take over so that the amino acid sequences could vary because of point mutations of the genetic substance, shouldn't the sequences have changed with respect to the primeval sequences? If that's the case, why should contemporary nearest-neighbor frequencies still resemble the dipeptide frequencies in the primitive Earth experiments?

A: The preferences we did observe experimentally were not absolutely identical to what we find in nature at the present time, but they did show similarity in trends. Undoubtedly, Darwinian evolution over geological time resulted in certain modifications in the structure and function of proteins, but the basic underlying pattern initially built into the system from prebiological stages apparently has been retained to a recognizable degree in these systems.

B: Are you suggesting that there has not been enough time during the Darwinian phase in the history of life for polypeptide sequences to change so that they would no longer resemble the primeval sequences, or that there are intrinsic limits to the variability that protein sequences can assume within the context of biological evolution?

A: It is very possible that the present degree of order resulted from a combination of those two factors. For example, if one looks at the sequences of particular proteins from several sources (cytochrome, as an example), there are many portions of the sequences which are the same going from very simple organisms to the most complex which have been examined. [See the section on comparative biochemistry later in this discussion.] This would suggest that there are certain aspects of these sequences which are essential for the stability and function of these proteins, and many of the changes which have come about really have had very little effect on the survival potential of the organism.

B: Therefore, the concept of unique or preferred molecular ordering in probiogenesis would seem to extend to the *allowable* polypeptide sequences in order for life to exist at all.

A: Another thing which we mentioned before was that the very simple compounds which could well have been found on the primitive Earth also exhibit an inherent degree of supermolecular morphogenicity of a unique kind, that is, the ability to form **cell-like structures.**

B: Here I presume you're referring to things like thermal microspheres and the coacervate droplets.

A: Yes, and if we take all these points together, it would seem that not only the required compounds but also the fundamental structures could well have been produced primordially. In other words, with any one of a variety of conditions which we now think could have occurred on the primitive Earth, the appearance of living systems as we know them today would seem to have been a very likely occurrence, *in fact, one which may have been rather difficult to prevent.*

B: It appears as though there are inherent tendencies in the reacting substances at several levels of organization to form polymers and then aggregates of polymers which resemble simple living cells in some respects. In a lot of previous thinking, one sees the terms "chance," "rare event," and "chain of improbable events" referred to quite often in attempts to account for the origin of life. In our examination of the types of phenomena that may have led up to the development of living systems, we see the evolution of complex compounds which are not haphazard in their organization but instead have very definite molecular and structural characteristics. Also, we are observing localized concentration of these substances.

A: The proposed increase in order through chemical evolution might seem to be contrary to the laws of **thermodynamics**, which require that any process taking place in nature must go toward a more random state [1]. If one isolated event takes place in such a fashion that randomness is decreased, this must be done at the expense of another where the **entropy**, or randomness, is increased. That such is the case in the reactions we have been discussing does not appear to be immediately evident. It has been suggested for many years that biogenesis would have to be the result of a very improbable, chance event because of this entropy problem. However, when one is discussing entropy using classical thermodynamics, he is talking about a *closed* system. On the other hand, living cells are *open* systems by their interaction with the environment through mass and energy exchange. On the basis of the ideas of Onsager, Prigogine, and others, we have now come to a new realization—namely, closed systems strive to reach a state of *maximum entropy;* open systems try to reach a state in which *minimum changes of entropy* occur at some particular level.

B: It could well be that in the latter case the preferred state is one of high organization and, therefore, low entropy.

A: In addition to the experiments which we have discussed in Chaps. 1 to 6, several other studies can be cited which show that this **inherent tendency toward organization** is observed on many levels of biological order. For example, the interaction of an antigen and an antibody is very specific. If the protein and nucleic acid components of tobacco mosaic virus are separated, they will spontaneously rejoin upon mixing [2]. In this reunion, the active virus is again reconstituted. Similarly, the separated subunits of the lactate dehydrogenase complex spontaneously reunite into the active quaternary structure under appropriate conditions [3]. The point which becomes quite clear is that throughout the range of biological order, from the interactions of simple biomonomers to the association of complex polymers, there appears to be an inherent tendency toward the type of organization which we observe in living cells. This we might call **Biochemical Predestination.**

B: Biochemical what?

A: I said, Biochemical Predestination. By this I mean that the association of units toward the ultimate development of the living cell is determined by the physicochemical properties possessed by the simplest starting compounds from which these systems evolved. In other words, the ultimate characteristics of the living cell can be traced back to the nature of the starting compounds from which it was produced. Therefore, we should not look upon the appearance and development of the living cell as an improbable phenomenon but rather as one which followed a definite course governed and promoted by the properties of the simple compounds from which the process began.

It is worthwhile noting some remarks made recently by Needham; he stated that

> *Laboratory work therefore has in general strengthened the view that bio-logical reactions are the innate, spontaneous properties of materials which are synthesized spontaneously under natural conditions, and that life ori-ginated and evolved for this reason . . . Applied to the eobiological systems the contention is that life has always been precisely this most probable, opportunist exploitation of the most spontaneous pathways. [4]*

B: If I understand you correctly, what you seem to be saying is that the direction of chemical evolution is determined largely, if not solely, by **constraints** operating within the reacting chemicals them-selves. What about the general **environment** in which these chemicals were reacting? Could it also have influenced the course of chemical evolution?

A: Undoubtedly, the nature of the environment could have had an effect. For example, it was shown in Chap. 5 that either the avail-ability of UV light or changes in the pH of the medium can influence the sequencing of amino acids. Therefore, the ultimate characteristics of the systems produced from the simplest compounds were functions of the properties inherent in these reactants as they were influenced and modified by the characteristics of the environment.

Of course we can never be absolutely certain of the suggested over-all schemes we have discussed in earlier chapters, but taken as a whole, the evidence reviewed in this book leads to a relatively consistent pic-ture. This picture is supported by the various successes or failures in the laboratory. In any theory, of course, there is some degree of uncertainty about how much we really understand of the system, and this is one of the reasons why it is called a "theory." Can we say that, for example, the atomic theory is subject to the same degree of uncertainty as our Theory of Biochemical Predestination?

B: It seems to me that the atomic theory, on the one hand, and the Theory of Biochemical Predestination, on the other, are fundamen-tally different in nature in certain respects. In the case of the atomic theory we are attempting to describe the fine structure of matter. But we can return to samples of the matter at will and subject them to certain experimental procedures of increasing resolution. This eventu-ally allows us to construct a consistent set of hypotheses. With the Biochemical Predestination Theory, we are dealing with something which happened in the remote antiquity of the Earth; it may have happened only once, and we're not studying at the outset the fine structure of the chemical events because we don't know for sure what these chemical events were. With the atomic theory, we know that a piece of matter has an ultimate structure, and then we go after it and try to find out what it is. In the case of the origin of life, we don't know what phenomena were involved when we start the inquiry.

A: From what you have said, it would appear that one of the primary difficulties in expounding the Theory of Biochemical Predestination is that biogenesis from inanimate material is not taking place at the present time in nature. In other words, we do not now observe the appearance and evolution of new living systems starting from nonbiological sources and thus cannot study the actual process at will.

B: Yes. The Theory of Biochemical Predestination is not based primarily upon observations and indications of **neobiogenesis,** but rather upon experiments conducted within the simulation paradigm. In the simulation paradigm you're not returning to a naturally occurring phenomenon; you are artificially simulating what you think were natural conditions and then seeing what happens in the reaction vessel.

A: I agree; but we should pay attention to some recent observations. For example, amino acids have been found in rainwater and snow, and these amino acids apparently cannot be attributed to biological sources [5]. It has been suggested that these compounds are produced in the atmosphere by natural processes of a nonbiological nature. If this is true, then our thinking on the production of amino acids and other biocompounds in gaseous reaction mixtures using natural energy sources may well be founded on phenomena which occur in nature as well.

B: As I understand it, the Theory of Biochemical Predestination is quite broad in its scope in the sense that it extends from the formation of specific biomonomers all the way up through the spontaneous morphogenesis of protocellular structures exhibited by biopolymers. The observations of contemporary abiotic events in nature, however, seem to be restricted to the possible formation of amino acids under present conditions and do not extend to polymer-forming reactions and the like.

A: It is possible that this is just a shortcoming of the scope of experimentation that has been carried out. In the future, such observations might be made. However, it is also conceivable that because of the presence of hungry microbes throughout the natural environment, one will never be able to observe complete biogenesis in nature again.

B: Alright then, let's for the moment accept the Theory of Biochemical Predestination as a reasonable induction from the great bulk of experimental evidence reviewed in this book. What does it tell us about subsequent stages in chemical evolution leading up to the first living cell?

A: This theory suggests that all of the steps ultimately leading to biogenesis were subject to known physical and chemical phenomena, and that the ultimate character of the organisms produced was a direct function of the inherent nature of the simplest materials from which the earliest stages of chemical evolution began. In our present state of knowledge, it is relatively easy to see how simple interactions could have dictated the ultimate characteristics of the biomonomers and biopolymers that were synthesized. However, it undoubtedly will be more difficult to isolate particular processes in studies to be made on later stages of biogenesis and relate the results to properties possessed by the starting materials. With increased sophistication of our knowledge and ability to understand complex processes, the applicability of the Theory of Biochemical Predestination to all stages of biogenesis should become more evident.

B: I see your point. If what you say is true, then the Theory should also have something to say about events following primordial biogenesis, i.e., **Darwinian biological evolution.** Can we make any statements about constraining forces behind the evolution of organisms as we know them today and also about what may lie ahead in future stages of biological evolution?

A: I think it would be improper for us to stretch our necks out too far beyond the actual experimental data that we have on hand at the present time. Hopefully, future investigators will return to this question with the aid of more advanced insights into evolutionary processes. With the introduction of increasing complexity during the transition from protocells to the first living cells and during the earliest stages of biological evolution, the possibilities of different directions for evolution to take would seem to increase. What the Theory of Biochemical Predestination would tell us, however, is that the choices that would be made, i.e., the limits beyond which evolutionary processes could not stray, would be determined largely by properties inherent in the evolving bodies as preset by the materials from which the systems were fabricated. Modern thinking sees evolutionary processes being regulated by genetic factors responding in certain well-prescribed fashions to forces in the environment.

B: The parallel to our prior discussions on chemical evolution is evident.

A: As we discussed in Chap. 5, the tertiary structure of proteins is apparently governed by the primary sequence of residues. Efforts are now being made by several investigators to determine which residues or groupings of residues lead to the particular three-dimensional structures found in native proteins. Someday it should be possible with such data to predict the overall structure of a given polypeptide on the basis of its primary sequence alone. In the same sense, we should eventually be able to predict the overall course of evolution, both pre-biogenetic and Darwinian, on the basis of a known assemblage of starting compounds with particular properties and a given set of environmental circumstances, as the Theory of Biochemical Predestination suggests. We are not in that position as yet.

B: A point that's bothering me about Biochemical Predestination is that you say constraints operate in simulation experiments to force certain products and special ordering to appear. But every chemical reaction which the chemist studies involves its own intrinsic set of constraints, the most simple example of which is steric hindrance, which govern the course that a reaction will take under the conditions of the experiment. So what is so special about the operation of constraints in prebiological chemical evolution?

A: There would not appear to be anything unique about constraints operating on biocompounds as compared to other organic compounds. The great need up to the present time has been to demonstrate that, in fact, such constraints do operate in the synthesis and reactions of biocompounds. However, one significant distinguishing feature is that in the simulation experiments one could visualize the synthesis of almost any organic compound imaginable; it is very interesting to note, however, that those compounds which are produced in the greatest yields are the ones which are also found in biological systems today. Evolving systems conceivably could have utilized essentially any of the products of chemical evolution; the ones which finally became incorporated into living systems were those which were produced in high yields from simple substances and which at the same time could participate in further reactions of the greatest utility, and all others were rejected.

Let's consider a related point. We have been concerned here with what laboratory-based experiments can tell us about the origin of life on the Earth. Are there any other implications of Biochemical Predestination as we've defined it? For instance, there is great current interest in **exobiology,** the investigation of the possibility of life on other planets. Would these chemical evolution experiments suggest to us that, given the types of conditions we may find on a number of other planets in our own solar system or in other solar systems, we might anticipate the evolution of living systems there as well?

B: Yes, I think it's very likely on the basis of what we've discussed so far that life should occur quite generally throughout the universe and should arise under natural conditions whenever those conditions are suitable for the emergence of life. I would expect life to be a quite **widespread phenomenon** rather than a very rare one in the cosmos as a whole.

A: Thus, we can assume that should the appropriate reaction conditions be available, life would evolve. The calculations have been made as to the probability of another planet somewhere in the universe bearing properties conducive to lifelike systems [6]. This calculation has been based upon such things as the probability of a planet being a certain distance from its sun and having a certain mass (which would determine the composition of its atmosphere and its surface temperature). One can conclude that, on the average, there should be two habitable planets within 24 light years of each other. Within a radius of 100 light years away from the Earth, one could expect to find 50 such planets (our galaxy is 80,000 light years in diameter). In other words, we can conclude that there are many planets in the universe that do bear physical characteristics very similar to the Earth's. On the basis of the Theory of Biochemical Predestination, one can expect that biological systems would emerge on these planets as a result of interactions of the types that we have discussed in Chaps. 1 to 6.

B: What you're saying is that since our evidence seems to indicate that the emergence of life on the Earth was a highly probable series of events rather than a very rare or even miraculous event, Earth life should not be thought of as being unique in the cosmos. Let's go a step further. If the Theory of Biochemical Predestination is true and life is a common phenomenon in the universe, then wouldn't we expect the **chemical details** of life on different planets to be very similar, one to another?

A: This depends upon the chemical makeup of the particular planet that we happen to be considering. It also depends on the validity of the assumption that the laws of nature experienced on the Earth are the same on other cosmic bodies.

B: But among planets that have general environments similar to the Earth's, would we expect that if any life is present there, it would chemically resemble Earth life?

A: I think we're really making that suggestion, and if the evolving system had "a choice," say, with respect to the **solvent** system in which it could be dispersed, it would seem to "prefer" water as the medium.

B: Are you suggesting that on other planets in the universe, where the conditions are different from terrestrial conditions, possibly some solvent other than water might provide a suitable medium for the emergence of life?

A: Yes, this is true. For example, we know that on the large planets in our own solar system, liquid ammonia constitutes a good deal of the mass of the planet. It is quite conceivable that this ammonia could serve as a solvent in which some type of system could evolve. But let's imagine a planet on which both liquid ammonia and liquid water exist; in other words, we have extremes of conditions where both of these could be found.

B: Are you speaking about local variations in microenvironments on the surface of the planet?

A: That's right. The thing we should ask ourselves is if an evolving system had a choice of the **ammonia** or the **water** as its primary solvent, which would it prefer? There are a few characteristics of these two solvents that we could cite [4], and from this it might be possible to anwer this question. It is interesting to note that most warm-blooded animals on the Earth have a body temperature of about 37.5°C, the temperature at which the specific heat of water is minimal. As you know, water is liquid between 0 and 100°C, whereas ammonia is liquid between —78 and —33°C. Most aqueous solutions of salts have a minimum volume at 37°C, thus enhancing miniaturization of cells. Water has a uniquely high surface tension, and this makes it ideal for the formation of discrete bodies with lipid-water interfaces. Ammonia has a higher specific heat than water, and the viscosity of liquid ammonia is much less than that of water, making it much less suitable for the maintenance of certain molecular structures such as apoenzyme-coenzyme complexes. The dipole moment of ammonia is less than that of water, making polar substances less soluble in it than in water. For example, chlorides, sulfates, sulfides, hydroxides, and oxides are insoluble in liquid ammonia. We know that Earth-based living systems utilize these compounds in their makeup.

B: It seems to me that all of these points that you have raised with respect to the properties of water are related to the fact that Earth-based life is an aqueous system. But isn't it conceivable that on another planet where ammonia might be the solvent the chemical properties of the life that emerged might be considerably different, to take advantage of the peculiar properties of ammonia? You might find, for example, a minimum solubility or a maximum solubility or some other properties at an intermediate temperature in the liquid range of ammonia toward which all those forms of life have gravitated. At this point we can't exclude the possibility that an ammonia-based life might have developed elsewhere in the cosmos where ammonia is much more abundant than water.

A: Another question can be brought up: Why must Earth-bound systems be based entirely upon **carbon** compounds? Why not the ubiquitous element **silicon?**

B: Carbon has the remarkable property that it can link up with itself in a variety of combinations. It can make chains of different lengths, and it can form various branching compounds. Although silicon can also do this, the stability of the resulting chain compounds of silicon is considerably lower than the corresponding compounds of carbon. In bonding with itself, a carbon-to-carbon bond is about twice as strong thermodynamically as a silicon-to-silicon bond. Silicon has a high affinity for oxygen and forms silicate crystalline-mineral arrays which are highly stable. This would tend to lock up a considerable fraction of the available silicon. On the other hand, carbon, when it combines with oxygen, is a gaseous compound. Therefore, if we have evidence indicating that a planet does have carbon, nitrogen, oxygen, and other elements available to it in the same or similar chemical forms of the type we observe on the Earth, we can expect to find living systems (if such did evolve) bearing many of the same classes of compounds being utilized for their existence and maintenance.

A: Are you saying that there is a high likelihood that wherever life emerged in the cosmos, it would be carbon-based rather than based on some other element?

B: Yes, if carbon compounds were available for utilization. I think there is one further point that can be made here. This type of reasoning can be applied to the design of **life-detection** systems for the space program currently underway. The obvious guideline that such thinking might provide for life-detection systems is that they should be designed specifically to detect the presence of compounds of the type which now occur in terrestrial life.

A: Let us imagine a space probe designed to look exclusively for such compounds as glucose, adenosine triphosphate, proteins, nucleic acids, and things of this sort, and let us say that this experiment did not turn up such compounds. Would this be sufficient to conclude that, first, living systems did not exist on these planets and, secondly, that such planets did not provide the appropriate circumstances for living systems to evolve at a later date?

B: If we don't find biocompounds, we simply might not have looked at the right place on the surface of the planet, or possibly the sensitivity of our tests was too low.

A more interesting possibility is that any particular object in the cosmos we examine for the presence of life might simply not have reached the biological stage; it might be at a more primitive stage of chemical evolution characterized by uniquely **prebiological substances,** such as nitriles, formaldehyde, and so forth. Therefore, when we design so-called *life-detection systems,* we must not only consider compounds which we presently find in *biological* systems but also those which origin of life experiments have indicated may well have served as *primitive precursors* to these biocompounds.

A: Then, let us assume that we have sent up a space probe to specifically look for the types of chemical precursors to biocompounds that we have found in primitive Earth simulation experiments. Let us say we find nitriles that have been shown in the laboratory to lead ultimately to amino acids. What can this tell us about the origin of life experiments which we have carried out on the Earth?

B: This might corroborate our conclusion that nitriles were involved in terrestrial biogenesis.

A: Do we have any evidence yet to indicate that nitriles may be found on other cosmic bodies?

B: Yes. You'll recall that in our discussion of the Oparin-Haldane hypothesis and, specifically, the methane-ammonia view of the primitive atmosphere, we cited spectroscopic evidence that cyanide, as a prototype for nitriles, is rather widespread in various bodies in the cosmos. Such evidence may be a further indication that we might find either living systems on some of these other bodies or prototype systems which may serve as precursors to the ultimate evolution of lifelike entities.

A: It may also be that the cosmic bodies to be examined will have only some of the physical and chemical characteristics which were found on the primitive Earth and will lack some of the others. This may permit chemical evolution to reach an intermediate stage on these bodies and not go quite as far as living biological entities, as we find them now on the Earth.

B: What we're saying is that not only is life likely in the cosmos, but in addition, wherever it emerged, it probably followed a similar course of chemical evolution if conditions were similar. This leads to a very interesting extension of the doctrine of uniformitarianism as applied to the Earth (Chap. 1). We might have a **universal type of uniformitarianism** with respect to biogenesis which extends throughout the cosmos in both time and space. (There is the tacit assumption here that the laws of chemistry and physics are the same in the entire universe.) Am I to take it that one possible implication of the Biochemical Predestination Theory is that if we should encounter extraterrestrial living forms, they would probably resemble *morphologically* forms that have occurred on the Earth either in the fossil record or in contemporary life?

A: No, I wouldn't go that far. From the results that we have discussed, we can say that there are certain inherent ordering tendencies in bioorganic reactions, e.g., polypeptide synthesis. However, it is known that very small changes in the amino acid sequence of certain proteins, for example, can lead to very large changes in gross morphology. A very good illustration of this is the case of S-hemoglobin and its related syndrome, sickle cell anemia. The change of only one amino acid causes complete alteration in the morphology of the red blood cell [4]. Therefore, even though similar trends may have occurred in the linking together of amino acids at many different terrestrial sites or on many different planets, it may very well be that the supermolecular forms that result from them would be quite different in their overall appearance. Although the gross characteristics may very well be similar as a result of common physicochemical phenomena, unique local conditions would probably lead to identifiable biological differences from one planet to another. This is evident when one considers the general biochemical similarities found in nearly all Earth-bound living systems as well as the particular differences which distinguish one species from another.

B: Good point! We've mentioned that one of the implications of the Biochemical Predestination Theory is that life on other planets and other astronomical bodies would resemble Earth life chemically if those astronomical bodies had the same general environmental conditions as the Earth. From this we might be able to shed some light on the problem of monophyletic vs. polyphyletic origins of life on the Earth that we discussed in Chap. 1. It seems to me that the two situations are really very similar. In the case of polyphyletic origins we have the possibility that life arose at different points on the same globe. That's really the same as life originating on different globes of similar environmental conditions. In other words, the similarity in biochemistry of nearly all contemporary organisms is not inconsistent with the idea that life might have started at several different places on the Earth at several different times, each one of which gave rise to its own part of present phylogeny. In each case of possible separate origin on the Earth, the same chemical and physical constraints presumably would operate. It doesn't seem to make any difference in principle whether the origin takes place on different astronomical bodies or at different places on the same body, because in all cases the same fundamental constraints would be operating.

A: In some of our discussions thus far, we have been attempting to apply the information which has been gained from primitive Earth simulation experiments to particular problems that may not have been related initially to this area of investigation. It may be that we are taking information and attempting to apply it with a minimum amount of justification and reliability. However, what this type of inquiry can do is help us to design **investigations in related areas.** For example, we have pointed out in a few places in previous chapters that the findings of chemical evolution experiments have added significant knowledge to **organic chemistry.** In the synthesis of adenine from HCN, much information has been gleaned about the nature of cyanide chemistry and the addition of one cyanide molecule to another. As we pointed out, this synthesis of adenine has now been adapted to a commercial preparation of the base.

B: Also, there is a renewed interest in cyanamide chemistry, and many of the details that we learn about cyanamide reactions in our chemical evolution studies will enhance the likelihood that other applications will be found.

Extrapolating a little beyond the present state of our knowledge, one of the great difficulties in the origin of life field is that we just don't know enough about the molecular details of how living cells operate. Do you suppose that we could turn the coin over and see on the other side the possibility of gaining new insights into **molecular biology** on the basis of chemical evolution studies?

A: This is quite correct. I visualize this type of research being a two-way street. First of all, the more we understand about how a cell operates at its molecular level, the more readily we can design experiments to determine how the living cell did evolve. For example, you recall that in Chap. 5 it was suggested that sequenced polypeptides may have preceded sequenced polynucleotides on the primitive Earth. In this model, the information found in these sequenced polypeptides could then be transferred to (or in some way influence) the linking together of nucleotides. However, when experiments were carried out in an attempt to demonstrate such interactions, this evidence was not found. In the same sense that the living cell does not directly transmit information between messenger RNA and amino acid sequencing into new proteins (there is a transmission of information via enzyme intermediaries), so it may well be that during the development of primitive biodynamic functions some additional factor was involved in the interaction of polypeptides and polynucleotides. We who are working in the area of chemical evolution and primitive metabolism must await a more complete understanding of how the cell is able to carry out various processes. From this we would then be able to design experiments to show how these phenomena could have originated from the simple reaction patterns in protocells.

B: Do you think the experiments with simple systems related to chemical evolution can in turn provide us with **insights into biodynamic operations** themselves?

A: I definitely think this is true. For example, in Chap. 5 we discussed experiments which examined the interaction of amino acids with one another. The model systems employed were simple enough to isolate certain phenomena from others that in a more complex system would also be involved. When one examines enzymes and the way enzymes react, he is confronted with a complex macromolecular system where many forces are involved, and the identification or the isolation of any one of these forces becomes rather difficult. In the model systems which we examined in our primordial experiments, the simplified conditions allow us to develop a more intimate understanding of individual forces. Once this understanding of isolated forces has been derived, these findings can be used in the synthesis of an overall picture of molecular phenomena in the cell.

B: Can you cite a specific example of such an isolation of a single force?

A: In Chap. 6 in our discussion of the possible modes by which the primitive cell could have evolved, we looked at the way lipid and protein components, when isolated from one another and recombined, could have interacted to bring about the appearance of **primitive membrane-like structures.** In such an examination, one is able to come up with a more complete understanding and a more intimate appreciation of the interaction of lipids and proteins as it may be involved in contemporary membranes, as well as in the most primitive states of membrane development. We also looked at the **colloidal phenomenon** of coacervation. Whereas the colloid chemist may not be interested specifically in the relationship between coacervation and biogenesis, the chemical evolutionist has examined means by which coacervates can interact with enzymes dissolved in the medium, concentrate these enzymes, and carry on isolated, localized metabolic processes. Such a phenomenon may be involved in the functioning of the cell now. Actually, too little has been done in the context of biogenesis to determine how colloidal properties might have influenced primordial evolution and metabolism and ultimately the construction of the cell prototype. There is room for much effort in this direction. Through this type of inquiry, we can also develop a more complete understanding of basic physicochemical forces operating within the living cell.

B: We've emphasized evidence which shows that there are constraints operating in the way amino acids link up one with another. This raised the possibility that such constraints can also affect the way that nucleotides combine. This is something that has not been investigated in detail yet because it is difficult to analyze the sequence of units in **polynucleotides.** This is undoubtedly an area that will receive considerable attention in the future. Since we have studied the relative probability of formation of different dipeptides in their chemical evolutionary context, an obvious extension of this would be to study the relative frequency of formation of specific dinucleotides. Such a study is perfectly feasible now since dinucleotides have been synthesized under primitive Earth conditions. The point here is that the synthetic system is a very simple one and allows us to focus on the constraints operating at the nucleotide-nucleotide level.

7-2 PROSPECTUS

A: One thing that is important for us to realize at this point is that we are certainly a long way from solving the problem of the origin of life. What has been done already is far from synthesizing the simplest living cell. We suspect now that we'll ultimately be able to understand the origin of the first cells on the Earth on the basis of known chemical and physical laws. It is possible that some new physical principles may be discovered that are relevant, but we don't think we need to invoke such things as **vitalism, neovitalism, and supernatural influences.**

B: Some people have made the suggestion that the **virus particles** represent a transition state between nonliving matter and the living cell. Recently an active form of virus has been synthesized in vitro and in the presence of the purified viral DNA as the initial template [7]. The question might be raised as to whether this achievement actually brings us closer to solving the origin of life problem. We should point out that although viruses exhibit some of the characteristics of living systems (e.g., replication), they can carry out many of these processes only in the interior of a full-blown organism. They do this by cannibalizing the protein-synthesizing machinery of the host cell, and they're totally incapable of self-replication *on their own.* It seems likely to me that the virus particles might actually be evolutionary side-products of the genetic substance of already-evolved bacteria.

A: Some people think that if one mixed together the **DNA-polymerase** enzyme plus an appropriate array of monomeric nucleotide units and had a DNA template available, he would have the essential components of a self-duplicating, lifelike system. Is this correct?

B: Not exactly. There are two points that can be made here. The first one concerns the likelihood of finding, under primitive Earth conditions, molecules of DNA and DNA-polymerase (a complex enzyme system) both synthesized *and* localized together in the same small region of space. The second point is that the in vitro DNA-polymerizing system is really not self-replicating. True enough, the template DNA is reproduced, but the polymerase enzyme itself is not replenished in this process. So, the polymerase system taken alone cannot be considered self-replicating.

A: Is it true, according to what you have said, that the system "lives" or "dies" on the availability of a unique, particular enzyme?

B: I would require in a crude definition of "life" that all the components essential to the operation of this system would have to be replicated. I wouldn't say that the DNA-polymerase system is "living" because eventually the enzyme molecule will be thermodynamically degraded. Unless it is manufactured again to replenish what is lost, the polymerization process will come to a halt.

A: At several points in our discussion we have been using the terms "life" and "living systems," but what do we really mean by this?

We've touched upon this problem in Chap. 6. We indicated that the *potential* for organization was an essential factor in defining a living system. When we talk about the "origin of life," what are we really saying?

B: You raise one of the most difficult problems we have to face, namely, what is "life"? How do we set up criteria which allow us to identify whether or not a given chemical system is living? Many attempts have been made to list the minimum requirements of living systems. These lists have many points in common, but they differ in essential respects. Finding an unequivocal definition for "life" is an ongoing problem, and there simply isn't any satisfactory formula available that would be totally adequate for a definition.

A: Do you think it is correct to say that the types of experiments we are doing can really be defined as investigations into "the origin of life," and I emphasize the word "life" in this case?

B: No; I think that what has been done so far can be summarized by saying that we have learned something about the earliest stages in the transformation of inanimate matter into prebiological systems. But the most complex systems so far made in the simulation studies are a long way from the simplest, independent living cell.

A: I would agree and emphasize that much work remains to be done. It would appear that we need a more intimate understanding of what we mean by a living cell and how a living cell operates at its most basic molecular levels.

B: Yes. I would go a little further and say that the possibility of synthesizing a living cell from scratch in a test tube is, in the present state of our knowledge, very remote.

A: But it's worth stressing that what we have learned already has been rather thoroughly documented with numerous careful experiments. Let us consider a few examples of the **specific problems** on which we can expect to see intensive work during the next few years.

B: To begin with, there are some notable gaps in our picture of how essential biocompounds could have appeared on the primeval Earth. For example, a basic building block of **triglycerides,** namely, glycerol, has to date not been identified in simulation experiments, although there's no reason to believe that it's not there, and I suspect that we shall find it in the future. Also, triglycerides themselves, which are fundamental to membrane formation, have not yet been isolated in primitive Earth experiments. In addition, the coenzymes have not been detected. Aside from these exceptions, virtually all of the major classes of biocompounds have been found.

A: It's possible that this specific compound glycerol has been synthesized in the simulation experiments but its yield is so little that it may be difficult to identify. Since glycerol is such a very important and widely occurring compound in biological systems, it could also be that the synthetic methods employed thus far may not represent the most prominent means by which this compound actually appeared on the primitive Earth. However, what the simulation experiments have shown is that the synthesis of such compounds must have been subject to very simple interactions.

B: At this point I would like to suggest some extensions of the study of constraining influences to several specific problems:

1. We might investigate the addition of amino acids to selected already-formed oligopeptides or polypeptides in order to get at the possible influence of secondary structure on peptide sequencing. So far we've just studied the influence of the nearest-neighbor interaction. It seems to me that we could now add another level of organization of proteins, namely, secondary structure, and study the forces operating there.

2. We could examine sequence generation as it takes place at the interface between two different phases (e.g., an air-water interface or, in a model system, even an oil-water interface). This would allow us to get at the possible influence of the colloidal state of matter, insofar as it influences reactions of biological interest.

3. Another possibility would be to study catalytic activity in small peptides synthesized under primitive Earth conditions. The aim here would be an attempt to understand the origin of enzyme activity. For example, the simple tripeptide glutathione, which has been identified in primitive Earth simulation experiments, can serve as a simple model for ferredoxin if we add iron to the system.

4. I'd like to see a study of the interactions between nucleotides on the one hand and free amino acids on the other hand. This would be an attempt to understand how these two classes of biocompounds originally might have been dynamically coupled to eventually lead to the transmission of hereditary information from polynucleotides to amino acid sequences in proteins. Here I'm thinking of the search at the simplest level for physical interaction forces between nucleotides or small polynucleotides and various amino acids.

5. We might extend the sequence-ordering studies already done in the case of amino acids at the dimer level to the study of sequence ordering in the formation of small oligonucleotides.

6. We could examine the effects of already synthesized polypeptides on the rate of synthesis of small oligonucleotides and on the sequence in growing polynucleotides.

7. Another topic for serious consideration could be the partial degradation of selected macromolecules and biodynamic systems, followed by observation of the probability of reestablishment of the native functions under suitable conditions. This would tell us if Predestination

had a role in determining the characteristics of the macromolecular and supermolecular systems we find in nature today.

8. We should considerably extend our scope of allowable model systems. Virtually all the work that we've discussed has been done within the confines of the biochemical similarity principle. We study simplified versions of chemical interactions involving compounds which occur in contemporary life or, in the case of the nitriles and aldehydes, some obvious precursors. But it seems to me that we shouldn't rule out the possibility that many areas of chemistry other than biochemistry could provide us with useful model systems for studying more conveniently certain aspects of the origin of life problem. Here we can think of sequence ordering of certain synthetic polymers such as polystyrenes and various plastic materials. It may be that general polymer chemistry, although it doesn't necessarily involve biological polymers in particular, could provide us with very fruitful model systems and valuable insights.

A: That's a tantalizing list of research problems! Let me just add the following points: At the end of Chap. 5 we reviewed the problem of the origin of **optical uniqueness.** The conclusion we came to at that time was that we really cannot make any conclusive statements at this state of knowledge as to how such uniqueness evolved in nature. The Theory of Biochemical Predestination gives us no clues at the moment. Perhaps we're looking at this enigma incorrectly, and fresh ideas are needed.

Certainly another major problem which remains is how **metabolism** developed; how did the complex metabolic schemes that we now find in biological systems originally appear?

B: Yes, you'll recall that the great bulk of the experimental data accumulated so far in chemical evolution studies relates to the production of specific molecular species with relatively little emphasis on how complex **reaction sequences,** such as glycolysis and the citric acid cycle, might have evolved.

A: Perhaps a major reason for this is that when we consider the origin of metabolism, we are faced with the same sort of difficulty that examination of the whole origin of life problem entails. One can make speculations upon how these phenomena could have occurred, but the **design of specific experiments** to show that the origin of metabolism, for example, was the result of the interaction of very simple compounds and forces, as the Theory of Biochemical Predestination would suggest, is very difficult to formulate. In other words, how do we design a laboratory experiment to plausibly demonstrate how very simple compounds and very simple chemical interactions could have led to the evolution of the complex systems of metabolism that we find today?

B: One plausible avenue of investigation is suggested by the reaction sequences involved in the formation of the porphyrins under possible primitive Earth conditions. You'll recall that δ-amino-levulinic acid is a suitable starting material for the abiotic formation of pyrroles, which eventually condense into tetrapyrroles. Also, δ-amino-levulinic acid itself is produced in simulation experiments, probably by the condensation of glycine and succinic acid. Now, these steps resemble the steps which occur in the contemporary biosynthesis of porphyrins [8]. It might be that, at least in terms of the origin of biosynthetic metabolic sequences, we can gain some clues by studying the mechanisms of formation of particular products in our simulation experiments. This is not true in every case, but in some instances valuable insights can be gained.

A: This is a good example of how biochemical and biogenetic investigations can proceed hand-in-hand.

B: But the difficulty in this particular example is that in the contemporary biosynthetic sequences, enzymes are involved in each of the intermediate reactions, and we can't invoke similar complex catalysts in the primitive situations. Our problem is still one of how catalytic **enzymes** got involved in the sequence.

A: Undoubtedly, as we gain a much more complete understanding of the way enzymes operate in general, we shall be in a position to make some more definitive statements on how primitive catalytic, and therefore metabolic, systems arose. It's very likely that the evolution of primitive metabolic systems resulted from the implementation of relatively simple reaction mechanisms without the sophisticated types of apparatus found in a living cell today. Another point is that the most primitive forms of enzymes may not have been totally unique, sequenced polymers. Many similar peptides may have exhibited catalytic functions on a much simpler level than one now finds in particularly sequenced, highly specific enzymes.

B: Of course, we know today that in different species of animals the same enzyme catalyst can have different detailed amino acid sequences. Evolutionary schemes have been derived on this basis [9]. So your point is well established from what we know of comparative biochemistry, though it's not surprising. Is it also possible that a primitive system might have arisen which did not contain either DNA or RNA? If so, sequenced polypeptides could have acted as templates for ordering nucleotide polymerization, the opposite of what takes place in contemporary cells. At a later stage of evolution the procedure could have been reversed.

A: We have already seen that amino acid polymers can be sequenced abiotically by mechanisms which do *not* require the participation of nucleic acids. It was also shown that the production of polypeptides could be influenced by already-synthesized amino acid polymers and, perhaps most interestingly, by the normal substrates of contemporary enzymes.

B: Another point that can be brought up in favor of this particular idea is that there is an organism which has been recently identified and characterized, known as the Scrapie agent, which is completely devoid of nucleic acid [10]. This is certainly one example of a system we find in nature today which does not require its own combination of nucleic acids and nucleotide polymerases to carry on its biological machinations.

A: In addition, amino acids appear in considerably higher yields in most simulation experiments than, for example, purines. Also, you know the difficulty encountered in trying to synthesize naturally coupled dinucleotides compared to the relative ease with which amino acids are linked up abiotically. Undoubtedly, the subsequent evolution of a nucleic acid-based system would have increased the efficiency of replication, but what we can conclude is that the most primitive aspects of biogenesis could have centered around a protein-based system.

In Chaps. 5 and 6 we reviewed the observation that the particular character and function of any given protein are not only determined by the relative abundance and primary sequence of residues, but also by its overall three-dimensional aspect in space. Furthermore, it now appears that the tertiary structure itself is a function of the primary sequence, and the mode of folding is not directly engineered by genetic factors. Now, even if the primordial association of nucleotides were nonrandom, there does not seem to be any reason why those polypeptides whose synthesis would be directed by these prebiotic polynucleotides should necessarily exhibit biologically pertinent functions. On the other hand, we have seen that both properties found in the environment and inherent within the reacting units can act to constrain the resultant primary sequence of amino acids in terms of neighbor-neighbor relationships and three-dimensional interaction with other molecules in the medium. If the protein-based model suggested is correct, it would provide an efficient means for retaining in polynucleotide sequences information pertaining only to those polypeptides which have "proven" biological significance. The opposite case would most likely lead to many "meaningless" polypeptides, and the problem of low returns of a trial-and-error system, discussed in Chap. 5, would be in operation here. Another way of putting it is that, with polypeptides, the sequences produced are the result of direct interaction of monomers and of interplay between the environment and the polymer-synthesizing system. If nucleic acids had been a prerequisite, there is no immediately obvious reason why the subsequent amino acid sequences coded for would necessarily yield functional macromolecules.

B: In summary, then, we're saying that not only can we liberate ourselves from the necessity of relying on rare events and on chance (we have relatively high-probability reactions going on), we also don't need to depend solely on the polynucleotides for a primitive model of self-replication. At any rate, we can expect that one future area of endeavor in chemical evolution studies will be an increasing concern with the development and interplay of *reaction patterns* as opposed to the search for just the production of particular biological compounds.

A: Yes, I think that much of our research activity should be devoted to this area. And just as it has been in the past, future experiments in chemical evolution and biogenesis must be based upon a multidisciplinary approach. The knowledge and understanding which are attained in many seemingly unrelated fields will have a bearing upon an understanding of the overall picture of primordial biogenesis.

B: Not only are we going to continue to draw on knowledge emerging in many different fields, but there are obviously going to be several different ongoing approaches in chemical evolution work. For example, as we've already seen, an area that has been utilized and will probably continue to be fruitful in the future is **comparative biochemistry.** In addition to the points already discussed, this approach to the problem has yielded valuable conclusions such as the realization that certain compounds, because they occur universally in contemporary life, appear to be very primitive (e.g., the coenzymes). Relationships between different enzymes from similar sources have pointed to the possibility of common evolutionary precursors [11], at least among higher organisms.

A: And studies in comparative biochemistry have suggested that ferredoxin is apparently a very ancient enzyme [12]. Therefore, one area of study in primitive metabolism can be an attempt to synthesize simple compounds bearing some of the chemical properties of ferredoxin, such as iron sulfide groupings, and then to look for evidence of catalytic characteristics similar to those exhibited by the contemporary protein.

B: You're talking here about a *particular feature* of contemporary ferredoxin, namely, the interaction between iron and sulfur, as being a focal point of future work. Right?

A: Yes, that's true and, in fact, this is an approach which is under active consideration in certain laboratories at the present time.

B: Another possible avenue of investigation is to extend the simulation paradigm to include a much more complex set of conditions than has usually been employed.

A: Especially in view of the criticism often raised that primitive Earth experiments done thus far were carried out under very specified conditions using carefully selected and highly purified compounds.

B: Right! An obvious extension of such simple experiments would be to make the conditions of these reactions more complex with respect to the chemicals that are introduced and to the number of phases. In addition to the gas phase, you might also have an aqueous phase and a solid phase all in the same system, so that you would attempt to duplicate what a small piece of the surface of the primitive Earth might have been like in detail. It's been suggested [13] that one could simulate a **primitive seashore** in an artificial system by including a solid phase consisting of sand, an aqueous phase with many dissolved ions, a source of ultraviolet light, and provisions for imitating the tides and the diurnal cycle of light and dark. After the system has been running for a while, it can be examined for the emergence of biologically interesting substances and structures. We've already seen in Chap. 6 that mimicking tidal action can lead to the production and sophistication of interesting cell-like microspheres. An additional point is that in a primitive atmosphere experiment, the starting gases are used up eventually, and the system will come to a stable equilibrium, or at least a steady state. On the primitive Earth, however, we would expect the overall environmental conditions to continuously change, and this feature hasn't been incorporated yet in these simple experiments.

A: We should also point out that it's perfectly legitimate to carry out one experiment producing amino acids and then to do a follow-up study in which you begin with greatly enhanced concentrations of amino acids to form polymers. One could then do a third experiment based on the results of the first two in which he starts off with an appreciable concentration of the polypeptides to see what they will do. In this way the **time factor** of millions of years available for chemical evolution is overcome.

The areas of research just outlined are certainly of great interest and demand the attention of experimental chemists and biologists, but are there any areas that can be pursued by the theoretician or others involved in mathematically based research?

B: What we've talked about in Chaps. 1 to 6 is based almost exclusively on experimental results, and we've said relatively little about **theory.** But one of the most difficult problems for the future in this area is to attempt to construct some theory which would help us understand how an evolving aggregate of organic chemicals would move toward the self-replicating state. There exists a great need for theoreticians in physics and in mathematics to extend the early ideas, in particular, to provide some **rationale for future experimental work.** What we need is some sound theoretical thinking at this point.

As we stated earlier, it is difficult to design biogenetic experiments. The point bears repeating that we may have reached the stage where we can say that the primordial synthesis of nearly all essential monomers and polymers is readily understandable in terms of known physical and chemical properties. Now we must seek **new avenues of approach** to determine how the subsequent stages of evolution occurred. We must try to come up with a more general theoretical framework that would provide us with some guidelines.

A: Have any such applicable theoretical approaches been proposed so far?

B: Very little has been done in this area. One suggestion that comes to mind is Pattee's thinking about the emergence of sequence ordering in growing polypeptides [13,14]. This may be on the way to solving the problem of self-duplication, at least at the polymer level, because it can be shown from computer theory that virtually any set of constraints operating on the linking together of monomers in a growing polymer will lead to a periodic sequence, however long. If this theoretical conclusion can be demonstrated in the laboratory, then we might have some clue to at least part of the self-duplication problem.

A: Will it be sufficient for the next efforts in the study of the origin of life to be centered upon the development of purely theoretical approaches?

B: Oh, no! Any theory that is constructed has to be **testable.** A good deal of speculation has been published in the literature with no obvious, explicitly stated means of experimentally testing such theories. The virtue of Pattee's theory, as an example, is that it offers the possibility of suggesting concrete experiments which can either support or refute the point. What we need are additional theories of this kind which are testable.

A: I couldn't agree with you more! As a final point let me offer a general reflection: Contrary to most biochemical research which is done, I find certain characteristics of chemical evolution investigations which are unique to this area. It appears that most biochemical research is concerned with the development of analytical procedures for the elucidation of the nature of certain phenomena observed in living systems. In this sense, biochemical research is primarily *analytical* in nature. On the other hand, I visualize chemical evolution and biogenetic studies as being essentially *synthetic.* We know what living systems are like now and that the conditions of the primitive Earth were very simple and the energy sources available were general. As a result, we must devise or synthesize an overall scheme which can take these factors into consideration and ultimately show us how living systems may have evolved. I see the opportunity for much new, original thinking here.

B: So do I. Furthermore, as Professor Oparin has pointed out, it may be essential to understand how life arose in order to comprehend its present nature [15]. The discovery of amino acids in a fossiliferous sediment over 3 billion years old [16] tends to corroborate our thinking as formulated by the principle of biochemical similarity (see Chap. 1).

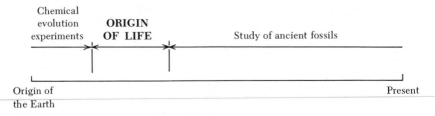

FIG. 7-1 Schematic picture of the basic approaches to the elucidation of the origin of living systems on the Earth.

Biochemists may go on analyzing the details of how the cell operates at the molecular level and may eventually be able to write down all the chemical reactions that occur in a living cell. When that job is done, we still shall not be able to understand why particular reaction sequences occur rather than others. We need the evolutionary, historical dimension as an essential feature of our understanding.

Finally, it should be pointed out that one other area which could certainly profit from chemical evolution studies is the world food problem. Although the benefits we have already cited are significant to the development of scientific insight, the synthesis of nutritionally important compounds from simple, readily available substances (for example, CO, N_2, and H_2O) and applied energy sources (e.g., heat, sunlight) may prove to be an exploitable solution to a pressing general social problem.

Figure 7-1 represents a summary view of the current status of the biogenesis field. We have seen that there are essentially two kinds of studies, one proceeding from the present backward in the examination of fossil remains of increasing antiquity. On the other hand, we have the chemical evolution work which has brought us from primitive gaseous mixtures all the way up to protocell-like structures. It is the large gap between these two limits, in which such things as the origin of metabolic sequences and self-duplication are located, that will occupy our future research efforts.

REFERENCES

1. Lewis, G. N., and M. Randall: "Thermodynamics," rev. by K. S. Pitzer and C. Brewer, McGraw-Hill Book Company, New York, 1961.
2. Fraenkel-Conrat, H., and R. C. Williams: *Proc. Natl. Acad. Sci.,* **41:**690 (1955).
3. Markert, C. L., *Science,* **140:**1329 (1963).
4. Needham, A. E.: "The Uniqueness of Biological Materials," Pergamon Press, New York, 1965.
5. Sidle, A. B.: Tellus, **19:**128 (1967); *Nature,* **216:**408 (1967).

6. Dole, S. H.: "Habitable Planets for Man," Blaisdell Publishing Co., New York, 1964.
7. Goulian, M., A. Kornberg, and R. L. Sinsheimer: *Proc. Natl. Acad. Sci.*, **58**:2321 (1967).
8. Shemin, D.: "Currents in Biochemical Research," p. 518, Interscience Publishers, New York, 1956; Gaffron, H.: *Grad. J.*, **4**:82 (1961).
9. Eck, R. V., and M. O. Dayhoff: "Atlas of Protein Sequence and Structure," National Biomedical Research Foundation, Silver Spring, Md., 1966.
10. Gibbons, R. A., and G. D. Hunter: *Nature*, **215**:1041 (1967); Griffith, J. S.: *Nature*, **215**:1043 (1967).
11. Neurath, H., K. A. Walsh, and W. A. Winter: *Science*, **158**:1638 (1967).
12. Eck, R. V., and M. O. Dayhoff: *Science*, **152**:363 (1966).
13. Pattee, H. H.: *Biophys. J.*, **1**:683 (1961); in S. W. Fox (ed.), "The Origins of Prebiological Systems," p. 385, Academic Press Inc., New York, 1965.
14. Pattee, H. H.: in F. F. Nord and C. H. Werkman (eds.), "Advances in Enzymology," vol. 27, p. 831, John Wiley & Sons, Inc., New York, 1965.
15. Oparin, A. I.: "Life: Its Origin, Nature and Development," Academic Press Inc., New York, 1964.
16. Schopf, J. W., K. A. Kvenvolden, and E. S. Barghoorn: *Proc. Natl. Acad. Sci.*, **59**:639 (1968).

selected general references

Bernal, J. D.: "The Physical Basis of Life," Routledge & Kegan Paul, Ltd., London, 1949.
————: "The Origin of Life," Weidenfeld & Nicolson, London, 1967.
Blum, H. F.: "Time's Arrow and Evolution," Harper & Row, Publishers, Incorporated, New York, 1962.
Calvin, M.: "Chemical Evolution," Condon Lectures, University of Oregon Press, Eugene, Ore., 1961.
————: Chemical Evolution, *Proc. Royal Soc.,* **288A**:441 (1965).
———— and G. J. Calvin: Atom to Adam, *Am. Scientist,* **52**:163 (1964).
Fox, S. W. (ed.): "The Origins of Prebiological Systems," Academic Press Inc., New York, 1965.
Horowitz, N. H., and S. L. Miller: Current Theories on the Origin of Life, *Fortschr. Chem. Org. Naturstoffe,* **20**:423 (1962).
Keosian, J.: "The Origin of Life," 2d ed., Reinhold Publishing Corporation, New York, 1968.
Oparin, A. I.: "The Origin of Life," Dover Publications, Inc., New York, 1953.
————: "The Origin of Life on the Earth," Academic Press Inc., New York, 1957.
———— (ed.): "The Origin of Life on the Earth," Pergamon Press, New York, 1959.
————: "Life: Its Nature, Origin ad Development," Academic Press, New York, 1962.
Oró, J.: Studies in Experimental Organic Cosmochemistry, *Ann. N. Y. Acad. Sci.,* **108**:464 (1963).
Rutten, M. G.: "Geological Aspects of the Origin of Life on Earth," Elsevier Publishing Company, Amsterdam, 1962.
Urey, H. C.: "The Planets," Yale University Press, New Haven, Conn., 1952.
Wald, G.: The Origins of Life, *Proc. Natl. Acad. Sci.,* **52**:595 (1964).
Young, R. S., and C. Ponnamperuma: Early Evolution of Life, *Am. Inst. Biol. Sci., BSCS Pamph. No. 11,* D. C. Heath & Company, Boston, 1964.

index

This book was set in Caledonia, printed on permanent paper and bound by The Maple Press Company. The designer was Richard Paul Kluga; the drawings were done by B. Handelman Associates, Inc. The editors were James L. Smith and Janet Wagner. Robert Laffler supervised the production.